MERCHANT SHIPS: WORLD BUILT

1963 Volume XI

SAVANNAH. *The world's first nuclear-powered cargo/passenger vessel.*

1963 VOLUME

*Compiled by the Publishers, with
an Introduction by* PETER DUFF

Merchant Ships : World Built

Vessels of 1000 tons gross and over completed in 1962

ADLARD COLES LIMITED
IN ASSOCIATION WITH
RUPERT HART-DAVIS LTD., 36 *Soho Square, London, W.*1
JOHN DE GRAFF, Inc., *New York*

VOLUME XI
FIRST PUBLISHED 1963
COPYRIGHT IN ALL COUNTRIES
SIGNATORY TO THE BERNE CONVENTION
© ADLARD COLES LTD. 1963

PUBLISHERS' NOTE AND ACKNOWLEDGMENTS

DESPITE the depression in shipping and the falling off of orders for new ships, the launching output for 1962 was 8,374,754 tons, an increase of 434,749 tons over 1961 and less than a million tons under the record of 1958.

In this volume (XI) of *Merchant Ships: World Built* particulars are given of the merchant ships delivered during 1962. Few passenger liners were completed during the year compared with the vintage year of 1961 but the output included a wide variety of interesting vessels. The *Savannah* can be regarded as the merchant ship of the Year and indeed of the Century as she is the first nuclear-powered vessel designed for normal commercial usage. The *Nissho Maru*, also delivered in 1962, is the world's largest oil tanker to date. Broadly, the ships represented in Volume XI are notable for size, speed and increasing efficiency in cargo handling and automation. It is to the credit of the late A. C. Hardy that he forecast all these developments in the introductions he contributed to the earlier volumes of *Merchant Ships: World Built*.

The Publishers are indebted to the Editor of *The Shipping World* for the majority of the photographs and plans reproduced, and for the particulars appearing in the descriptions of the vessels. They also wish to express their thanks to Lloyd's Register of Shipping and to the shipowners, shipbuilders and correspondents for information supplied.

PRINTED IN GREAT BRITAIN
BY SYDENHAM AND COMPANY LIMITED, BOURNEMOUTH

Contents

Publishers' Note and Acknowledgments   *Page*   4

Introduction   *Page*   7
By Peter Duff

Conversion Tables—feet to metres   *Page*   14

Alphabetical Register of Ships of 1,000 tons gross and over   *Page*   14

Merchant Ships launched during 1962   *Page* 178

Abbreviations—English, French and German   *Page* 184

Introduction

By **PETER DUFF**

formerly Editor of the Shipping World

'BIGGER and faster.' Those words encompass the principal feature of merchant ship production in 1962. Once upon a time both terms would at once imply that one was talking about crack passenger liners. In a way it epitomizes the changing emphasis of the shipping scene that this is no longer so. 'Bigger' refers mostly to tankers and bulk carriers; 'faster' concerns, in the main, cargo liners. The 'biggest' passenger liner is still the *Queen Elizabeth*, completed twenty years ago. The fastest is the *United States*, which went into service, and captured the Atlantic Blue Riband, in 1952. When the *Queen Elizabeth* was completed in the early years of the last war, to serve at first as the most outstandingly successful troop carrier ever known, the largest all-cargo carriers were tankers of about 15,000 tons d.w., and the fastest cargo liners in service had speeds of about 17 knots. In 1962 a tanker was completed with a deadweight tonnage of 130,000 and a cargo liner with a speed in excess of 24 knots. I refer to the *Nissho Maru* and the *American Challenger*; I will say more about each later on.

One slight qualification is needed to those remarks. The French Line's *France*, which went into service early last year, is actually the *longest* passenger liner in the world. At 1,035 ft., her overall length is slightly more than that of the *Queen Elizabeth*.

But the size of a passenger ship is best measured by her gross tonnage, which roughly represents the cubic capacity, converted to 'tons,' of the working spaces of a ship, with allowances for machinery spaces (100 cu. ft. equals one gross ton). The gross tonnage of the *France* is 66,300 tons; of the *Queen Elizabeth* it is 83,673. The *France* is now generally regarded as the last of the great North Atlantic passenger liners owing direct lineage to a famous cosmopolitan fleet which goes back to the *Lusitania*. She was covered fully in the last volume of this publication, so I will say no more about her now, except to remark that her first year's service has gone without a hitch. While her first class accommodation is generally acknowledged to have established a new peak in luxury, combined with a graciousness which seems to come naturally to the French, the inability to cope with a full complement of passengers at one sitting in the dining saloon has evoked some criticism.

Nuclear Power

In the realm of technical achievement the year had at least two outstanding prizes to offer. One was the coming into service of the world's first nuclear-powered cargo ship, the American *Savannah*. Badly publicized, landed with a series of labour problems and coming up against other difficulties, this vessel did not make the impact she might otherwise have done. Conceived as an experimental venture into a new field, with scant regard to economics, she failed to achieve the fame which attaches to her earlier namesake, the first vessel using steam power (albeit as an adjunct to her sails, rather than the other way round) to cross the Atlantic. The new *Savannah* did not achieve the distinction of being the first non-naval vessel to use nuclear machinery. That was won by the large Soviet ice-breaker *Lenin*, which, according to reports, continued to do valuable work in Arctic waters during 1962. In the case of the *Lenin* the choice of steam generator was directly related to the service requirement of long voyage duration without the need for refuelling. The *Savannah* had no specific service requirements of this kind.

The *Savannah* is operated by the States Marine Lines as general agents for the U.S. Atomic Energy Commission and the Maritime Administration. She has a designed speed of 20 knots. A lengthy series of trials were carried out in the spring and early summer, during which the designed speed was comfortably exceeded. Her first operational voyage took her to the port of Savannah in August, 1962. The vessel—which is described in this volume—is mainly a cargo carrier, with passenger accommodation. Her machinery develops 22,300 s.h.p. at full power. No technical troubles were reported during the extensive trials.

Builders of the reactor for the *Savannah* were Babcock & Wilcox. During her early voyages to American ports this firm announced that they had designed a new atomic power plant which represented a vast stride forward from the *Savannah*'s machinery. Called the Consolidated Nuclear Steam Generator (CNSG), it was said to weigh only 685 tons as against the 2,452 tons for the *Savannah* plant and to occupy one-fifth of the space. For a group of ships, it was claimed, transportation costs would work out just as economically as with conventional machinery.

Early British nuclear marine studies have now been abandoned in favour of a joint Anglo-Belgian project known as the Vulcain reactor, and an integral boiling reactor developed by the British Atomic Energy Authority. The proposal to build a British nuclear vessel, with work probably starting in 1964, was announced in February, 1963. In Sweden, Germany and France other projects are under way, but the nearest they have got to fruition is the placing of a contract for a 16,000-ton d.w. nuclear cargo ship with Kieler Howaldtswerke in Germany to be completed by 1965-66. Oddly, the choice of reactor type was not settled at the time the contract was placed. So much for the atomic ship. At least the year marked a milestone.

Hovercraft

What of the other technical achievement? I was thinking of the hovercraft, or air-cushion vehicle. In this field Britain has been leading, and during the year the first essay in commercial operation of this revolutionary form of semi-ship was carried out on an experimental basis across the estuary of the River Dee. The craft used for the purpose was the VA-3, built by Vickers-Armstrongs Ltd. Weighing 11 tons and powered by four Blackburn gas turbines, two providing lift and two propulsion, the craft carried loads of 25 passengers at speeds of up to 70 m.p.h. The route was 20 miles across, and at both ends simple terminals were provided on the beaches, so the craft had the opportunity of demonstrating its unique amphibious character. The programme was carried out under a 'Certificate of Construction and Performance' issued by the Ministry of Aviation in conjunction with the Ministry of Transport.

A different type of cushion craft, the Denny D2, built by Denny Hovercraft Ltd., a subsidiary of Wm. Denny & Bros. Ltd., of Dumbarton (famous for their cross-Channel and other specialized ships), was also scheduled to carry out an experimental passenger service during the year. This was to have operated on the Thames, but unfortunately development problems conspired against it. The commercial debut of this more sedate and more ship-like sidewall type hovercraft will probably be made on the Thames during the summer of 1963. On a barge-like hull measuring 83 ft. by 19 ft. the craft carries 70 passengers at a speed of 20 knots. Two diesel engines drive lifting fans, and two more provide propulsion through shafts resembling outboard motors.

In other countries, principally Russia and Japan, further progress was made with the commercial operation of the hydrofoil. The Russians completed a vessel called the *Vikhr* claimed to be the largest sea-going hydrofoil in the world. For service on the Black Sea, she can carry 300 passengers in three saloons at a speed of 50 knots. British participation in hydrofoil development has centred on the acquisition of the Dutch and Luxemburg Aquavion interests by a new British concern known as International Aquavion (G.B.) Ltd. A small, nine-seater craft was demonstrated on the Solent in August, and larger prototypes are being built. Experiments are to be made with a 40-seater craft for the Orkneys. A Japanese builder, towards the end of the year, was reported to be turning down export orders because capacity was insufficient to meet the home demand.

Passenger Vessels

It is a far cry from these experimental fringes of passenger transport by sea to the 'real thing.' The *France* apart, the year was not particularly notable for large passenger liner completions; indeed, as much interest lay in conversions and reconditionings as in new buildings.

The most impressive of the new vessels was the *Northern Star*, built for the Shaw Savill Line by Vickers-Armstrongs on the Tyne. She is a running mate for the *Southern Cross*, and like that vessel is engaged in voyaging round the world, with the Antipodes as the main distant focal point. The *Southern Cross* normally sails westerly via the Panama Canal, and the *Northern Star* goes eastwards via the Cape of Good Hope. Superannuated from the service as a result was the *Dominion Monarch*, which carried 500 first class passengers and made two and a half round trips in the year. The *Northern Star* carries about 1,400 tourist passengers (like the *Southern Cross* she is a one-class vessel) and makes four round voyages a year. The new liner is a little larger than the earlier ship (650 ft. overall against 604 ft., 24,733 tons gross against 20,203 tons) but in main design and general appearance has very much in common.

One other passenger ship of fair size built during the year was the *Ancerville* for service between Marseilles, Moroccan ports, the Canary Islands and Dakar. Of 14,500 tons gross, she carries 756 passengers in three classes, but can easily be arranged as a one-class cruising ship during the off season. On twin screws she has a machinery output of 24,000 b.h.p., which gives her a speed of 22½ knots and puts her among the world's most powerful diesel engined passenger liners afloat.

Italy entered the field of passenger ship building rather late in the post-war years. One consequence is that the majority of passenger liners now building in the world are under construction in that country for Italian owners. One exception is the trans- atlantic liner for the Norske Amerika Linje of Oslo, the coveted order for which went to a French shipyard during 1962. From Italy in 1963 will come the *Michelangelo* of 43,000 tons gross and the sister ships *Galileo Galilei* and *Guglielmo Marconi*, each of 27,000 tons. From France will come the *Shalom*, 23,000 tons, to be Israel's largest liner.

Speed

Earlier on I referred to the *American Challenger*. This is the cargo liner with a top speed of 26 knots. That was the speed she attained on trials with the special reserve power (provided under an extra subsidy as a defence feature) in use. This extra power is not normally available. But even without it the *American Challenger* reached an average speed of 24·47 knots on her maiden voyage across the Atlantic. The normal service speed is 21 knots.

The *American Challenger* is a notable ship for various reasons besides her speed. First, she is very aptly named, because she does represent a challenge to established practice in the North Atlantic cargo liner trades. There is, incidentally, an interesting sidelight about her name. When her keel was laid this was the name provisionally allotted to the ship. Then the United States Lines Far East services were somewhat disrupted by the loss of a ship. So this ship, the first of the new building programme, was allocated to the Far East route and launched as the *Pioneer Moon*. Just before she ran trials the company policy was changed and the vessel switched to the Atlantic run and renamed *American Challenger*. Later she was renamed once again *Pioneer Moon* and replaced in the Atlantic service by a sister ship now sailing under the name of *American Challenger*.

Of more significance is the fact that the vessel is the first of a new class. There will eventually be 10 ships of the class on the Atlantic routes. They will be the forerunners of a huge replacement programme comprising no less than 43 ships. The *American Challenger* has several points of interest in her design and equipment which are referred to in this volume.

The main machinery is a straightforward turbine installation which follows normal American practice, but with extra power added. The normal maximum output is 18,150 s.h.p. On trials, with emergency power in use, the machinery developed 23,500 s.h.p. Part of the secret of her speed lies in an unusually fine-lined hull form.

Though exceptional for the comparatively short Atlantic run, high speeds of this order are not so unusual on other routes, particularly those concerned with the Far East. The 'Challenger' class remains the fastest cargo liner class in the world, but across the Pacific the Japanese have been providing ships capable of 20 knots, and between North European ports and the Far East are now operating several British cargo liners with speeds of up to 21 knots. Three outstanding ships coming within this category

built during 1962 are the *Glenlyon* and *Glenogle* of the Glen Line Ltd., and the Ben Line's *Benvalla*. The first of these, which gave her name to the class of four ships (the others are the *Flintshire* and the *Glenfalloch*), was built by the Nederlandsche Dok en Scheepsbouw Mij. of Amsterdam. The *Glenogle* (actually the first to be completed) was built by the Fairfield Shipbuilding & Engineering Co. Ltd. And the Ben Line ship was built by Charles Connell & Co. Ltd. The *Glenogle* reached a speed on trials of 22·8 knots. Her normal service speed is 20 knots, achieved by a Sulzer turbocharged diesel engine developing 16,600 b.h.p. She has fine lines and a bulbous bow. The deadweight tonnage is 13,000 and the gross just under 12,000.

The *Benvalla* is also one of a group of four, but she breaks new ground when compared with her earlier sister ships. Principally she marks a switch from turbine machinery to diesel—also of the Sulzer type. Other changes include a repositioning of the bipod mast and the 50-ton heavy derrick and also of the two 5-ton deck cranes, and a longer deckhouse to allow for an increase in passenger accommodation from 10 to 12. It has been estimated that the change from turbine to diesel machinery brought about a 10 per cent. saving in machinery cost and a reduction in consumption of heavy fuel oil from 80 to 50 tons a day. These are large savings to set against the extra maintenance required. The *Benvalla*'s British-built Sulzer engine develops 15,000 s.h.p.

and gives her a speed of 21 knots. Her dimensions and tonnage compare closely with those of the 'Glenlyon' class (which, incidentally, also have 12-passenger accommodation).

Automation

Another notable British-built cargo liner is the *Clan Macgillivray*, which is the first British merchant ship to have a large element of automatic and remote control of the machinery. Built by the Greenock Dockyard for the Clan Line, she has a Barclay-Curle-Sulzer diesel engine of 8,500 b.h.p. and a service speed of 16½ knots. The machinery is controlled from an air-conditioned room at the forward end of the main engine on the first engine room flat. Main engine, diesel generator and electrical controls are operated from here; also in the control room is a very complete set of instruments and gauges. There is a push-button starting for the principal pumps. Such a degree of automation makes possible a saving in engine room man power of 20 per cent.

Still leading in this field of automation are the Japanese. The *Sadoharu Maru*, delivered during the year by the Hitachi Co. to the Shinnihon Steamship Co., was said to be the most highly automated ship then built in that country. The console control for the main machinery is placed in the bridge house, and gauges, meters and other controls are taken to a soundproof booth in the engine room. The wheelhouse is of an unusual circular type providing exceptional vision to the navigating officers. In Sweden, Norway and in Denmark special studies have been made of this subject of automation. They have examined technical, economic, trades union and what might be termed the human side of the various issues which must arise when people are replaced by machines.

Tankers

At the beginning of this survey I mentioned particularly the question of ship size. The world's largest tanker, the *Nissho Maru*, was launched in July and delivered at the beginning of October—in itself a remarkable achievement for a vessel of this colossal size. Her keel was laid in November, 1961. She has a deadweight of 132,334 tons and a draught of more than 54 ft. Across her beam of over 141 ft. she has four instead of the usual three rows of tanks. To propel this monster through the water at a speed of 16 knots there is a single screw driven by high-pressure high-temperature steam turbines developing 25,500 s.h.p. at normal service output. The *Nissho Maru* was built by Sasebo Heavy Industries Ltd. A sister ship is on order with the Ishikawajima-Harima Co. The next largest tanker delivered in 1962 came from America, the 106,568 tons d.w. *Manhattan*, built at the Quincy yard of Bethlehem Steel Co. Of less than half the tonnage, but still a large tanker, is the *British Hussar*, delivered by John Brown & Co. Ltd. She represented the first of the specially designed 50,000-ton BP tankers. Like the *Nissho Maru*, these vessels have their bridge house amidships. The 48,470-ton *Otina* was the first of the large tankers to be built for Shell Tankers with navigating bridge and all accommodation aft. The 87,200-ton *Esso Spain*, delivered in September by Howaldtswerke A.G. to Standard Tankers (Bahamas), was the largest oil carrier built in a Continental shipyard at that time. Another 'largest' was the *P. J. Adams*, of 32,250 tons, built for Ampol Petroleum Ltd., New South Wales, by the Broken Hill Pty. Co. Ltd. and the largest vessel to be built in an Australian shipyard.

A good example of the very large ore carriers now being built in Japan is the *Andes Maru*. She has a deadweight of 52,744 tons and is now running regularly between Chile and Japan under a long-term charter arranged between the Kawasaki Steel Corporation and the owners, the Nihon Suisan K.K. These shipowners are new entrants into the ore carrier field; their normal line of country is fishing and canning. Another large Japanese ore carrier built earlier in the year—and said to be the largest built for a Japanese owner up to that time—was the *Nichiho Maru*, of 48,735 tons d.w., a product of the Nippon Steel & Tube Co. The service speed of this ship, which has a high-tensile steel hull, is about $14\frac{1}{2}$ knots, but she reached just under 18 knots on trials. A feature of the vessel is her cylindrical shaped bow, which has an unusually large radius increasing into a bulb at the foot.

The size of general purpose bulk carriers, besides that of the more specialized ore carriers, also continued to grow during the year. The *Barlby*, built by Sir James Laing & Sons Ltd. for the Ropner Shipping Co. Ltd., represented one of the largest of this class of ship to be built for British owners. So far British ship-owners have on the whole tended to neglect the potentialities of the bulk carrier but it has become evident that fresh thinking on the subject is now being done. In the meantime the initiative has passed to the Norwegians, who continue to add many notable vessels to their impressive bulk carrier fleet.

Among other specialized ocean-going ships which should be mentioned are the following: *Wakasa Maru*, 10,051 tons d.w., with a 200-ton derrick of special design; *Maratha Endeavour*, a 15,380-ton tramp ship built in Germany for Chowgule Steam-ships (Bahamas) with a 160-ton derrick; *Argyll*, a 53,000-ton bulk salt carrier built for National Bulk Carriers Inc. at this company's Kure (Japan) shipyard, with a complicated and revolutionary self-unloading system comprising twin grab-bucket travelling cranes and conveyor belts spanning all holds; *Bridge-stone Maru*, 25,626 tons d.w., specially designed for the carriage of refrigerated liquefied petroleum gas.

Among smaller vessels one of the most significant and most successful is the trawler *Junella*, one of the first British-built distant water stern trawlers and the first non-factory British trawler to be fully refrigerated. She has an overall length of $238\frac{1}{2}$ ft. and was built by Hall, Russell & Co. Ltd. for J. Marr & Son Ltd., of Hull.

Alphabetical Register of Merchant Ships
1000 tons gross and over

CONVERSION TABLES - FEET TO METRES

Feet	Metres	Feet	Metres	Feet	Metres	Feet	Metres	Feet	Metres	Feet	Metres	Feet	Metres
1	0·305	40	12·192	250	76·2	370	112·8	490	149·3	610	185·9	730	222·5
2	0·610	50	15·240	260	79·2	380	115·8	500	152·4	620	189·0	740	225·6
3	0·914	60	18·288	270	82·3	390	118·9	510	155·5	630	192·0	750	228·6
4	1·219	70	21·336	280	85·3	400	121·9	520	158·5	640	195·1	760	231·7
5	1·524	80	24·384	290	88·4	410	125·0	530	161·5	650	198·1	770	234·7
6	1·829	90	27·432	300	91·4	420	128·0	540	164·6	660	201·2	780	237·8
7	2·134	100	30·480	310	94·5	430	131·1	550	167·6	670	204·2	790	240·9
8	2·438	200	60·9	320	97·5	440	134·1	560	170·7	680	207·3	800	243·9
9	2·743	210	64·0	330	100·6	450	137·2	570	173·7	690	210·3		
10	3·048	220	67·1	340	103·6	460	140·2	580	176·8	700	213·4		
20	6·096	230	70·1	350	106·7	470	143·2	590	179·8	710	216·4		
30	9·144	240	73·2	360	109·7	480	146·3	600	182·9	720	219·5		

For Explanations and Abbreviations see page 184

ABADESA. *British.* Tanker. Built by Swan, Hunter & Wigham Richardson Ltd., Newcastle-upon-Tyne, for Furness-Houlder Argentine Lines Ltd., London. 13,571 tons gross, 20,180 tons d.w., 565 ft. l.o.a., 72·2 ft. breadth, 31·75 ft. draught, 6-cyl. Doxford diesel by the shipbuilders, 8,100 b.h.p., 14¼ knots.

ABAGUR. *Russian.* Tanker. Built by Rauma-Repola O/Y, Rauma, Finland, for U.S.S.R. 3,360 tons gross, 4,400 tons d.w., 344·82 ft. l.o.a., 48·58 ft. breadth, 20·42 ft. draught, 5-cyl. diesel by B. & W., 2,900 b.h.p., 14 knots.

ABAGURLES. *Russian.* Cargo. Built by United Polish Shipyards, Gdansk, for U.S.S.R. 4,653 tons gross, 5,900 tons d.w., 406·42 ft. l.o.a., 54·9 ft. breadth, 22·33 ft. draught, 5-cyl. Sulzer diesel, 4,500 b.h.p., 14½ knots.

ACHGELIS HUGO STINNES. *German.* Cargo. Built by Rheinstahl Nordseewerke, Emden, for Koholyt Hugo Stinnes Persönlich K.G., Bremen. 3,130 tons gross, 4,100 tons d.w., 331·42 ft. l.o.a., 47·5 ft. breadth, two 6-cyl. grd. diesels by M.A.K., 2,840 b.h.p., 12½ knots.

ADA GORTHON. *Swedish.* Tanker. Built by Oresundsvarvet A/B, Landskroner, for Stig Gorthon, Helsingborg. 13,349 tons gross, 20,100 tons d.w., 559·75 ft. l.o.a., 72 ft. breadth, 30·67 ft. draught, 7-cyl. Götaverken diesel, 8,750 b.h.p., 15½ knots (trials).

AEGEAN MARINER. *Greek.* Cargo. Built by At. & Ch. de Dunkerque & Bordeaux (France-Gironde), Bordeaux, for Porto Nacional Cia. Nav. S.A., London. 11,063 tons gross, 15,670 tons d.w., 518·33 ft. l.o.a., 67·75 ft. breadth, 30·75 ft. draught, 6-cyl. B. & W. diesel by Creusot, 7,500 b.h.p., 15½ knots.

AFRAM RIVER. *Ghanaian.* Refrigerated cargo. Built by N.V. Kon. Maats. 'De Schelde,' Flushing, for Black Star Line Ltd., Accra. 5,315 tons gross, 6,800 tons d.w., 460·9 ft. l.o.a., 60·2 ft. breadth, 23·25 ft. draught, 5-cyl. Sulzer diesel by the shipbuilders, 4,500 b.h.p., 15 knots.

AFRICAN COMET. *American.* Refrigerated cargo. Built by Ingalls S.B. Corp., Pascagoula, Miss., for Farrell Lines Inc., New York. 11,350 tons gross, 12,401 tons d.w., 572 ft. l.o.a., 75·2 ft. breadth, 30·5 ft. draught, 2 grd. turbs. by G.E.C., 16,500 s.h.p., 20 knots.

AFRICAN METEOR. *American.* Refrigerated cargo. Built by Ingalls S.B. Corp., Pascagoula, Miss., for Farrell Lines Inc., New York. 11,350 tons gross, 12,501 tons d.w., 572 ft. l.o.a., 75·2 ft. breadth, 30·5 ft. draught, 2 grd. turbs. by G.E.C., 16,500 s.h.p., 20 knots.

AIDA III. *Egyptian.* Lighthouse tender. Built by Zaanland Schps. Maats., Zaandam, for United Arab Maritime Co., Alexandria. 2,733 tons gross, 286 ft. l.o.a., 44·75 ft. breadth, tw-sc. two 8-cyl. diesels by Deutz, 4,000 b.h.p., 16½ knots.

ALAPAEVSKLES. *Russian.* Cargo. Built by United Polish Shipyards, Gdansk, for U.S.S.R. 4,653 tons gross, 5,900 tons d.w., 406·42 ft. l.o.a., 54·9 ft. breadth, 22·33 ft. draught, 5-cyl. Sulzer diesel, 4,500 b.h.p., 14½ knots.

ALATYRLES. *Russian.* Cargo. Built by United Polish Shipyards, Gdansk, for U.S.S.R. 4,653 tons gross, 5,900 tons d.w., 406·42 ft. l.o.a., 54·9 ft. breadth, 22·33 ft. draught, 5-cyl. Sulzer diesel, 4,500 b.h.p., 14½ knots.

ALGAZAYER. *Egyptian (U.A.R.).* Refrigerated cargo and passenger. Built by Deutsche Werft A.G., Hamburg, for The United Arab Maritime Co., Alexandria. 4,444 tons gross, 1,327 tons d.w., 354·33 ft. l.o.a., 54·58 ft. breadth, 14·5 ft. draught, 9-cyl. M.A.N. diesel, 3,240 b.h.p., 16 knots.

A

ALEKSIN. *Russian.* Tanker. Built by Rauma-Repola O/Y, Rauma, for U.S.S.R. 3,360 tons gross, 4,400 tons d.w., 344·82 ft. l.o.a., 48·58 ft. breadth, 20·42 ft. draught, 5-cyl. diesel by B. & W., 2,900 b.h.p., 14 knots.

ALTAFJORD. *Norwegian.* Cargo. Built by A/S Bergens M/V, Bergen, for Den Norske Amerikalinje A/S, Oslo. 8,356 tons gross, 11,300 tons d.w., 462·2 ft. l.o.a., 63·33 ft. breadth, 26 ft. draught, 6-cyl. Sulzer diesel, 6,650 b.h.p., 16½ knots.

ALUKSNE. *Russian.* Tanker. Built by Rauma-Repola O/Y, Rauma, for U.S.S.R. 3,360 tons gross, 4,400 tons d.w., 344·82 ft. l.o.a., 48·58 ft. breadth, 20·42 ft. draught, 5-cyl. diesel by B. & W., 2,900 b.h.p., 14 knots.

AMALIENBORG. *Danish.* Tanker. Built by Hitachi S.B. & E. Co. Ltd., Osaka, for A/S D/S Dannebrog, Copenhagen. 12,400 tons gross, 19,813 tons d.w., 560 ft. l.o.a., 72·2 ft. breadth, 29·5 ft. draught, 6-cyl. B. & W. diesel by the shipbuilders, 7,500 b.h.p., 15¼ knots.

AMERICAN CHALLENGER. *American.* Refrigerated cargo. Built by Newport News S.B. & D.D. Co., Newport News, for United States Lines Co., New York. 11,308 tons gross, 13,100 tons d.w., 560·5 ft. l.o.a., 75·42 ft. breadth, 31·5 ft. draught, 2 grd. turbs. by Westinghouse, 18,150 s.h.p., 21 knots.

AMPHIOPE. *French.* Ore carrier. Built by Ch. Reunis-Normandie Gd., Quevilly, for Soc. Nav. Caennaise & Union Navale, Caen. 19,372 tons gross, 26,900 tons d.w., 618·58 ft. l.o.a., 79·33 ft. breadth, 33·75 ft. draught, 7-cyl. diesel by l'Atlantique, 8,750 b.h.p., 15 knots.

AMSTELLAND. *Dutch.* Refrigerated cargo. Built by Verolme United Shipyards, Alblasserdam, for Kon. Hollandsche Lloyd, Amsterdam. 6,792 tons gross, 9,513 tons d.w., 517·58 ft. l.o.a., 64·66 ft. breadth, 26·25 ft. draught, 7-cyl. Sulzer diesel by Werkspoor, 8,400 b.h.p., 17 knots.

AMSTELSTAD. *Dutch.* Cargo. Built by Werf de Noord, Alblasserdam, for N.V. Reederij 'Amsterdam,' Amsterdam. 9,617 tons gross, 14,000 tons d.w., 509 ft. l.o.a., 63·66 ft. breadth, 29·66 ft. draught, 5-cyl. Sulzer diesel, 5,500 b.h.p., 14 knots.

ANADYRLES. *Russian.* Cargo. Built by United Polish Shipyards, Gdansk, for U.S.S.R. 4,653 tons gross, 5,900 tons d.w., 406·42 ft. l.o.a., 54·9 ft. breadth, 22·33 ft. draught, 5-cyl. Sulzer diesel, 4,500 b.h.p., 14½ knots.

ANAPA. *Russian.* Tanker. Built by Rauma-Repola O/Y, Rauma, Finland, for U.S.S.R. 3,330 tons gross, 4,400 tons d.w., 344·82 ft. l.o.a., 48·56 ft. breadth, 20·42 ft. draught, 5-cyl. diesel by B. & W., 2,900 b.h.p., 14 knots.

ANARIS. *Swedish.* Bulk carrier. Built by A/B Götaverken, Gothenburg, for Trafik A/B Grängesberg-Oxelösund, Stockholm. 10,849 tons gross, 15,360 tons d.w., 490 ft. l.o.a., 64·2 ft. breadth, 30·75 ft. draught, 7-cyl. Götaverken diesel, 5,000 b.h.p., 14¼ knots.

ANCERVILLE. *French.* Passenger. Built by Ch. de l'Atlantique, St. Nazaire, for Cie. de Navigation Paquet, Marseilles. 14,500 tons gross, 3,000 tons d.w., 548·75 ft. l.o.a., 71·5 ft. breadth, 21·58 ft. draught, tw-sc. two 12-cyl. B. & W. diesels by the shipbuilders, 24,000 b.h.p., 22½ knots.

ANDES MARU. *Japanese.* Ore carrier. Built by Ishikawajima-Harima H.I., Aioi, for Nippon Suisan K.K., Tokyo. 32,068 tons gross, 52,744 tons d.w., 743 ft. l.o.a., 100·75 ft. breadth, 39 ft. draught, 2 grd. turbs. by the shipbuilders, 17,600 s.h.p., 16 knots.

ANDOMALES. *Russian.* Cargo. Built by United Polish Shipyards, Gdansk, for U.S.S.R. 4,653 tons gross, 5,900 tons d.w., 406·42 ft. l.o.a., 54·9 ft. breadth, 22·33 ft. draught, 5-cyl. Sulzer diesel, 4,500 b.h.p., 14½ knots.

AFRICAN COMET. *The first of a series of six high-speed cargo liners of about 12,000 tons d.w. ordered by the American shipping company Farrell Lines Inc. from the Ingalls Shipbuilding Corporation. The African Comet is the largest ship to be built under the present U.S. Government shipbuilding subsidy programme. Of the next three vessels, the African Meteor was also completed in 1962 and the African Mercury and African Neptune were launched. The six vessels will serve on the United States South and East Africa routes. They have been designed for a service speed of 20 knots and should cut the present steaming time for the 6,786 miles run from New York to Cape Town from 18 to 14 days. A special feature of the African Comet is the amount of aluminium sheet and extruded shapes that have been used for the midship structure. About 200,000 lb. of this material have been used, making it the largest structure yet fabricated in light alloy for an American-built cargo vessel. Defence measures incorporated into the ship's structure will permit rapid conversion to a military auxiliary with heavy-lift gear in case of national emergency. The cargo capacity bale is 688,026 cu. ft., 28,000 cu. ft. refrigerated, and the deep tanks have a capacity of 1,016 tons liquid cargoes. First class accommodation is provided for 12 passengers. The propelling machinery consists of a steam turbine installation of 16,500 s.h.p. driving the propeller shaft at 105 r.p.m. at design conditions. Two bent-tube boilers provide steam at 600 p.s.i. and 850 deg. F.*

A

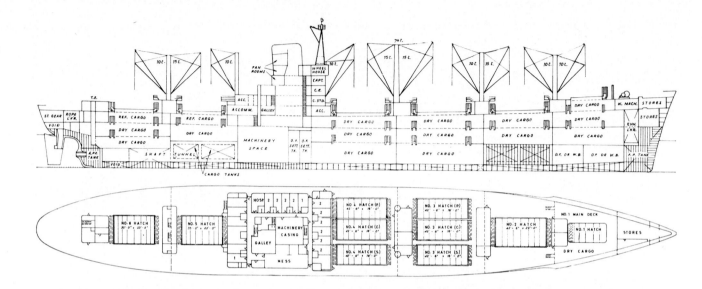

AMERICAN CHALLENGER. *This ship is the first of a new class of 13,100 tons d.w. cargo liners for the United States Lines. She has the high maximum commercial speed of 24½ knots, and a service speed of 21 knots. The class was designed by Gibbs & Cox Inc., who also designed the African Comet. The American Challenger was built by Newport News Shipbuilding & Dry Dock Co., who are building three others of the class; the remaining six are being built by the Bethlehem Steel Co. Her speed, achieved by a fine-lined hull form combined with turbine machinery developing a commercial maximum of 18,150 s.h.p., is the outstanding characteristic, but she has a number of other notable features. These include a system of derricks which provides centralized control of hoisting and slewing from positions giving a clear view into the hold; triple hatches fitted to Nos. 3 and 4 holds, the cargo gear for these holds including a 70-ton Stulcken derrick; flush decks to facilitate the use of forklift trucks and the stowage of containers; wing ballast tanks along the upper tweendecks forward of the machinery space; main hold lengths up to 75 ft.; hydraulically controlled weather deck hatch covers; provision for carrying over 1,000 tons of liquid cargoes in lined and heated tanks; and refrigerated spaces totalling nearly 30,000 cu. ft., with additional spaces convertible to refrigeration. The dry cargo capacity grain is 625,775 cu. ft., bale 580,102 cu. ft. The main engine comprises a Westinghouse cross-compound double-reduction geared turbine driving a single screw. Superheated steam is supplied by two Foster Wheeler two-drum bent-tube boilers at 600 p.s.i.g. and 850 deg. F. Now renamed Pioneer Moon.*

A

ALTAFJORD. *A motor cargo liner of 8,356 tons gross for the Norwegian American Line. This ship was the first to be built by A/S Bergens Mek. Verksteder with lines faired mathematically by the digital computer at the University of Bergen. There are two tweendecks in all cargo spaces except No. 1 hold, and a raised tweendeck as well over No. 5 hold. Weatherdeck hatches are either of Velle or MacGregor Megronest type.*

ANDREA MANTEGNA. *Italian.* Passenger. Built by Cant. Nav. Apuania, Marina di Carrara, for Linee Maritime Dell' Adriatico S.p.A., Rome. 1,800 tons gross, 312 ft. l.o.a., 41 ft. breadth, 12·42 ft. draught, tw-sc. two 5-cyl. diesels by Fiat, 5,500 b.h.p., 19¾ knots.

ANETTE MAERSK. *Danish.* Cargo. Built by Mitsui S.B. & E. Co. Ltd., Tamano, for A. P. Möller, Copenhagen. 6,238 tons gross, 500 ft. l.o.a., 62·75 ft. breadth, 9-cyl. B. & W. diesel by the shipbuilders, 9,800 b.h.p., 17½ knots.

ANGARSKLES. *Russian.* Cargo. Built by United Polish Shipyards, Gdansk, for U.S.S.R. 4,653 tons gross, 5,900 tons d.w., 406·42 ft. l.o.a., 54·9 ft. breadth, 22·33 ft. draught, 5-cyl. Sulzer diesel, 4,500 b.h.p., 14½ knots.

ANNA NERY. *Brazilian.* Passenger. Built by Brodogradiliste Uljanik, Pula, Yugoslavia, for Cia. Nacional de Nav. Costeira Autarquia, Rio de Janeiro. 10,444 tons gross, 492·2 ft. l.o.a., 72·25 ft. breadth, 17·9 ft. draught, tw-sc. two 7-cyl. B. & W. diesels by Krupp, 9,000 b.h.p., 17½ knots.

ANNE BOGELUND. *Danish.* Cargo. Built by E. J. Smit & Zoon's Scheeps., Westerbroek, for Rederiet Bogelund-Jensen I/S, Copenhagen, 1,503 tons gross, 2,060 tons d.w., 264 ft. l.o.a., 39 ft. breadth, 16 ft. draught, 7-cyl. diesel by Werkspoor, 1,630 b.h.p., 13 knots.

ANNEMARIE. *German.* Cargo. Built by Jos. L. Meyer, Pappenburg-Ems, for Hans Kruger, Hamburg. 3,400 tons gross, 310 ft. b.p., 46·58 ft. breadth, 23 ft. draught, Fiat diesel by Borsig A.G., 3,600 b.h.p., 15 knots.

ANNE MILDRED BROVIG. *Norwegian.* Tanker. Built by Oresundsvarvet A/B, Landskroner, for Th. Brövig, Farsund. 25,454 tons gross, 40,550 tons d.w., 700·33 ft. l.o.a., 96·25 ft. breadth, 35·82 ft. draught, 10-cyl. Götaverken diesel, 18,350 b.h.p., 17 knots.

ANTRIM. *British.* Cargo. Built by Alex. Stephen & Sons Ltd., Glasgow, for Avenue Shipping Co. Ltd., London. 6,461 tons gross, 9,900 tons d.w., 460·33 ft. l.o.a., 59 ft. breadth, 27·2 ft. draught, 5-cyl. Doxford diesel by the shipbuilders, 5,500 b.h.p., 14 knots.

A O 9. *Uruguay.* Tanker. Built by Ishikawajima-Harima H.I., Aioi, for Government of Uruguay. 17,500 tons gross, 28,267 tons d.w., grd. turb. by the shipbuilders, 11,300 s.h.p., 16¾ knots.

ARAMIS. *Norwegian.* Cargo. Built by Short Bros. Ltd., Sunderland, for Bernhard Hanssen & Co., Flekkefjord. 10,023 tons gross, 14,000 tons d.w., 511 ft. l.o.a., 66 ft. breadth, 27·2 ft. draught, 4-cyl. H. & W.-B. & W. diesel by Kincaid, 6,500 b.h.p., 14¾ knots.

ARAMOANA. *New Zealand.* Passenger, train and car ferry. Built by Wm. Denny & Bros. Ltd., Dumbarton, for New Zealand Government. 4,700 tons gross, 1,050 tons d.w., 368 ft. l.o.a., 61 ft. breadth, 15·5 ft. draught, tw-sc. diesel-electric, 10,500 s.h.p., 17 knots.

ARGYLL. *British.* Bulk salt carrier. Built by Nat. Bulk Carriers Inc. (Kure Shipyard Div.), Kure, for Argyll Shipping Co. Ltd., Hamilton, Bermuda. 39,665 tons gross, 53,090 tons d.w., 763·5 ft. l.o.a., 106·2 ft. breadth, 39·2 ft. draught, 2 grd. turbs. by G.E.C., 12,500 s.h.p., 15 knots.

ARISTOTELES. *Dutch.* Cargo. Built by N.V. Schps. Gebr. Pot., Bolnes, for Konink. Nederl. Stoomb. Maats. N.V., Amsterdam. 5,700 tons gross, 7,100 tons d.w., 423 ft. l.o.a., 57·66 ft. breadth, 24·42 ft. draught, 7-cyl. diesel by the shipbuilders, 4,900 b.h.p., 16¼ knots.

ARLINGTON COURT. *British.* Cargo. Built by Bartram & Sons Ltd., Sunderland, for Court Line Ltd. 9,662 tons gross, 11,250 tons d.w., 498·66 ft. l.o.a., 63·2 ft. breadth, 30·33 ft. draught, 5-cyl. B. & W. diesel by Kincaid, 7,250 b.h.p., 17½ knots (trials).

A

Opposite:

ANCERVILLE. *14,500 tons gross. The largest diesel-engined passenger liner yet built for French owners was delivered in 1962 by Chantiers de l'Atlantique (Penhoet-Loire), Saint Nazaire, to the Compagnie de Navigation Paquet. She has been designed for service between Marseilles, Tangier, Casablanca, Teneriffe, Las Palmas and Dakar. The Ancerville is a twin-screw ship and is fitted with two high-pressure turbocharged Burmeister & Wain diesel engines, the first of this type to be installed. This is a short-stroke engine allowing more head room so that a smaller engine room can be used, thus making it particularly suitable for installation in passenger liners and ferries. One main difference from standard B. & W. engines is that there are two exhaust valves instead of one. The ship has twin exhaust outlets instead of a conventional funnel. Accommodation is arranged for 756 passengers in three classes: first, tourist and standard. As the vessel will be sailing in warm waters, a maximum of open promenade space has been provided. About 100 motor cars are carried and there is refrigerated space of 17,557 cu. ft. The service speed of the ship is 22·5 knots.*

ANDES MARU. *The delivery of the Andes Maru, 52,744 tons d.w. ore carrier, to the Nihon Suisan K.K. affords an interesting example of diversification on the part of the owning company which is one of the leading Japanese fishing and canning companies. The Andes Maru was built at the Aioi ship-yard of Ishikawajima-Harima Heavy Industries Ltd. and is employed in regular service between Chile and the Chiba Works of the Kawasaki Steel Corporation. Kawasaki guaranteed a 15-year requirement for the ore service when the order was placed. The hull is double and has two longitudinal bulk-heads for the carriage of heavy ores. Ten hatches have been provided for the central hold. This central hold has wings designed for ballast when the vessel is light.*

A

ARAMOANA. The delivery of this twin-screw diesel-electric passenger carrying train and car ferry, 4,700 tons gross, to the New Zealand Government marked a new era in the country's internal transport. Built by William Denny & Brothers Ltd., Dumbarton, at a cost of about £1,800,000, this ship is the first train ferry to operate in New Zealand, and will link the railway and road systems of the North and South Islands between Wellington and Picton. She will be operated by the Union Steam Ship Co. of New Zealand Ltd. on behalf of New Zealand Railways. The Aramoana has a lateral bow thrust unit consisting of a Voith-Schneider design propeller working in an athwartships tunnel. Retractable-type Denny-Brown stabilizers are fitted and a stern door for loading vehicles is constructed in halves and fitted with a Götaverken Hydrautorque hinge. The vessel is capable of a speed of 19 knots and it is hoped to operate a daily, and in busy periods twice

AROMOANA—*continued*

daily, service over the 51-mile stretch from Wellington to Picton. The vessel is subdivided by 11 watertight bulkheads and is fitted with vehicle, upper, promenade and boat decks with a mezzanine deck arranged port and starboard, forward and aft, between the vehicle and upper deck. She is fitted with a complete cellular double bottom, forward and aft trimming tanks and also heeling tanks. The heeling tanks are required to counteract the heavy off-centre loading of trains and are of sufficient capacity to ensure that the maximum angle of heel when loading railway wagons will not exceed 5 degrees. The main vehicle deck is fitted with three 3 ft. 6 in. gauge railway tracks, the three tracks converging into one by means of a three-throw turnout at the after end. This deck has been designed to carry a full load of New Zealand Railway rolling stock while the aftermost 160 ft. of centre track is also capable of carrying locomotives up to 110 tons in weight. Alternatively this deck may carry a total of either 20-25 railway wagons and about 20 motor cars, or about 80-90 motor cars. Provision has also been made at the fore end of the vehicle deck for the carriage of motor cars, motor cycles and pedal cycles. A garage is also fitted on the upper deck aft, and is designed to carry 31 average-size cars. Accommodation has been provided for the carrying of about 1,150 passengers and 70 crew and includes the provision on the upper deck forward of eight four-berth private cabins for passengers.

ARLINGTON COURT. *The Court Line took delivery of this cargo vessel, 11,250 tons d.w., from Bartram & Sons Ltd., Sunderland. She is of open shelter-deck type with scantlings for closed shelterdeck. The machinery has been placed somewhat further aft than usual in this type of vessel and lies between Nos. 4 and 5 holds.*

A

ARNEB. *Dutch.* Cargo. Built by Sölvesborgs Varv A/B, Sölvesborg, for N.V. van Nievelt, Goudriaan & Co.'s Stoomv. Maats., Rotterdam. 1,190 tons gross, 2,300 tons d.w., 282·2 ft. l.o.a., 40·9 ft. breadth, 15·33 ft. draught, 8-cyl. diesel by Deutz, 2,100 b.h.p., 14½ knots.

ARTHUR STOVE. *Norwegian.* Bulk carrier. Built by At. & Ch. de Nantes (Bretagne-Loire), Nantes, for Lorentzens & Sonners Rederi A/S, Oslo. 11,430 tons gross, 15,340 tons d.w., 509·82 ft. l.o.a., 67 ft. breadth, 29·5 ft. draught, 6-cyl. Sulzer diesel by l'Atlantique, 6,300 b.h.p., 14¾ knots.

ASA V. CALL. *Liberian.* Tanker. Built by Sörviksvarvet A/B, Uddevalla, for California Transport Corp., Monrovia and San Francisco. 38,472 tons gross, 68,100 tons d.w., 824·66 ft. l.o.a., 116·58 ft. breadth, 43 ft. draught, 2 De Laval grd. turbs., 20,000 s.h.p., 16½ knots.

ATHOS. *Danish.* Cargo. Built by Frederikshavns V. & F. A/S, Frederikshavn, for Det Forenede D/S A/S, Copenhagen. 2,661 tons gross, 3,200 tons d.w., 362·42 ft. l.o.a., 50·9 ft. breadth, 20 ft. draught, 6-cyl. B. & W. diesel by Elsinore, 3,900 b.h.p., 16 knots.

ATLANTIC CHALLENGER. *Liberian.* Tanker. Built by S.A. Cockerill-Ougrée, Hoboken, for Tankers Transport Inc., Monrovia and Philadelphia. 29,699 tons gross, 47,800 tons d.w., 743 ft. l.o.a., 105·2 ft. breadth, 37·82 ft. draught, 2 grd. turbs. by the shipbuilders, 17,000 s.h.p., 17 knots.

ATLANTIC COMPETITOR. *Liberian.* Tanker. Built by S.A. Cockerill-Ougrée, Hoboken, for Tankers Transport Inc., Monrovia and Philadelphia. 29,699 tons gross, 47,797 tons d.w., 743 ft. l.o.a., 105·33 ft. breadth, 37·82 ft. draught, 2 Westinghouse grd. turbs., 17,132 s.h.p., 17 knots.

ATLANTIC PRESTIGE. *American.* Tanker. Built by Newport News S.B. & D.D. Co., Newport News. 21,200 tons gross, 32,240 tons d.w., 669·42 ft. l.o.a., 82·75 ft. breadth, 34·58 ft. draught, 2 grd. turbs. by the shipbuilders, 15,000 s.h.p., 17 knots.

AVENIR. *Swedish.* Bulk carrier. Built by Bremer Vulkan, Vegesak, for Rederi A/B Fraternitas, Gothenburg. 11,098 tons gross, 15,249 tons d.w., 510 ft. l.o.a., 66·75 ft. breadth, 28·5 ft. draught, 6-cyl. M.A.N. diesel by the shipbuilders, 6,120 b.h.p., 18 knots (trials).

AVISFAITH. *British.* Cargo. Built by Bartram & Sons Ltd., Sunderland, for The Aviation & Shipping Co. Ltd., London. 7,868 tons gross, 11,200 tons d.w., 460·5 ft. l.o.a., 60·2 ft. breadth, 28·58 ft. draught, 5-cyl. Götaverken diesel by N.E.M., 6,300 b.h.p., 14 knots.

AXENFELS. *German.* Cargo. Built by A.G. 'Weser' Werk Seebeck, Bremerhaven, for D.D.G. 'Hansa,' Bremen. 5,495 tons gross, 7,150 tons d.w., 417 ft. l.o.a., 54·2 ft. breadth, 25·42 ft. draught, 7-cyl. B. & W. diesel by Krupp, 4,900 b.h.p., 15½ knots.

ARGYLL. *This unusual ship is a 53,090 tons d.w. salt carrier which was delivered by the Kure Shipyards Division of National Bulk Carriers Inc. to the Argyll Shipping Co. of Bermuda, an affiliate of National Bulk Carriers Inc. This vessel was designed to carry salt from Mexico to the Pacific North-west of the United States and Canada and is said to be the world's largest salt carrier. Built to an American Bureau of Shipping classification, the Argyll is of self-unloading type and can also be used for carrying other dry bulk cargoes such as ore, coal and grain, while oil could be carried in the tanks normally used for ballast. The most striking feature of the vessel (which has a grain capacity of 1,908,600 cu. ft.) is the cargo-handling equipment.*

This consists of twin grab-bucket travelling cranes and a conveyor belt system mounted on the main deck. Operation of this equipment over all holds is achieved by placing the bridge right forward and the main engine aft, with the holds and cargo-handling equipment occupying the space between. One crane is to port and one to starboard. Each can be operated independently, but both are mounted on a single trolley chassis which spans the deck above the hatch covers. The wheels of the trolley run on rails extending along the sides of the deck between the deckhouse aft and the bridge. The same rails serve two other trolleys, one aft of the cranes and one forward, which carry cross conveyors and boom conveyors with telescopic chutes. All are self-propelled. In operation the trolleys are fixed in the required positions by clamping them to the rails. The cranes have grab-buckets which dump the salt taken from the holds into hoppers mounted in the bases of the cranes. The hoppers supply it to belt feeders which in turn feed it to a centre conveyor running on deck and extending the length of the holds. This centre conveyor feeds it to the aft cross conveyor or forward cross conveyor as required. One or other of these will feed it to its respective boom conveyor which will then carry it overboard to the discharge point. Each of the two belt feeders is 84 in. wide with a capacity of 1,344 tons per hour.

A

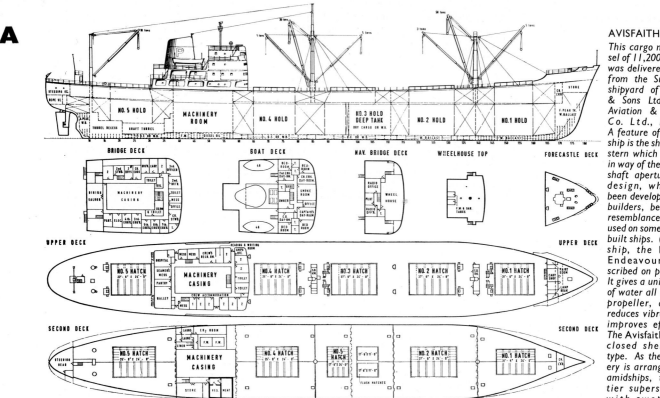

BRIDGE DECK   BOAT DECK   NAV. BRIDGE DECK   WHEELHOUSE TOP   FORECASTLE DECK

UPPER DECK

SECOND DECK

AVISFAITH

This cargo motor vessel of 11,200 tons d.w. was delivered in 1962 from the Sunderland shipyard of Bartram & Sons Ltd. to the Aviation & Shipping Co. Ltd., London. A feature of this new ship is the shape of the stern which is bossed in way of the propeller shaft aperture. This design, which has been developed by the builders, bears some resemblance to that used on some German-built ships. (One such ship, the Maratha Endeavour, is described on page 104.) It gives a uniform flow of water all round the propeller, and thus reduces vibration and improves efficiency. The Avisfaith is of the closed shelterdeck type. As the machinery is arranged aft of amidships, the four-tier superstructure with swept-back rounded front is correspondingly positioned. This superstructure houses the entire ship's complement and is surmounted by a well proportioned funnel. Transverse watertight subdivision is effected by seven bulkheads, dividing the vessel into three holds and a deep tank forward of the engine room and one hold abaft, all with corresponding tweendeck spaces. Cargo handling is effected by one 50-ton, one 30-ton, two 10-ton and eight 5-ton derricks.

BACCHUS. *British.* Refrigerated cargo. Built by Henry Robb Ltd., Leith, for British India S.N. Co. Ltd., London and Calcutta. 4,823 tons gross, 5,200 tons d.w., 379 ft. l.o.a., 55·2 ft. breadth, 22 ft. draught, 5-cyl. Sulzer diesel by Swan Hunter, 5,500 b.h.p., 15 knots.

BAIKAL. *Russian.* Passenger and cargo. Built by VEB Mathias-Thesen Werft, Wismar, for U.S.S.R. 4,800 tons gross, 360·95 ft. b.p., 53 ft. breadth, 16·95 ft. draught, tw-sc. M.A.N. diesel, 8,000 b.h.p., 18 knots.

BALAKLAVA. *Russian.* Tanker. Built by United Polish Shipyards, Gdansk, for U.S.S.R. 13,365 tons gross, 19,000 tons d.w., 580·33 ft. l.o.a., 71·82 ft. breadth, 30·2 ft. draught, 6-cyl. Sulzer diesel by Cegielski, 9,000 b.h.p., 16 knots.

BALLADE. *Swedish.* Refrigerated cargo. Built by Ch. Nav. La Ciotat, La Ciotat, for Salenrederierna A/B, Stockholm. 6,929 tons gross, 9,500 tons d.w., 450·25 ft. l.o.a., 59·66 ft. breadth, 26 ft. draught, 2 De Laval grd. turbs., 9,500 s.h.p., 18¼ knots.

BALLYRUSH. *British.* Collier. Built by Hall, Russell & Co. Ltd., Aberdeen, for John Kelly Ltd., Belfast. 1,575 tons gross, 2,000 tons d.w., 256 ft. l.o.a., 39·5 ft. breadth, 15·75 ft. draught, 8-cyl. Nohab-Polar diesel, 1,520 b.h.p.

BALTIC SUN. *British.* Refrigerated cargo. Built by Krogerwerft G.m.b.H., Rendsburg, for United Baltic Corp. Ltd., London. 2,800 tons gross, 4,300 tons d.w., 390·25 ft. l.o.a., 55·58 ft. breadth, 21 ft. draught, two 10-cyl. M.A.N. grd. diesels, 4,780 b.h.p., 16½ knots.

BANAK. *Norwegian.* Bulk carrier. Built by Deutsche Werft A.G., Hamburg, for Torvold Klaveness, Oslo. 10,500 tons gross, 16,000 tons d.w., 492 ft. l.o.a., 70 ft. breadth, 30·25 ft. draught, 7-cyl. Sulzer diesel, 7,700 b.h.p., 15½ knots.

BANSHU MARU No. 5. *Japanese.* Fish carrier. Built by Taiyo S.B. Co., Nagasaki, for Taiyo Gyogyo K.K., Tokyo. 3,700 tons gross, 4,400 tons d.w., 362 ft. l.o.a., 49·9 ft. breadth, 20·9 ft. draught, 6-cyl. diesel by Kobe Hatsudoki, 3,800 b.h.p., 13½ knots.

BARBARA. *Swedish.* Bulk carrier. Built by Sir J. Laing & Sons Ltd., Sunderland, for Tore Ulff A/B, Stockholm. 14,660 tons gross, 22,000 tons d.w., 566 ft. l.o.a., 73·33 ft. breadth, 32 ft. draught, 6-cyl. Götaverken diesel by N.E.M., 7,500 b.h.p., 15 knots.

BARCAROLLE. *Swedish.* Refrigerated cargo. Built by Ch. Nav. de La Ciotat, La Ciotat, for A/B Ekensbergs Varv, Stockholm. 6,750 tons gross, 450 ft. l.o.a., 59·5 ft. breadth, 20·75 ft. draught, 2 grd. turbs. by De Laval, 8,500 s.h.p., 18½ knots.

BARDU. *Norwegian.* Bulk carrier. Built by Deutsche Werft A.G., Hamburg, for I/S Bulktrading, Oslo. 11,276 tons gross, 16,000 tons d.w., 492 ft. l.o.a., 70 ft. breadth, 30·25 ft. draught, 7-cyl. Sulzer diesel, 7,700 b.h.p., 14½ knots.

BARILOCHE. *Swiss.* Bulk carrier. Built by Brodogradiliste 3 Maj, Rijeka, for Oceana Shipping A.G., Basle. 12,500 tons gross, 18,500 tons d.w., 575 ft. l.o.a., 73·33 ft. breadth, 30 ft. draught, 6-cyl. Sulzer diesel.

BARLBY. *British.* Bulk carrier. Built by Sir J. Laing & Sons Ltd., Sunderland, for Ropner Shipping Co. Ltd., Darlington. 16,565 tons gross, 24,850 tons d.w., 598·42 ft. l.o.a., 74·5 ft. breadth, 32·58 ft. draught, 5-cyl. Doxford diesel, 7,500 b.h.p., 15½ knots.

BAUSKA (ex *Professor Huber*). *Russian.* Tanker. Built by United Polish Shipyards, Gdansk, for U.S.S.R. 13,269 tons gross, 580·5 ft. l.o.a., 71·82 ft. breadth, 30·33 ft. draught, 6-cyl. Sulzer diesel, 7,800 b.h.p.

BAXTERGATE. *British.* Cargo. Built by Burntisland S.B. Co. Ltd., Burntisland, for Turnbull Scott Shipping Co. Ltd., London. 6,132 tons gross, 10,650 tons d.w., 470 ft. l.o.a., 61·75 ft. breadth, 26·66 ft. draught, 4-cyl. Doxford diesel by Hawthorn Leslie, 6,640 b.h.p., 15¼ knots.

B

B

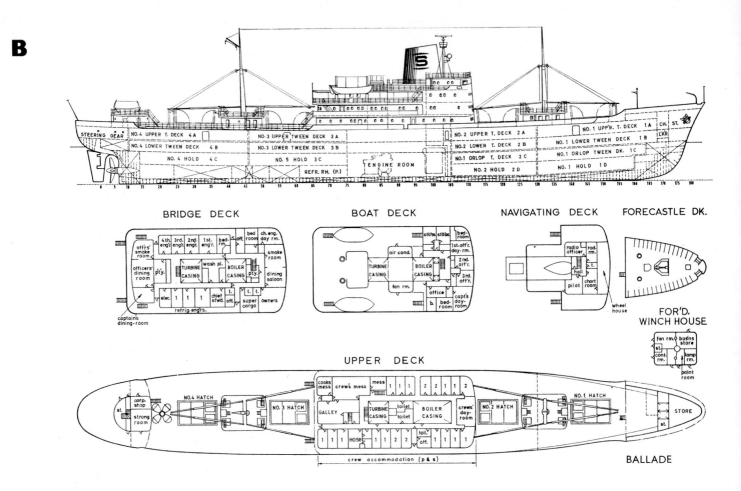

STEERING GEAR

NO.4 UPPER T. DECK 4A	NO.3 UPPER TWEEN DECK 3A	NO.2 UPPER T. DECK 2A	NO.1 UPP'R. T. DECK 1A	CH. ST.
NO.4 LOWER TWEEN DECK 4B	NO.3 LOWER TWEEN DECK 3B	NO.2 LOWER T. DECK 2B	NO.1 LOWER TWEEN DECK 1B	LKR
NO.4 HOLD 4C	NO.5 HOLD 3C	NO.1 ORLOP T. DECK 2C	NO.1 ORLOP TWEEN DK. 1C	
REFR. RM. (P.)	ENGINE ROOM	NO.2 HOLD 2D	NO.1 HOLD 1D	

BRIDGE DECK

BOAT DECK

NAVIGATING DECK

FORECASTLE DK.

FOR'D.
WINCH HOUSE

UPPER DECK

crew accommodation (p & s)

BALLADE

30

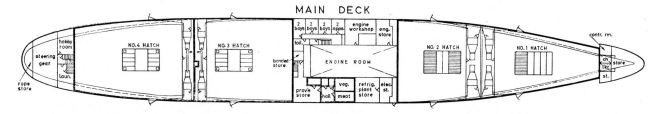

hobby room

steering gear

laun.

rope store

NO.4 HATCH

NO.3 HATCH

2 boys | 2 boys | 2 boys | 2 apps | engine workshop | eng. store

toil.

bonded store

ENGINE ROOM

provn store | hall | meat | veg. | refrig. plant store | elec. st.

NO. 2 HATCH

NO. 1 HATCH

contr. rm.

ch. | store
lkr.
st.

BALLADE. *This ship is the second of three sister ships ordered from Chantiers Navals de la Ciotat by the Swedish shipowners Salen-rederierna A/B Stockholm. They have been added to the owners' existing fleet of refrigerated cargo vessels employed in world-wide trade. The Ballade is powered by De Laval steam turbines supplied with steam generated in two of the latest type Foster Wheeler E.S.D.II boilers. The steam turbine with double-reduction gearing is designed for a maximum output of 9,500 s.h.p. (metric) at 124 r.p.m. and normal continuous service output of 8,600 s.h.p. (metric) at about 120 r.p.m. The ship obtained a maximum speed of 20·5 knots in rough water and in unloaded conditions. The Ballade has been built with two complete decks using Siemens-Martin steel for the hull. The cargo holds are divided into eight compartments, four forward and four aft as shown in the accompanying drawing. All four holds and tweendeck spaces are insulated and arranged for the carriage of refrigerated or frozen cargo at —4 deg. F. (—20 deg. C.). The ship is subdivided by six bulkheads watertight to the upper deck. There are four cargo side ports measuring about 6 ft. by 4 ft. 9 in. and one bunker port about 6 ft. by 2 ft. on each side of the upper tweendeck. Cargo hatches on the upper deck are fitted with MacGregor three-section insulated steel covers, while those on the decks below are of the pontoon type. The holds and tweendecks are served by eight A.S.E.A. 5-ton cargo winches fitted on top of the mast houses, four forward and four aft.*

BALLYRUSH. *This 2,000 tons d.w. motor collier was completed by Hall Russell & Co. Ltd., Aberdeen, for John Kelly Ltd., Belfast, and is the first of a pair of ships on order for these owners at the yard. The ship has been designed as a self-trimming collier and also as a general cargo carrier, for coastwise trading between the North of Ireland, British ports and on short international runs.*

BARLBY. *Built by Sir James Laing & Sons Ltd. for the Ropner Shipping Co. Ltd., the Barlby, 24,850 tons d.w., is one of the largest general purpose bulk carriers yet built for British owners. The ship is powered by a 5-cylinder 'P' turbocharged Doxford oil engine, the first of this size to be built. She has been designed for St. Lawrence Seaway trading. The Barlby is a single-deck bulk cargo vessel with a cargo capacity of 1,294,030 cu. ft. The hull is divided into seven main cargo holds having watertight bulkheads extending up to the main deck. All transverse bulkheads, with the exception of the forward engine room bulkhead and lower parts of the fore and after peaks, are corrugated. The height of the double bottom in the holds is about $52\frac{1}{4}$ in. with the sides carried up to 14 ft. 6 in. to form a partial hopper. So that the vessel shall be self-trimming, two longitudinal bulkheads are fitted extending from the hatch to the ship's side, an arrangement which allows the ship to have water ballast tanks to port and starboard in way of all holds. The spaces so formed, except those in way of No. 1 hold, can be used for the carriage of grain. These grain tanks have two steel watertight hatches with hinged covers, so that they can be employed when the ship is loading light grain. There are seven main cargo hatches of the MacGregor single-pull steel watertight type and fitted with towing chains.*

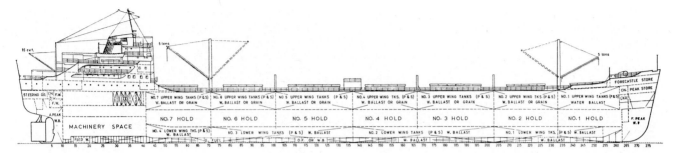

BARLBY—*above*

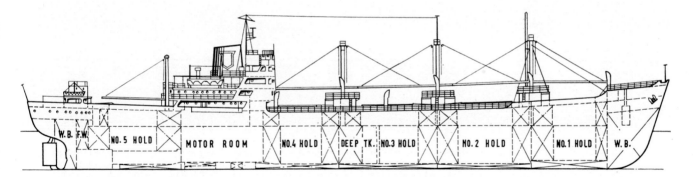

BAXTERGATE. *This general cargo ship was handed over to the Turnbull Scott Shipping Co. Ltd., London, by the Burntisland Shipbuilding Co. Ltd. She has four cargo holds and a dual-purpose deep tank forward and one cargo hold aft of the machinery space. This arrangement ensures a good trim under all conditions of loading. Tweendecks are arranged above the cargo holds and abreast the machinery casings where special lock-up cargo spaces are arranged with compartments for CO_2 bottles and the domestic dry and refrigerated store rooms.*

BEAVERPINE. *Built by the Burntisland Shipbuilding Co. Ltd. for Canadian Pacific Steamships Ltd., who now have seven cargo ships operating and the three passenger liners Empress of Canada, Empress of Britain and Empress of England. The new ship is powered by a diesel engine and has an average speed of 15 knots and will be employed on the company's services from the U.K., Continental and Canadian seaboard and Great Lakes ports, together with the Beaverelm and Beaverfir. The Beaverpine has been built to Lloyd's Register Class +100 AI with Class II Ice Strengthening. She is fitted out to meet the requirements of the St. Lawrence Seaway Authority, having Port Colbourne fairleads, landing booms, navigating lights and a stern anchor. Three of the four holds and tweendecks are positioned forward of the machinery space, and all the living accommodation is situated in the midships superstructure. The cargo capacity is 323,000 cu. ft. bale, and 296,000 cu. ft. grain. Each hold and tweendeck is served by one hatch, the largest being No. 2 which measures 50 ft. by 22 ft. A section of No. 4 tweendeck is allocated for the carriage of special cargo, and the forecastle space can also be used for this purpose.*

BEAU. *Norwegian.* Tanker. Built by Kaldnes M/V A/S, Tönsberg, for Biörn Biörnstad & Co., Moss. 18,417 tons gross, 28,000 tons d.w., 666·33 ft. l.o.a., 81·2 ft. breadth, 33·5 ft. draught, 2 De Laval grd. turbs. by Marinens Hovedverft, 12,000 s.h.p., 16 knots.

BEAVERPINE. *British.* Cargo. Built by Burntisland S.B. Co. Ltd., Burntisland, for Canadian Pacific Steamships Ltd., Montreal. 4,540 tons gross, 6,050 tons d.w., 371 ft. l.o.a., 52·75 ft. breadth, 23·67 ft. draught, 6-cyl. Sulzer diesel by Fairfield, 4,000 b.h.p., 15 knots.

BELGULF ENTERPRISE. *Belgian.* Tanker. Built by Kawasaki Dockyard Co. Ltd., Kobe, for Belgulf Tankers S.A., Antwerp. 12,319 tons gross, 17,757 tons d.w., 561 ft. l.o.a., 71 ft. breadth, 30 ft. draught, 2 grd. turbs. by the shipbuilders, 8,500 s.h.p., 15½ knots.

BELGULF STRENGTH. *Belgian.* Tanker. Built by Kawasaki Dockyard Co. Ltd., Kobe, for Belgulf Tankers S.A., Antwerp. 12,319 tons gross, 17,757 tons d.w., 561 ft. l.o.a., 71 ft. breadth, 30 ft. draught, 2 grd. turbs. by the shipbuilders, 8,500 s.h.p., 15½ knots.

BELGULF UNION. *Belgian.* Tanker. Built by Kawasaki Dockyard Co. Ltd., Kobe, for Belgulf Tankers S.A., Antwerp. 12,319 tons gross, 17,757 tons d.w., 561 ft. l.o.a., 71·2 ft. breadth, 30 ft. draught, 2 grd. turbs. by the shipbuilders, 8,500 s.h.p., 15¼ knots.

BELLAMI. *Norwegian.* Bulk carrier. Built by Kockums M/V A/B, Malmö, for Skibs A/S Oiltank, Tönsberg. 10,826 tons gross, 15,950 tons d.w., 492 ft. l.o.a., 65·2 ft. breadth, 29·82 ft. draught, 8-cyl. M.A.N. diesel by the shipbuilders, 6,960 b.h.p., 14½ knots.

BELMONA. *Norwegian.* Bulk carrier. Built by Rheinstahl Nordseewerke, Emden, for Georg Vefling, Tönsberg. 12,230 tons gross, 17,110 tons d.w., 522·9 ft. l.o.a., 70·58 ft. breadth, 30·66 ft. draught, 5-cyl. B. & W. diesel by Krupp, 7,500 b.h.p., 15¼ knots.

BELORETSK. *Russian.* Cargo. Built by A/S Nakskov Skibsv., Nakskov, for U.S.S.R. 10,651 tons gross, 14,485 tons d.w., 526 ft. l.o.a., 69·75 ft. breadth, 31·67 ft. draught, 6-cyl. B. & W. diesel, 12,600 b.h.p., 18½ knots.

BELOVODSK. *Russian.* Cargo. Built by A/S Nakskov Skibsv., Nakskov, for U.S.S.R. 10,651 tons gross, 14,485 tons d.w., 526 ft. l.o.a., 69·75 ft. breadth, 31·67 ft. draught, 6-cyl. B. & W. diesel, 12,600 b.h.p., 18½ knots.

BELTANA. *Norwegian.* Bulk carrier. Built by Kaldnes M/V A/S, Tönsberg, for Skibs A/S Oiltank, Tönsberg. 10,165 tons gross, 15,000 tons d.w., 500·33 ft. l.o.a., 66 ft. breadth, 28·58 ft. draught, 6-cyl. M.A.N. diesel by Kockums, 5,220 b.h.p., 14 knots.

BENEFACTOR (ex *Olau Ege*). *Danish.* Cargo. Built by Helsingborgs Varfs A/B, Helsingborg, for Olau-Line A/S, Copenhagen. 3,815 tons gross, 4,950 tons d.w., 361·58 ft. l.o.a., 47·66 ft. breadth, 19·66 ft. draught, 6-cyl. B. & W. diesel, 3,300 b.h.p., 16 knots (trials).

BENVALLA. *British.* Refrigerated cargo. Built by Chas. Connell & Co. Ltd., Glasgow, for Ben Line Steamers Ltd., Edinburgh. 11,391 tons gross, 13,080 tons d.w., 549·58 ft. l.o.a., 71·25 ft. breadth, 30 ft. draught, 10-cyl. Sulzer diesel by Rowan, 15,000 b.h.p., 21 knots.

BERGE EDDA. *Norwegian.* Tanker. Built by A/S Rosenberg M/V, Stavanger, for Sig. Bergesen d.y. & Co., Stavanger. 31,835 tons gross, 51,000 tons d.w., 734 ft. l.o.a., 104·33 ft. breadth, 39·33 ft. draught, 10-cyl. B. & W. diesel, 17,300 b.h.p., 15½ knots.

BERGE JARL. *Norwegian.* Tanker. Built by A/S Rosenberg M/V, Stavanger for Sig. Bergesen d.y. & Co., Stavanger. 33,835 tons gross, 51,000 tons d.w., 734 ft. l.o.a., 104·2 ft. breadth, 39·25 ft. draught, 10-cyl. B. & W. diesel, 17,300 b.h.p., 15½ knots.

BERNES. *Norwegian.* Bulk carrier. Built by Lithgows Ltd., Port Glasgow, for A/S Kristian Jebsens Rederi, Bergen. 10,485 tons gross, 15,000 tons d.w., 500·5 ft. l.o.a., 67 ft. breadth, 28·2 ft. draught, 6-cyl. B. & W. diesel, 6,000 b.h.p., 14¾ knots.

B

BELORETSK. *V/O Sudoimport of Russia have taken delivery of a number of vessels built in Denmark and Japan. The Beloretsk is the first of a quartet of 14,485 tons d.w. vessels building in Denmark. This vessel and her sister ship Belovodsk were built by A/B Nakskov Skibsvaerft, while the other pair are under construction by Burmeister & Wain of Copenhagen. An interesting point is that the bilge and tank piping is provided with hydraulic valves operated from the engine room.*

BENEFACTOR. *The Olau Line Ltd. of Copenhagen took delivery of the cargo motorship Benefactor from Helsingborgs Varfs A/B, Helsingborgs, Sweden. The deadweight capacity open is 3,740 tons on a draught of 19 ft. 8 in., and with shelterdeck closed she will carry 4,960 tons on a draught of 23 ft. 1 in.*

BENVALLA. *This 13,080 tons d.w. ship has been built for the Ben Line to the same very fine lines as her sister ships* Bengloe *('Merchant Ships: World Built,' Vol. X) and* Benloyal *('Merchant Ships: World Built,' Vol. VIII). Between the Benvalla and Bengloe, however, there are five immediately apparent differences. In the first place the Benvalla has her forward bipod mast and heavy derrick located between Nos. 2 and 3 holds, whereas the Bengloe had these fitted between Nos. 3 and 4 holds. Secondly, the Benvalla has three mast houses, two forward and one aft, whereas the Bengloe has one only located on the foredeck. Thirdly, in the new ship the boat deckhouse has been increased in length by about 15 ft. to enable 12 passengers to be accommodated—the Bengloe only carries 10 passengers. The Benvalla has six cargo holds, four forward of the superstructure and two aft, with an additional cargo space in the poop. The total grain capacity, excluding that of the oil cargo tanks and refrigerated cargo spaces, is 668,750 cu. ft. The new ship, built by Charles Connell & Co. Ltd., unlike her earlier sister ships which are steam turbine driven, is powered by diesel machinery.*

BESSEGEN. *Built to the order of Chr. Ostberg, of Oslo, by Kaldnes Mek. Verksted, this carrier is specially designed and constructed for the carriage of newsprint in bulk. The vessel is of the single-deck type with machinery and accommodation aft. In order to facilitate the carriage of deck cargo, the six hatches are fitted with covers of special design, made by MacGregor International, and when closed they present a flat and unbroken surface, which extends practically the whole breadth of the ship between Nos. 2 and 6 hatches. The width of these hatches is 46 ft. The cargo handling equipment consists of three Munck rolling gantry cranes, travelling fore and aft on rails mounted on the deck. The cranes are equipped with hydraulically operated hinged extension arms, which give a long reach over the ship's sides when loading or discharging. The lifting part of the crane comprises a hoist operating from a trolley running on rails along the main girders and hinged extension pieces of the gantry. The three cranes give a total working capacity of more than 1,000 tons per hour. By means of a special yoke eight reels of newsprint can be handled simultaneously by each crane in one operation. To handle 9,000 tons of newsprint loading or discharging would normally take three days and employ 60 men, but with these cranes it is expected that 10 men will be able to accomplish the task in 10 hours.*

BESSEGGEN. *Norwegian.* Newsprint carrier. Built by Kaldnes M/V A/S, Tönsberg, for Chr. Ostberg, Oslo. 7,200 tons gross, 9,250 tons d.w., 459 ft. l.o.a., 64·2 ft. breadth, 25·33 ft. draught, 6-cyl. diesel by Gebr.-Stork, 6,300 b.h.p., 14½ knots.

BETH. *Norwegian.* Bulk carrier. Built by Deutsche Werft A.G., Hamburg, for I/S Gibisary, Oslo. 11,200 tons gross, 16,310 tons d.w., 492 ft. l.o.a., 70·2 ft. breadth, 30·42 ft. draught, 7-cyl. Sulzer diesel by Buckau-Wolf, 7,700 b.h.p., 15½ knots.

BETTY. *Norwegian.* Bulk carrier. Built by Deutsche Werft, Hamburg, for L. Gill-Johannessen Ltd., Oslo. 10,500 tons gross, 16,300 tons d.w., 465 ft. b.p., 70 ft. breadth, 30·2 ft. draught, diesel by Sulzer, 7,700 b.h.p., 15½ knots.

BHARATA JAYANTI. *Indian.* Bulk carrier. Built by Mitsuibishi S.B. & E. Co. Ltd., Nagasaki, for Jayanti S. Co. Pte. Ltd., Bombay. 21,600 tons gross, 32,250 tons d.w., 627 ft. l.o.a., 90 ft. breadth, 6-cyl. Sulzer diesel by Uraga, 10,500 b.h.p., 16 knots.

BILBAO. *Spanish.* Tanker. Built by Empresa Nac. 'Bazan,' El Ferrol, for Naviera Vizcaina S.A., Bilbao. 21,592 tons gross, 32,000 tons d.w., 665 ft. l.o.a., 87·5 ft. breadth, 34·82 ft. draught, 2 Parsons grd. turbs., 14,000 s.h.p., 16¼ knots.

BIRIM RIVER. *British.* Cargo. Built by N.V. Kon. Maats. 'De Schelde,' Flushing, for Black Star Line Ltd., Accra. 5,315 tons gross, 6,800 tons d.w., 460·9 ft. l.o.a., 60·2 ft. breadth, 23·25 ft. draught, 5-cyl. Sulzer diesel by the shipbuilders, 4,500 b.h.p., 15 knots.

BLANDFORD. *British.* Tanker. Built by Kockums M/V A/B, Malmö, for Blandford Shipping Co. Ltd., Fred Dessen & Co. Ltd. and Fruit Lines Ltd., London. 26,100 tons gross, 41,750 tons d.w., 699·5 ft. l.o.a., 97·25 ft. breadth, 36·75 ft. draught, 2 De Laval grd. turbs. by the shipbuilders, 16,500 s.h.p., 17¾ knots.

BLANKAHOLM. *Swedish.* Refrigerated cargo. Built by Wärtsilä Kon. Crichton-Vulcan, Abo, for A/B Svenska Amerika Linien, Gothenburg. 5,400 tons gross, 7,000 tons d.w., 421·9 ft. l.o.a., 57·8 ft. breadth, 26·25 ft. draught, 7-cyl. diesel by Götaverken, 5,800 b.h.p., 16 knots.

BLEASDALE. *British.* Hopper dredger. Built by Simons-Lobnitz Ltd., Renfrew, for British Transport Commission. 1,140 tons gross, 192·9 ft. l.o.a., 40·42 ft. breadth, tw-sc. diesel-electric, two 8-cyl. diesels by Mirrlees, Bickerton & Day, 904 b.h.p., 10½ knots.

BOBRUISKLES. *Russian.* Cargo. Built by United Polish Shipyards, Gdansk, for U.S.S.R. 4,653 tons gross, 5,900 tons d.w., 406·42 ft. l.o.a., 54·9 ft. breadth, 22·33 ft. draught, 5-cyl. Sulzer diesel, 4,500 b.h.p., 14½ knots.

BOGATYRLES. *Russian.* Cargo. Built by United Polish Shipyards, Gdansk, for U.S.S.R. 4,653 tons gross, 5,900 tons d.w., 406·42 ft. l.o.a., 54·9 ft. breadth, 22·33 ft. draught, 5-cyl. Sulzer diesel, 4,500 b.h.p., 14½ knots.

BOLERO. *Swedish.* Refrigerated cargo. Built by Ch. Nav. de La Ciotat, La Ciotat, for A/B Ekensbergs Varv, Stockholm. 6,936 tons gross, 450·25 ft. l.o.a., 59·44 ft. breadth, 26 ft. draught, 2 grd. turbs. by De Laval, 9,500 s.h.p., 18¼ knots.

BONGO. *French.* Wine and vegetable oil tanker. Built by At. & Ch. de La Rochelle-Pallice, La Rochelle-Pallice, for Cie. de Nav. Paquet, Marseilles. 2,278 tons gross, 3,020 tons d.w., 315 ft. l.o.a., 42·5 ft. breadth, 17 ft. draught, 8-cyl. Pielstick diesel, 2,940 b.h.p.

BONGO. *Norwegian.* Cargo. Built by P. Lindenau, Kiel, for Paal Wilson & Co. A/S, Bergen. 2,750 tons gross, 300·2 ft. l.o.a., 48 ft. breadth, 19·75 ft. draught, 6-cyl. M.A.N. diesel.

B

B

BORDER CHIEFTAN. *British.* Tanker. Built by Smith's Dock Co. Ltd., Middlesbrough, for The Lowland Tanker Co. Ltd., Newcastle-upon-Tyne. 13,238 tons gross, 19,635 tons d.w., 569 ft. l.o.a., 72·66 ft. breadth, 31·58 ft. draught, 6-cyl. Doxford diesel by Hawthorn Leslie, 7,500 b.h.p., 14¼ knots.

BOSTON MARU. *Japanese.* Cargo. Built by Mitsubishi S.B. & E. Co. Ltd., Hiroshima, for Mitsubishi Kaiun K.K., Tokyo. 9,350 tons gross, 12,000 tons d.w., 513·33 ft. l.o.a., 64·2 ft. breadth, 30·66 ft. draught, 9-cyl. U.E.C. diesel by the shipbuilders, 13,000 b.h.p., 18 knots.

BRECON BEACON. *British.* Cargo. Built by Werf de Noord, Alblasserdam, for Medomsley Steam Shipping Co. Ltd., London. 9,322 tons gross, 12,850 tons d.w., 499·58 ft. l.o.a., 64·5 ft. breadth, 29·58 ft. draught, 6-cyl. M.A.N. diesel by Wilton Fijenoord, 7,760 b.h.p., 15 knots.

BREGAGLIA. *Swiss.* Bulk carrier. Built by Brodogradiliste 3 Maj, Rijeka, for Oceana Shipping A.G., Lausanne. 14,112 tons gross, 18,500 tons d.w., 575 ft. l.o.a., 73·33 ft. breadth, 30 ft. draught, 6-cyl. diesel by Sulzer, 7,800 b.h.p., 14 knots.

B. RESIT PASA. *Turkish.* Cargo. Built by Nipponkai H.I. Co. Ltd., Toyama, for Denizcilik Bankasi T.A.O., Istanbul. 2,750 tons gross, 5,150 tons d.w., 349·75 ft. l.o.a., 49·42 ft. breadth, 21·82 ft. draught, 5-cyl. Sulzer diesel by Uraga, 3,200 b.h.p., 15½ knots.

BREVIK. *Norwegian.* Bulk carrier. Built by A/B Götaverken, Gothenburg, for A/S Borgestad, Borgestad. 12,103 tons gross, 16,600 tons d.w., 518·25 ft. l.o.a., 70·2 ft. breadth, 30·33 ft. draught, 8-cyl. Götaverken diesel, 6,000 b.h.p., 14½ knots.

BRIANSKLES. *Russian.* Cargo. Built by United Polish Shipyards, Gdansk, for U.S.S.R. 4,638 tons gross, 5,900 tons d.w., 406·42 ft. l.o.a., 54·9 ft. breadth, 22·33 ft. draught, 5-cyl. Sulzer diesel, 4,500 b.h.p., 14½ knots.

BRIDGEPOOL. *British.* Bulk carrier. Built by Austin & Pickersgill Ltd., Sunderland, for Pool Shipping Co. Ltd., Durham. 11,428 tons gross, 16,100 tons d.w., 522 ft. l.o.a., 67·2 ft. breadth, 30 ft. draught, 5-cyl. Götaverken diesel, 6,300 b.h.p., 14½ knots.

BRINTON LYKES. *American.* Refrigerated cargo. Built by Bethlehem Steel Co., Sparrows Point, for Lykes Brothers S.S. Co. Inc., New Orleans. 10,200 tons gross, 11,000 tons d.w., 495 ft. l.o.a., 69 ft. breadth, 29·58 ft. draught, 2 grd. turbs. by G.E.C., 11,000 s.h.p., 18 knots.

BRIDGESTONE MARU. *Japanese.* L.P.G. carrier. Built by Mitsubishi Nippon H.I., for Bridgestone Liquefied Petroleum Gas Co. Ltd., and Nippon Yusen Kaisha, Tokyo. 20,516 tons gross, 25,626 tons d.w., 602·75 ft. l.o.a., 82·2 ft. breadth, 34·42 ft. draught, 9-cyl. M.A.N. diesel, 13,000 b.h.p., 16 knots.

BRISSAC. *Norwegian.* Ore carrier. Built by Ch. Réunis Loire-Normandie, Nantes, for Fred Olsen & Co., Oslo. 11,430 tons gross, 15,650 tons d.w., 497·2 ft. l.o.a., 67 ft. breadth, 29·5 ft. draught, 7-cyl. Sulzer diesel, 6,300 b.h.p., 14¾ knots.

BRITISH BOMBARDIER. *British.* Tanker. Built by Alex. Stephen & Sons Ltd., Glasgow, for BP Tanker Co. Ltd., London. 32,351 tons gross, 50,000 tons d.w., 760 ft. l.o.a., 97·33 ft. breadth, 41 ft. draught, 2 Pametrada grd. turbs. by the shipbuilders, 16,000 s.h.p., 15½ knots.

BRITISH CAVALIER. *British.* Tanker. Built by J. L. Thompson & Sons Ltd., Sunderland, for BP Tanker Co. Ltd., London. 32,351 tons gross, 50,000 tons d.w., 760 ft. l.o.a., 97·33 ft. breadth, 41 ft. draught, 2 grd. turbs. by Parsons, 16,000 s.h.p., 15½ knots.

BRITISH CYGNET. *British.* Tanker. Built by Harland & Wolff Ltd., Belfast, for BP Tanker Co. Ltd., London. 11,174 tons gross, 15,303 tons d.w., 525·5 ft. l.o.a., 69·33 ft. breadth, 29·33 ft. draught, 6-cyl. B. & W. diesel by the shipbuilders, 7,600 b.h.p., 14½ knots.

BLANDFORD. This 41,750 tons d.w. tanker was delivered to the Blandford Shipping Co. Ltd., London, from the Malmo shipyard of Kockums Mekaniska Verstad, Sweden. The main propelling machinery consists of Kockums-De Laval steam turbines developing 16,500 s.h.p. at 106 r.p.m. A speed of 17·75 knots was attained on trials.

BREVIK. The Götaverken shipyard delivered in 1962 this motor bulk carrier to A/S Borgestad, Norway. The six cargo holds have a total grain capacity of 802,000 cu. ft. The hatch covers are of Götaverken's new design operated by Hydrautorque hinges. The main engine is an 8-cylinder Götaverken diesel which develops 6,000 b.h.p. at 112 r.p.m.

B

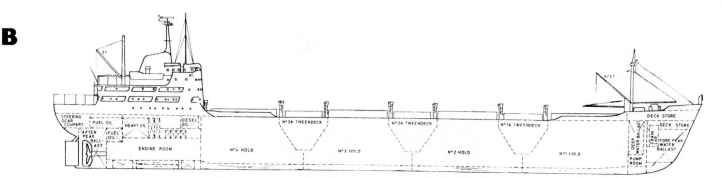

BREGAGLIA. *Two Universal Bulk Carriers have been completed in 1962 by the Yugoslav shipbuilders Brodogradiliste 3 Maj, Rijeka. The Bregaglia is owned by Oceana Shipping A.G., of Switzerland, and the Bariloche by Transglobe Shipping & Trading Corporation of Monrovia. Both ships are managed by the Société d'Armament Maritime Suisse-Atlantique S.A., Lausanne. It is only four years since the first ship was built to a design developed by the International MacGregor Organization known as the Universal Bulk Carrier. Today there are 16 ships of this type at sea or under construction, including the 22,075 tons d.w. Hoegh Transporter, see page 86. The U.B.C. can carry its deadweight of any of the normal bulk cargoes without excessive metacentric height and without the use of shifting boards; it can also carry ballast amounting to nearly 50 per cent. of the deadweight tonnage—again with a reasonably small metacentric height and consequently easy motion. The Bregaglia and Bariloche have been built in the conventional modern style with machinery and accommodation aft, and have a single deck. There are four main cargo holds extending from the main weather deck to the double bottom tank, having a total capacity of 850,500 cu. ft. grain. The main cargo holds are suitable for the carriage of all kinds of bulk cargo, such as grain, coal, ore, phosphate, sugar, salt, etc. There are three partial tweendecks which are of greater height than is found in conventional cargo ships.*

BRIDGESTONE MARU. *This ship was designed solely for the carriage of refrigerated liquefied petroleum gas and was built at the Yokohama shipyard of Mitsubishi Nippon Heavy-Industries Ltd. This vessel, 25,626 tons d.w., has been built for the Bridgestone Liquefied Petroleum Gas Co. Ltd., and is being used for the carriage of L.P.G. from Kuwait to Japan under a long-term contract with the British Petroleum Co. Ltd. Designed by Conch International Methane Ltd., the firm responsible for the design of the Methane Pioneer, the Bridgestone Maru employs the refrigerated storage system originally developed for the carriage of methane. She is the first vessel to use it for L.P.G. Conch International Methane Ltd. and Nippon Yusen Kaisha Ltd. are the joint owners. The Bridgestone Maru has been constructed with four cargo tanks of full hold length and width, and has internal centreline and transverse bulkheads. These tanks are constructed of nickel-alloy steel and measure about 88 ft. in length, 44 ft. in depth and 72 ft. in width. In this type of ship where the gases are carried at temperatures of about −40 to −42 deg. F., glass fibre insulation is used to reduce the influx of heat to the cargo: this is done to reduce the rate of vaporization and to protect the hull steel from embrittlement.*

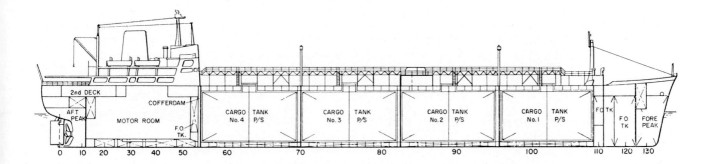

B

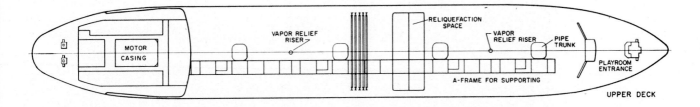

CARGO TANK No. 4 P/S
CARGO TANK No. 3 P/S
CARGO TANK No. 2 P/S
CARGO TANK No. 1 P/S

2nd DECK
COFFERDAM
AFT PEAK
MOTOR ROOM
F.O. TK.
F.O TK
F.O TK
FORE PEAK

0 10 20 30 40 50 60 70 80 90 100 110 120 130

MOTOR CASING
VAPOR RELIEF RISER
RELIQUEFACTION SPACE
VAPOR RELIEF RISER
PIPE TRUNK
PLAYROOM ENTRANCE
A-FRAME FOR SUPPORTING
UPPER DECK

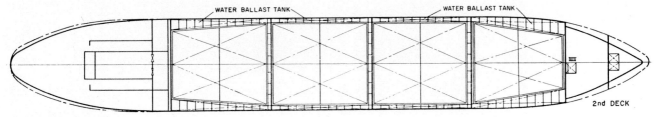

WATER BALLAST TANK
WATER BALLAST TANK
2nd DECK

BRIDGESTONE MARU

B

BRITISH GRENADIER. *British.* Tanker. Built by Vickers-Armstrongs (S.B.) Ltd., Barrow, for BP Tanker Co. Ltd., London. 32,500 tons gross, 52,400 tons d.w., 760 ft. l.o.a., 97 ft. breadth, 41 ft. draught, 2 grd. turbs. by the shipbuilders, 16,000 s.h.p., 15½ knots.

BRITISH HUSSAR. *British.* Tanker. Built by John Brown & Co. (Clydebank) Ltd., Clydebank, for BP Tanker Co. Ltd., London. 32,351 tons gross, 50,000 tons d.w., 760 ft. l.o.a., 97·33 ft. breadth, 41 ft. draught, 2 grd. turbs. by the shipbuilders, 16,000 s.h.p., 15½ knots.

BRITISH KESTREL. *British.* Tanker. Built by Wm. Hamilton & Co. Ltd., Port Glasgow, for BP Tanker Co. Ltd., London. 11,171 tons gross, 15,303 tons d.w., 525·25 ft. l.o.a., 69·33 ft. breadth, 29·33 ft. draught, 6-cyl. B. & W. diesel by Kincaid, 7,600 b.h.p., 14½ knots.

BRITISH MERLIN. *British.* Tanker. Built by Harland & Wolff Ltd., Glasgow, for BP Tanker Co. Ltd., London. 11,171 tons gross, 15,303 tons d.w., 525·75 ft. l.o.a., 69·33 ft. breadth, 29·33 ft. draught, 6-cyl. B. & W. diesel by the shipbuilders, 7,600 b.h.p., 14½ knots.

BRITISH OSPREY. *British.* Tanker. Built by Harland & Wolff Ltd., Glasgow, for BP Tanker Co. Ltd., London. 11,171 tons gross, 15,303 tons d.w., 525·75 ft. l.o.a., 69·33 ft. breadth, 29·33 ft. draught, 6-cyl. B. & W. diesel by the shipbuilders, 7,600 b.h.p., 14½ knots.

BRITISH PRESTIGE. *British.* Tanker. Built by Vickers-Armstrongs (S.B.) Ltd., Barrow, for BP Tanker Co. Ltd., London. 27,480 tons gross, 42,000 tons d.w., 710 ft. l.o.a., 95·42 ft. breadth, 38·66 ft. draught, 2 grd. turbs. by the shipbuilders, 16,000 s.h.p., 16 knots.

BRITISH PRESTIGE. *The second of two sister 42,000 tons d.w. turbine tankers delivered to the BP Tanker Co. Ltd. from the Barrow-in-Furness shipyard of Vickers-Armstrongs (Shipbuilders) Ltd. There are 44 cargo tanks, four abreast in the breadth of the vessel. The turbine machinery is capable of developing a service power of 16,000 s.h.p., giving a speed in service of 16 knots.*

BRITISH HUSSAR. This vessel, built by John Brown & Co. (Clydebank) Ltd., is the first of a series of six ships of about 50,000 tons d.w. on order for BP. A second ship of this tonnage delivered in 1962, the British Bombardier, was completed by Alexander Stephen & Sons Ltd., a third was delivered by J. L. Thomson & Sons Ltd., Sunderland, and a fourth by Vickers-Armstrongs Ltd., Barrow. The British Hussar is powered by steam turbine machinery operating on steam generated at 600 p.s.i.g. and 900 deg. F. Back-pressure turbo-alternators are fitted, and the overall effect of the design changes is calculated to show a considerable saving in fuel and reduction in the first cost. This has been designed for an output of 16,000 s.h.p. at 105 propeller r.p.m. The British Hussar has been constructed on the combined longitudinal and transverse system of framing, with three longitudinal bulkheads, two oiltight and one non-oiltight. The cargo space has

B

BRITISH HUSSAR. *The tall streamlined funnel is of a new design to keep smoke off the decks.*

Continued from previous page:

been divided into 36 tanks; the three wing tanks port and starboard at amidships being arranged for the carriage of water ballast, and the remaining 12 centre tanks and 18 wing tanks having a total capacity of about 2·2 million cu. ft. The oil cargo is handled by three Hayward Tyler-De Laval steam turbine driven pumps, each of 1,750 tons/hour capacity, and two stripping pumps, each of 250 tons/hour capacity. The pumps are of the horizontal type and are fitted in the pump room in way of the machinery space bulkhead. In addition, there is one 1,000 tons/hour turbine driven water ballast pump, and one bilge pump.

BRITISH KESTREL. *This 15,303 tons d.w. tanker, delivered to the BP Tanker Co. Ltd. by Wm. Hamilton & Co. Ltd., Port Glasgow, is the twelfth of a series of typical finished-product carrying vessels; the first of them being the* British Fulmar, *listed in 'Merchant Ships: World Built,' Vol. VIII. Three others of this class,* British Cygnet, British Merlin *and* British Osprey, *were delivered by Harland & Wolff during 1962.*

BRUNES. *Norwegian.* Bulk carrier. Built by Lithgows Ltd., Port Glasgow, for A/S Kristian Jebsens Rederi, Bergen. 10,485 tons gross, 15,030 tons d.w., 500·5 ft. l.o.a., 67 ft. breadth, 28·2 ft. draught, 6-cyl. B. & W. diesel by Kincaid, 6,000 b.h.p., 15½ knots.

BUCURESTI. *Roumanian.* Cargo. Built by Brodogradiliste 3 Maj, Rijeka, for NAVROM Roumanian Marit. & Fluvial Nav., Bucharest. 9,050 tons gross, 12,850 tons d.w., 496·82 ft. l.o.a., 62 ft. breadth, 29·5 ft. draught, 8-cyl. Sulzer diesel.

C

CACTUS MARU. *Japanese.* Tanker. Built by Yokohama S.B. Co. Ltd., Yokohama, for Nisso Shipping Co. Ltd., Tokyo. 29,000 tons gross, 48,300 tons d.w., 738·25 ft. l.o.a., 100·42 ft. breadth, 37·82 ft. draught, 9-cyl. M.A.N. diesel by Mitsub. Nippon H.I., 17,100 b.h.p., 17 knots.

CALIFORNIA. *American.* Cargo. Built by Newport News S.B. & D.D. Co., Newport News, for States Steamship Co., San Francisco. 12,693 tons gross, 565 ft. l.o.a., 76·2 ft. breadth, 31·58 ft. draught, 2 grd. turbs. by the shipbuilders, 19,250 s.h.p., 20 knots.

CALTEX GREENWICH. *British.* Tanker. Built by Hitachi S.B. & E. Co. Ltd., Innoshima, for Overseas Tankship (U.K.) Ltd., London. 35,720 tons gross, 54,850 tons d.w., 761·66 ft. l.o.a., 109·25 ft. breadth, 38·25 ft. draught, grd. turb. by the shipbuilders, 18,500 b.h.p., 16½ knots (trials).

CAMPOGULES. *Spanish.* Tanker. Built by Union Nav. de Levante, Valencia, for Cia. Arrendataria del Monopolio de Petroleos S.A., Valencia. 7,053 tons gross, 9,300 tons d.w., 456·2 ft. l.o.a., 56·75 ft. breadth, 25·42 ft. draught, 5-cyl. B. & W. diesel by Maquinista, 4,500 b.h.p., 14 knots.

CAMPORROJO. *Spanish.* Tanker. Built by Union Nav. de Levante, Valencia, for Cia. Arrendataria del Monopolio Petroleos S.A., Valencia. 7,053 tons gross, 9,300 tons d.w., 456·2 ft. l.o.a., 56·75 ft. breadth 25·42 ft. draught, 5-cyl. B. & W. diesel by Maquinista, 4,500 b.h.p., 14 knots.

CANAL EL SUEZ. *United Arab Republic.* Cargo. Built by Suez Canal Authority, Port Fuad, for Suez Canal Authority. 1,983 tons gross, 3,200 tons d.w., 258·5 ft. l.o.a., 42·33 ft. breadth, 21·5 ft. draught, 7-cyl. M.A.N. diesel.

CAPE HOWE. *British.* Ore carrier. Built by Lithgows Ltd., Port Glasgow, for Lyle Shipping Co. Ltd., Glasgow. 16,000 tons gross, 26,500 tons d.w., 608 ft. l.o.a., 80 ft. breadth, 32·25 ft. draught, 6-cyl. B. & W. diesel by Kincaid, 6,410 b.h.p., 12 knots.

CAP SAN ANTONIO. *German.* Cargo. Built by Howaldtswerke Ham. A.G., Hamburg, for Hamburg-Südamerik. D/S, Hamburg. 7,434 tons gross, 10,700 tons d.w., 522 ft. l.o.a., 70·33 ft. breadth, 27 ft. draught, 9-cyl. M.A.N. diesel by the shipbuilders, 11,650 b.h.p., 20 knots.

CAP SAN DIEGO. *German.* Cargo. Built by Deutsche Werft A.G., Hamburg, for Hamburg-Südamerik. D/S, Hamburg. 7,432 tons gross, 10,300 tons d.w., 522 ft. l.o.a., 70·42 ft. breadth, 24·66 ft. draught, 9-cyl. M.A.N. diesel, 11,650 b.h.p., 20 knots.

CARDIFF CITY. *British.* Cargo. Built by Wm. Doxford & Sons (S.B.) Ltd., Sunderland, for Reardon Smith Line Ltd., Cardiff. 10,335 tons gross, 14,400 tons d.w., 499·5 ft. l.o.a., 67·25 ft. breadth, 30·58 ft. draught, 4-cyl. Doxford diesel, 6,600 b.h.p., 14½ knots.

CASTOR. *Finnish.* Cargo. Built by Wärtsila Kon. Crichton-Vulkan, Abo, for Finska Angfartygs A/B, Helsingfors. 2,256 tons gross, 3,100 tons d.w., 294·82 ft. l.o.a., 43·2 ft. breadth, 19·75 ft. draught, 6-cyl. Sulzer diesel by the shipbuilders, 2,400 b.h.p., 15½ knots.

CENTAURO. *Italian.* Bulk carrier. Built by Ansaldo S.p.A., Spezia, for 'Italsider' Alti Forni e Acciaierie Riuniti Ilva e Cornigliano S.p.A. 24,400 tons gross, 35,000 tons d.w., 679 ft. l.o.a., 92·25 ft. breadth, 34·25 ft. draught, 8-cyl. Fiat diesel, 16,800 b.h.p., 17 knots.

CENTAURUS. *Greek.* Cargo. Built by J. & K. Smit's Scheepsw., Kinderdijk, for Soc. Transoceanica Canopus S.A., Piraeus. 10,493 tons gross, 12,200 tons d.w., 516·25 ft. l.o.a., 64·2 ft. breadth, 31 ft. draught, 6-cyl. Stork diesel, 7,000 b.h.p., 16 knots.

CHAPEL RIVER. *British.* Bulk carrier. Built by Blyth D.D. & S.B. Co. Ltd., Blyth, for River Line Ltd., London. 16,398 tons gross, 23,000 tons d.w., 618·82 ft. l.o.a., 73·25 ft. breadth, 31 ft. draught, 7-cyl. Sulzer diesel by G. Clark, 10,500 b.h.p., 16 knots.

CALTEX GREENWICH. A 54,850 tons d.w. tanker delivered to Overseas Tankship (U.K.) Ltd., from the Innoshima shipyard of the Hitachi Shipbuilding & Engineering Co. Ltd. A sister ship to the Caltex Greenwich, the Caltex Southampton, is due for delivery in March, 1963.

CHARLES L.D. *French.* Ore carrier. Built by Soc. des Forg. de la Méditerranée, La Seyne, for Louis Dreyfus & Cie., Paris. 21,554 tons gross, 32,500 tons d.w., 652·9 ft. l.o.a., 87·2 ft. breadth, 35 ft. draught, 8-cyl. Götaverken diesel by the shipbuilders, 10,000 b.h.p., 14½ knots.

CHIKUMAGAWA MARU. *Japanese.* Tanker. Built by Kawasaki Dockyard Co. Ltd., Kobe, for Kawasaki Kisen K.K., Kobe. 29,600 tons gross, 50,396 tons d.w., 723·42 ft. l.o.a., 101·67 ft. breadth, 36·5 ft. draught, 2 grd. turbs. by the shipbuilders, 16,500 s.h.p., 15½ knots.

CHIRYU MARU. *Japanese.* Cargo. Built by Tohoku S.B. Co., Shiogama, for Taiheiyo Kisen K.K., Tokyo. 2,283 tons gross, 3,750 tons d.w., 299·5 ft. l.o.a., 43·33 ft. breadth, 19·2 ft. draught, 6-cyl. diesel by Kobe Hatsudoki, 2,000 b.h.p., 11½ knots.

CHRISTIANE OLDENDORFF. *German.* Cargo. Built by Werft Nobiskrug, Rendsburg, for Egon Oldendorff, Lübeck. 2,983 tons gross, 4,250 tons d.w., 347·5 ft. l.o.a., 49·66 ft. breadth, 19·5 ft. draught, two 6-cyl. grd. diesels by M.A.N., 3,000 b.h.p., 14 knots.

CIDADE DE BELEM. *Brazilian.* Refrigerated cargo. Built by Ishikawajima do Brasil, Rio de Janeiro, for Comissao de Marinha Mercanto, Rio de Janeiro. 4,950 tons gross, 5,860 tons d.w., 378·25 ft. l.o.a., 55·2 ft. breadth, 5-cyl. Sulzer diesel by Ishikawajima-Harima H.I., 2,500 b.h.p., 13½ knots.

CITY OF CANBERRA. The single-screw motorship City of Canberra was delivered to Ellerman Lines Ltd. in 1962 by Barclay, Curle & Co. Ltd. The new vessel is generally similar to the City of Sydney but she has increased refrigerated cargo capacity, and has been designed for use on her owners' trans-Pacific service between Australia and America. The ship has five cargo holds with upper and lower tweendecks throughout. No. 2 upper and lower tweendecks and hold, No. 3 upper and lower tweendecks and No. 4 upper and lower tweendecks and hold are insulated, with a capacity of 240,000 cu. ft. for the carriage of refrigerated cargoes.

CIDADE DE MANAUS (ex *Campo Grande*). *Brazilian.* Refrigerated cargo. Built by Ishikawajima do Brasil, Rio de Janeiro, for Comissao de Marinha Mercante, Rio de Janeiro. 4,950 tons gross, 5,860 tons d.w., 378·25 ft. l.o.a., 55·2 ft. breadth, 5-cyl. Sulzer diesel by Ishikawajima-Harima H.I., 2,500 b.h.p., 13½ knots.

CITTA DI NAPOLI. *Italian.* Passenger and cargo. Built by 'Navalmeccanica' Cant. Nav., Castellammare, for 'Tirrenia' S.p.A. di Nav., Naples. 5,500 tons gross, 395·33 ft. l.o.a., 55·25 ft. breadth, 18 ft. draught, tw-sc. two 9-cyl. Fiat diesels by Ansaldo, 12,600 b.h.p., 19½ knots.

CITTA DI NUORO. *Italian.* Passenger. Built by Cant. Nav. Riuniti, Ancona, for 'Tirrenia' S.p.A. di Nav., Naples. 5,200 tons gross, 395·33 ft. l.o.a., 55·25 ft. breadth, 17·82 ft. draught, tw-sc. two 9-cyl. Fiat diesels by Ansaldo, 12,600 b.h.p., 19½ knots.

CITY OF CANBERRA. *British.* Cargo. Built by Barclay, Curle & Co. Ltd., Glasgow, for Ellerman Lines Ltd., London. 10,543 tons gross, 11,130 tons d.w., 511 ft. l.o.a., 67·33 ft. breadth, 30 ft. draught, 9-cyl. Sulzer diesel by the shipbuilders, 10,000 b.h.p., 17½ knots.

CITY OF EASTBOURNE. *British.* Cargo. Built by Vickers-Armstrongs (S.B.) Ltd., Newcastle-upon-Tyne, for Ellerman Lines Ltd., London. 10,006 tons gross, 10,733 tons d.w., 508 ft. l.o.a., 66·75 ft. breadth, 29 ft. draught, 8-cyl. Sulzer diesel by shipbuilders, 9,300 b.h.p., 17½ knots.

CITY OF VANCOUVER. *Canadian.* Ferry. Built by Burrard D.D. Co. Ltd., Vancouver, for British Columbia Toll, Highways and Bridges Authority, Victoria. 3,541 tons gross, 342·42 ft. l.o.a., 78·58 ft. breadth, 12·5 ft. draught, tw-sc. four 16-cyl. diesels by Paxman, 6,664 b.h.p., 18 knots.

CITY OF VICTORIA. *Canadian.* Ferry. Built by Victoria Machinery Depot Co., Victoria, B.C., for British Columbia Toll Authority Ferry System, Victoria. 3,541 tons gross, 342 ft. l.o.a., 78·5 ft. breadth, 12·5 ft. draught, tw-sc. four 16-cyl. diesels by Paxman, 6,664 b.h.p., 18 knots.

CIUDAD DE BUENOS AIRES. *Argentine.* Passenger ferry. Built by Soc. Española de Const. Nav., Cadiz, for Flota Argentina de Nav. Fluvial, Buenos Aires. 7,157 tons gross, 1,200 tons d.w., 427·5 ft. l.o.a., 55·9 ft. breadth, 12 ft. draught, tw-sc. two 10-cyl. B. & W. diesels by the shipbuilders, 7,800 b.h.p., 18 knots.

CLAN FARQUHARSON. *British.* Cargo. Built by Swan, Hunter & Wigham Richardson Ltd., Wallsend-on-Tyne, for King Line Ltd., London and Glasgow. 9,242 tons gross, 10,230 tons d.w., 496·58 ft. l.o.a., 62·42 ft. breadth, 28·2 ft. draught, 6-cyl. Sulzer diesel by Wallsend Slipway, 7,100 b.h.p., 15 knots.

CLAN FINLAY. *British.* Cargo. Built by Swan, Hunter & Wigham Richardson Ltd., Wallsend-on-Tyne, for King Line Ltd. 9,242 tons gross, 10,230 tons d.w., 496·58 ft. l.o.a., 62·42 ft. breadth, 28·2 ft. draught, 6-cyl. Sulzer diesel by Wallsend Slipway, 8,500 b.h.p., 15 knots.

CLAN GRANT. *British.* Cargo. Built by Greenock Dockyard Co. Ltd., Greenock, for The Clan Line Steamers Ltd., London. 9,039 tons gross, 11,930 tons d.w., 507·82 ft. l.o.a., 63·25 ft. breadth, 28·2 ft. draught, 6-cyl. Sulzer diesel by Barclay Curle, 8,500 b.h.p., 16½ knots.

CLAN MACGILLIVRAY. *British.* Cargo. Built by Greenock Dockyard Co. Ltd., Greenock, for The Clan Line Steamers Ltd., London and Glasgow. 9,039 tons gross. 11,930 tons d.w., 507·82 ft. l.o.a., 63·25 ft. breadth, 28·5 ft. draught, 6-cyl. Sulzer diesel by Barclay Curle, 8,500 b.h.p., 16½ knots.

C

CITY OF EASTBOURNE. *The first of two sister ships ordered from Vickers-Armstrong (Shipbuilders) Ltd., Walker-on-Tyne. This vessel, 10,723 tons d.w., built for the Ellerman Line, is powered by the first Vickers-Sulzer marine diesel engine built at Barrow. The new ship has a cargo capacity of 674,130 cu. ft. grain, 615,740 cu. ft. bale, and a cargo oil capacity of 28,020 cu. ft. Her propelling machinery, which is located well aft, consists of a turbocharged 8-cylinder two-stroke Vickers-Sulzer type diesel engine, capable of a service power of 9,300 b.h.p. at 115 r.p.m. The service speed is 17·5 knots. Unlike her predecessors the new ship has no refrigerated cargo space.*

CLAN MACGREGOR. *British.* Cargo liner. Built by Greenock Dockyard Co. Ltd., Greenock, for The Clan Line Steamers Ltd., London. 9,039 tons gross, 11,930 tons d.w., 507·82 ft. l.o.a., 63·25 ft. breadth, 6-cyl. Sulzer diesel by Barclay Curle, 8,500 b.h.p., 16½ knots.

CLAN MACNAIR. *British.* Cargo. Built by John Brown & Co. (Clydebank) Ltd., for The Clan Line Steamers Ltd., London and Glasgow. 9,039 tons gross, 11,930 tons d.w., 507·82 ft. l.o.a., 63·25 ft. breadth, 28·2 ft. draught, 6-cyl. Doxford diesel by the shipbuilders, 6,000 b.h.p., 14½ knots.

CLARKFORTH. *British.* Cargo. Built by Lithgows Ltd., Port Glasgow, for H. Clarkson & Co. Ltd., London. 9,350 tons gross, 13,750 tons d.w., 505 ft. l.o.a., 66 ft. breadth, 30·82 ft. draught, 8-cyl. B. & W. diesel by Kincaid, 8,570 b.h.p., 16½ knots.

CLEE NESS. *British.* Drag suction hopper dredger. Built by Fleming & Ferguson Ltd., Paisley, for British Transport Commission. 1,436 tons gross, 223·9 ft. l.o.a., 45·58 ft. breadth, tw-sc. two 5-cyl. grd. diesels by Ruston & Hornsby, 1,310 b.h.p., 9 knots.

CONFEDERATION. *Canadian.* Passenger and car ferry. Built by Halifax Shipyards Ltd., Halifax, for Canadian Government. 2,371 tons gross, 282·6 ft. l.o.a., 61·58 ft. breadth, 13·75 ft. draught, quad-sc. diesel-electric, four 12-cyl. Ruston-Paxman diesels, 6,400 b.h.p., 13 knots.

CONGO ZOLE. *Belgian.* Refrigerated cargo. Built by N.V. Kon. Maats. 'De Schelde,' Flushing, for Cie. Africaine de Nav. S.A., Antwerp. 8,838 tons gross, 12,240 tons d.w., 482·5 ft. l.o.a., 62·2 ft. breadth, 29 ft. draught, 5-cyl. Sulzer diesel by shipbuilders, 6,500 b.h.p., 14 knots.

CLAN FINLAY. *The last of a class of five cargo liners of about 9,000 tons gross for members of the British & Commonwealth group of companies was delivered to the King Line Ltd. by the Wallsend shipyard of Swan Hunter & Wigham Richardson Ltd. The others in the class are Clan Fergusson, Clan Forbes, Clan Fraser and Clan Farquharson, the latter also being delivered in 1962.*

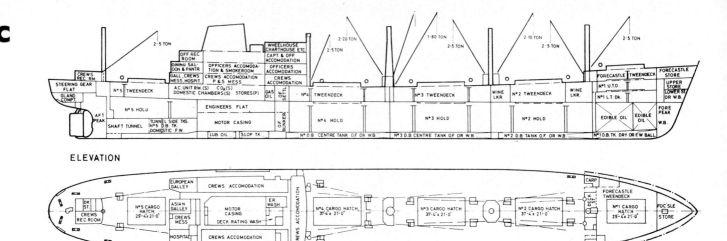

ELEVATION

UPPER DECK

CLAN MACGILLIVRAY. *This was the first British merchant ship to be fitted with an extensive system of automatic and remote controls and alarms in the engine room. The Clan Macgillivray, 11,930 tons d.w., was built by the Greenock Dockyard Co. Ltd. for The Clan Line Steamers Ltd., and was the first of an order for three vessels of similar tonnage which were delivered in 1962, the other ships being named Clan Grant and Clan Macgregor. A fourth vessel of similar class is the Clan Macnair delivered by John Brown & Co. (Clydebank) Ltd. The object of employing near-automation in the engine room has been to reduce the engine room complement to a minimum. There are now six engineers, one electrician and 12 Asian ratings, and the normal sea-going watch consists of one engineer and one Asian donkeyman. A ship of similar tonnage and without rationalization of the engine room requires a complement of 20 per cent. more. The rationalized engine system has cost no more to instal than would a conventional engine room layout. The Clan Macgillivray is generally similar to the Clan Maciver class though a little longer, broader and with more speed, which is 16½ knots in service. Operating practice with earlier vessels of this class has led to a certain amount of improvement and alteration in design, including the fitting of steel hatch covers throughout, a different layout in the wheelhouse, and improved accommodation. There are five main cargo holds and tweendeck spaces available for general cargo, four forward and one aft of the machinery space. No. I lower tweendeck is fitted to carry 150 tons weight of dangerous cargo (petroleum or allied substances in drums). The cargo capacity is 571,580 cu. ft. bale, 633,900 cu. ft. grain. The vessel has seven main watertight bulkheads. An additional transverse corrugated oiltight bulkhead has been fitted in No. I hold and the* *resulting after portion further subdivided with a fore and aft centreline corrugated oiltight bulkhead to provide three edible oil tanks which can also be used for dry cargo or water ballast. To facilitate the use of fork-lift trucks the sectional covers in the Nos. 2, 3 and 4 tweendecks are flush-fitting. The second deck is strengthened in Nos. 2, 3, 4 and 5 cargo spaces for fork-lift trucks having two wheels at the fork end and having a total combined load of $6\frac{3}{4}$ tons, and the slab hatch covers are also suitable to take this loading. Tank tops in Nos. 2, 3 and 4 cargo spaces and the tunnel top in No. 5 are suitable to carry similar fork-lift trucks having a total combined load of $6\frac{3}{4}$ tons. A total of 17 tubular steel derricks has been provided. These comprise one of 60 tons, two of 20 tons, four of 10 tons and ten of 5 tons capacity. All derrick posts and masts are unstayed to give space for deck cargo.*

CLARKFORTH. *The Scottish shipbuilders Lithgows Ltd. built this 13,750 tons d.w. cargo ship for H. Clarkson & Co. Ltd. (managers J. & J. Denholm (Management) Ltd., Glasgow). This vessel is a sister ship to the Clarkspey (see 'Merchant Ships: World Built,' Vol. IX), but her layout and machinery have been modified in a number of respects. The chief feature is that the main engine in the Clarkforth is of much higher output than her sister ship and gives her a couple of knots extra speed.*

CORAL ACROPORA. *Dutch.* Refrigerated cargo. Built by Ch. & At. Aug. Normand, Havre, for Dammers & v.d. Heide's Shipping & Trading Co Ltd., Rotterdam. 1,300 tons gross, 1,600 tons d.w., 260·5 ft. l.o.a., 36·66 ft. breadth, 15·82 ft. draught, 6-cyl. diesel by Deutz, 2,000 b.h.p., 13 knots.

CUBA (ex *Artsyz*). *Cuban.* Tanker. Built by Rauma-Repola O/Y, Rauma, for Republic of Cuba. 3,360 tons gross, 4,400 tons d.w., 344·82 ft. l.o.a., 48·58 ft. breadth, 20·42 ft. draught, 5-cyl. diesel by B. & W., 2,900 b.h.p., 14 knots.

CYGNUS. *Norwegian.* Cargo. Built by A/S Bergens M/V, Bergen, for Det Bergenske D/S, Bergen. 4,515 tons gross, 6,440 tons d.w., 441·5 ft. l.o.a., 58·2 ft. breadth, 23·25 ft. draught, 8-cyl. B. & W. diesel by Akers, 5,540 b.h.p., 16 knots (trials).

CZUKOTKA. *Russian.* Fish mother ship. Built by United Polish Shipyards, Gdansk, for U.S.S.R. 10,026 tons gross, 9,800 tons d.w., 509 ft. l.o.a., 65·58 ft. breadth, 26·95 ft. draught, tw-sc. steam recip. with exh. turb., 5,000 s.h.p., 13 knots.

DAGHILD. *Norwegian.* Tanker. Built by Burmeister & Wain, Copenhagen, for A/S Ocean, Oslo. 22,000 tons gross, 41,500 tons d.w., 684 ft. l.o.a., 98·2 ft. breadth, 36·42 ft. draught, 8-cyl. diesel by the shipbuilders, 16,800 b.h.p., 16½ knots.

DAIKAI MARU. *Japanese.* Cargo. Built by Namura S.B. Co., Osaka, for Nippon Yusen Kaisha & Namura Kisen Kaisha, Tokyo. 3,600 tons gross, 5,500 tons d.w., 350·2 ft. l.o.a., 50·25 ft. breadth, 21·25 ft. draught, 6-cyl. diesel by Kobe-Hatsudoki, 2,700 b.h.p., 12¼ knots.

DAINANOH MARU. *Japanese.* Cargo. Built by Mitsubishi H.I.R., Kobe, for Daian Shosen K.K., Tokyo. 6,500 tons gross, 9,590 tons d.w., 429·82 ft. l.o.a., 59·25 ft. breadth, 26·25 ft. draught, 6-cyl. Sulzer diesel by the shipbuilders, 6,300 b.h.p., 14½ knots.

DAINET. *Norwegian.* Cargo. Built by Porsgrunds M/V, Porsgrunn, for A/S Dione, Porsgrunn. 5,204 tons gross, 8,400 tons d.w., 381·58 ft. l.o.a., 52·58 ft. breadth, 26·75 ft. draught, 10-cyl. diesel by M.A.N., 3,860 b.h.p., 13½ knots.

DAIWA MARU. *Japanese.* Cargo. Built by Ishikawajima-Harima H.I., Tokyo, for Nitto Shosen K.K., Tokyo. 9,600 tons gross, 13,000 tons d.w., 511·82 ft. l.o.a., 64·58 ft. breadth, 10·25 ft. draught, 6-cyl. Sulzer diesel by the shipbuilders, 9,000 b.h.p., 16¼ knots.

DALMATIA. *Swedish.* Cargo. Built by A/B Lindholmens Varv, Gothenburg, for Rederi A/B Svenska Lloyd, Gothenburg. 3,772 tons gross, 4,600 tons d.w., 349 ft. l.o.a., 47·66 ft. breadth, 22·75 ft. draught, 8-cyl. Götaverken diesel by the shipbuilders, 3,000 b.h.p., 16 knots.

DAVID SALMAN. *Swedish.* Newsprint carrier. Built by Uddevallavarvet A/B, Uddevalla, for Swedish Gulf Line, Gothenburg. 7,052 tons gross, 7,810 tons d.w., 424·2 ft. l.o.a., 61·5 ft. breadth, 26 ft. draught, 6-cyl. Götaverken diesel, 5,600 b.h.p., 16 knots.

DENEB (ex *Frederika*). *Dutch.* Cargo. Built by A/B Falkenbergs Varv, Falkenberg, for N.V. van Nievelt Goudriaan & Co.'s Stoomv. Maats., Rotterdam. 1,190 tons gross, 2,300 tons d.w., 282·2 ft. l.o.a., 40·58 ft. breadth, 15·33 ft. draught, 8-cyl. diesel by Deutz, 2,100 b.h.p., 14½ knots.

DIANE. *Danish.* Cargo. Built by Porsgrunds M/V, Porsgrunn, Norway, for Chr. J. Reim, Porsgrunn. 7,600 tons d.w.

DIMITROVO. *Russian.* Bulk carrier. Built by Warnowwerft, Warnemünde, for U.S.S.R. 7,265 tons gross, 9,750 tons d.w., 457·5 ft. l.o.a., 59 ft. breadth, 26·25 ft. draught, M.A.N. diesel by D.M.R., 5,400 b.h.p., 14¼ knots.

DISCOVERY. *British.* Research ship. Built by Hall, Russell & Co. Ltd., Aberdeen, for National Oceanographic Council. 2,500 tons gross, 260·25 ft. l.o.a., 46 ft. breadth, diesel-electric, three 6-cyl. diesels by Ruston & Hornsby, 2,000 b.h.p., 10 knots.

DJAKARTA MARU. *Japanese.* Cargo. Built by Ishikawajima-Harima H.I., Aioi, for Tokyo Senpaku K.K., Tokyo. 6,800 tons gross, 9,669 tons d.w., 423·2 ft. l.o.a., 59 ft. breadth, 26·9 ft. draught, 6-cyl. Sulzer diesel by the shipbuilders, 6,600 b.h.p., 14½ knots.

DOMEYKO. *Polish.* Refrigerated cargo. Built by United Polish Shipyards, Szczecin, for Polish Government. 5,406 tons gross, 8,200 tons d.w., 478·5 ft. l.o.a., 60·82 ft. breadth, 25 ft. draught, 6-cyl. Sulzer diesel, 7,800 b.h.p., 17 knots.

DONA NANCY. *Panamanian.* Cargo. Built by Hitachi S.B. & E. Co. Ltd., Osaka, for Commonwealth S. Co. Ltd., Nassau. 9,814 tons gross, 14,883 tons d.w., 518·5 ft. l.o.a., 63·9 ft. breadth, 30·33 ft. draught, 6-cyl. B. & W. diesel by the shipbuilders, 6,500 b.h.p., 17¾ knots (trials).

D

DAVID SALMAN

Opposite:

DAVID SALMAN. *The feature of this newsprint carrier built by Uddevallavarvet A.B. for the Swedish Gulf Line, Gothenburg, is the use of twin hatches for cargo ship holds. The use of such hatches, although not entirely new, has not yet been applied to any great extent. The cargo liner Bandeirante, described in 'Merchant Ships: World Built,' Vol. IX, had three hatches side by side, and the interesting new ship Toulouse (described later in this volume) affords another example of twin hatches. In the David Salman cargo can be lowered into the hold directly and with the minimum of lateral movement to stow it away. Thus cargo is less easily damaged (which is important in a vessel carrying rolls of newsprint which are expensive and easily damaged) and it provides quicker loading and discharging. The David Salman is mainly welded construction. Bulkheads divide the ship into forepeak, afterpeak, engine room and a total of five cargo holds with a cargo capacity grain of 460,050 cu. ft. There are four stout derrick posts with outriggers, a crow's nest being fitted in the forward mast. A signal mast is incorporated in the funnel.*

DJAKATA MARU. *Ishikawajima-Harima H.I. Co. Ltd. delivered this 9,669 tons d.w. cargo liner to the Tokyo Shipping Co. Ltd. under the Japanese Government's 17th shipping programme. She will normally operate on the Japan-Indonesia service. A forecastle and long poop have been included in the design to provide maximum deck space for lumber shipments. The forecastle has a particularly heavy sheer. The engine room and midship superstructure has been arranged about two-thirds aft. As can be seen, the funnel is smaller than usual in order to cut the size of the superstructure to the minimum.*

D

DUKE OF ATHENS. *This diesel-powered, closed tweendeck, 16,100 tons d.w. cargo vessel of high cubic capacity has been built by Furness Shipbuilding Co. Ltd. for the Trent Maritime Co. Ltd., London, who are part of the very large group of S. Livanos (Shipbrokers) Ltd. The cubic capacity gross is 830,254 cu. ft. There are five main cargo hatches each 22 ft. wide. The lengths are: No. 1, 33 ft. 9 in.; No. 2, 45 ft.; Nos. 3 and 4, single-pull covers on the weather deck and wood covers, 37 ft. 6 in.; and No. 5, 35 ft. The five cargo holds, three forward and two aft of the engine room, are clear of obstructions. A special cargo hold is arranged in the tweendecks over the afterpeak tank. A steel centreline bulkhead in the holds and tweendecks, clear of hatchways, is arranged to take shifting boards when carrying grain cargoes. Refrigerating chambers of 2,817 cu. ft. capacity are fitted in the midship tweendecks and are operated by two electrically driven Freon type machines. There are ten 5-ton and two 8-ton electric winches to handle 15 tubular steel derricks, two of 3 tons, twelve of 5 or 10 tons, and one of 30 tons lifting capacity. Two of the winches at the after end of No. 1 hatchway have an additional heavy-duty barrel to handle the 30-ton derrick. A winch of 8 tons capacity has been fitted aft of No. 5 hatchway for cargo or warping duties in addition to an 8-ton electric capstan.*

DONA NANCY. *This cargo motorship, 14,883 tons d.w., was delivered to the Commonwealth Shipping Co. Ltd., Panama, from the Sakurajima shipyard of the Hitachi Shipbuilding & Engineering Co. Ltd. The cargo holds have a capacity of 20,296 cu. m. The main machinery consists of a 6-cylinder Hitachi-B. & W. diesel engine, type 662-VT2BF-140, developing 6,500 b.h.p. The maximum trial speed was 17·85 knots.*

DORIC FERRY. *British.* Ferry. Built by Ailsa S.B. Co. Ltd., Troon, for Atlantic Steam Navigation Co. Ltd., London. 2,563 tons gross, 1,529 tons d.w., 361·5 ft. l.o.a., 55 ft. breadth, 12·75 ft. draught, tw-sc. two 16-cyl. diesels by Davie-Paxman, 3,360 b.h.p., 14 knots.

DOROTHY ANN. *Liberian.* Cargo. Built by Nagoya S.B. Co. Ltd., Nagoya, for The Judith Ann Liberian Transport Co. Ltd., Monrovia and Hong Kong. 10,300 tons gross, 14,800 tons d.w., 472·33 ft. l.o.a., 66·5 ft. breadth, 25·5 ft. draught, 6-cyl. B. & W. diesel by Hitachi, 6,500 b.h.p., 14 knots.

DUKE OF ATHENS. *British.* Cargo. Built by Furness S.B. Co. Ltd., Haverton Hill, for Trent Maritime Co. Ltd., London. 10,823 tons gross, 16,100 tons d.w., 517·5 ft. l.o.a., 66·25 ft. breadth, 31·33 ft. draught, 5-cyl. Doxford diesel by Hawthorn Leslie, 5,500 b.h.p., 13¾ knots.

E

E. H. BIRD. *Liberian.* Bulk carrier. Built by Brodogradiliste Split, Split, for Atlantic Bulk Trading Corp., Monrovia and Boston. 15,300 tons gross, 23,000 tons d.w., 592·82 ft. l.o.a., 76·82 ft. breadth, 32·9 ft. draught, 9-cyl. diesel by Fiat, 10,800 b.h.p., 16 knots (trials).

EASTERN RANGER. *British.* Cargo. Built by J. L. Thompson & Sons Ltd., Sunderland, for Indo-China S.N. Co. Ltd., Hong Kong. 4,408 tons gross, 7,000 tons d.w., 404·25 ft. l.o.a., 57·25 ft. breadth, 23·33 ft. draught, 4-cyl. Doxford diesel by Hawthorn Leslie, 4,600 b.h.p., 14¼ knots.

EASTERN SAKURA. *British.* Cargo. Built by Hakodate Dock Co. Ltd., Hakodate, for World Log Carriers Ltd., Hong Kong. 10,250 tons gross, 15,000 tons d.w., 500·33 ft. l.o.a., 71·75 ft. breadth, 29 ft. draught, 6-cyl. Sulzer diesel by Ino S.B., 6,600 b.h.p., 14½ knots.

ECKENHEIM. *German.* Bulk carrier. Built by A.G. 'Weser' Werk Seebeck, Bremerhaven, for Unterweser Reederei G.m.b.H., Bremen. 6,800 tons gross, 11,400 tons d.w., 60·75 ft. breadth, 28 ft. draught, 6-cyl. diesel by M.A.N., 4,050 b.h.p., 13 knots.

ECUADORIAN REEFER. *Danish.* Refrigerated cargo. Built by Aalberg Vaerft A/S, Aalberg, for J. Lauritzen, Copenhagen. 5,065 tons gross, 5,900 tons d.w., 435·75 ft. l.o.a., 59·2 ft. breadth, 26 ft. draught, two 6-cyl. B. & W. diesels, 8,850 i.h.p., 17½ knots.

EDERA. *Italian.* Bulk carrier. Built by Ansaldo S.p.A., Spezia for Aretusa Soc. per Azioni di Nav., Palermo. 23,300 tons gross, 35,000 tons d.w., 679 ft. l.o.a., 92·25 ft. breadth, 36 ft. draught, 8-cyl. Fiat diesel, 16,800 b.h.p., 17 knots.

EDGAR ANDRE. *East German.* Bulk carrier. Built by Warnowwerft, Warnemünde, for Deutsche Seereederei, Rostock. 8,609 tons gross, 11,350 tons d.w., 498 ft. l.o.a., 62·2 ft. breadth, 27·25 ft. draught, 7-cyl. diesel by D.M.R., 5,850 b.h.p., 15 knots.

EGERO. *Norwegian.* Cargo. Built by Uddevallavarvet A/B, Uddevalla, for Skjelbreds Rederi A/S, Kristiansand. 6,350 tons gross, 12,400 tons d.w., 467·2 ft. l.o.a., 61 ft. breadth, 26·33 ft. draught, 7-cyl. Götaverken diesel, 6,550 b.h.p., 15½ knots.

EGTON. *British.* Cargo. Built by Bartram & Sons Ltd., Sunderland, for Rowland & Marwood's S.S. Co. Ltd., Whitby. 7,175 tons gross, 12,500 tons d.w., 507·58 ft. l.o.a., 66·2 ft. breadth, 27·33 ft. draught, 4-cyl. Doxford diesel, 6,640 b.h.p., 14 knots.

ELLEN KLAUTSCHKE. *German.* Cargo. Built by Orenstein-Koppel & Lbcr. Masch., Lübeck, for Reederei Bernhard Schulte A.G., Hamburg, 3,100 tons gross, 5,000 tons d.w., 321·25 ft. l.o.a., 46·75 ft. breadth, 22·75 ft. draught, 8-cyl. M.A.N. diesel, 2,880 b.h.p., 14¼ knots.

EMMA BAKKE. *Norwegian.* Refrigerated cargo. Built by A/B Götaverken, Gothenburg, for Knut Knudsen O.A.S., Haugesund. 7,200 tons gross, 8,750 tons d.w., 490 ft. l.o.a., 65·2 ft. breadth, 25·75 ft. draught, 7-cyl. Götaverken diesel by the shipbuilders, 8,750 b.h.p., 17 knots.

ERKOWIT. *Sudanese.* Cargo. Built by Brodogradiliste 'Uljanik,' Pula, Yugoslavia, for Sudan Shipping Lines Ltd., Port Sudan. 3,835 tons gross, 4,950 tons d.w., 395·2 ft. l.o.a., 53·9 ft. breadth, 22·2 ft. draught, 5-cyl. B. & W. diesel by the shipbuilders, 5,450 b.h.p., 16½ knots.

ERLING H. SAMUELSEN. *Norwegian.* Bulk carrier. Built by Kockums M/V A/B, Malmö, for Erling H. Samuelsen Rederi, Oslo. 16,495 tons gross, 25,100 tons d.w., 577 ft. l.o.a., 75 ft. breadth, 33·9 ft. draught, 6-cyl. M.A.N. diesel by the shipbuilders, 8,400 b.h.p., 15 knots.

ERNA OLDENDORFF. *German.* Cargo. Built by Werft Nobiskrug G.m.b.H., Rendsburg, for Egon Oldendorff, Lübeck. 2,933 tons gross, 4,250 tons d.w., 347·5 ft. l.o.a., 49·66 ft. breadth, 19·5 ft. draught, two 6-cyl. diesels by M.A.N., 3,000 b.h.p., 14 knots.

ERNE. *British.* Tanker. Built by C. Connell & Co. Ltd., Glasgow, for James Nourse Ltd., London. 14,244 tons gross, 20,000 tons d.w., 559·75 ft. l.o.a., 71·9 ft. breadth, 31 ft. draught, 2 grd. turbs. by Barclay Curle.

ESPADON. *French.* Refrigerated cargo. Built by At. & Ch. de Nantes (Bretagne-Loire), Nantes for Cie. Générale de Transports Maritimes, Marseilles. 4,900 tons gross, 6,400 tons d.w., 377·33 ft. l.o.a., 52·5 ft. breadth, 19·67 ft. draught, 2 Pielstick diesels, 8,520 b.h.p., 18 knots.

ECUADORIAN REEFER. *Rederiet J. Lauritzen, the Copenhagen shipping company whose polar vessels are well known both in the Arctic and Antarctic, also has a number of refrigerated vessels. The latest of these to enter service is the Ecuadorian Reefer, which was completed in 1962 by Aalborg Vaerft, the Lauritzen shipyard. She is a twin-screw diesel ship of 5,900 tons d.w. and is intended for the carriage of fruit though the design is such that meat and other refrigerated cargoes can also be carried. B. & W. diesel engines developing a total of 8,850 i.h.p. at 170 r.p.m. give her a speed of 17·5 knots loaded to her marks, or 18·5 knots with a cargo of fruit. Accommodation is provided for 10 passengers.*

E

EMMA BAKKE. *The Norwegian owners Knut Knutsen O.A.S., of Haugesund, took delivery of this cargo ship, 8,750 tons d.w., from Götaverken A/B, Gothenburg, Sweden. As can be seen, the holds are arranged three forward and three aft of the engine room. They have a capacity of 512,000 cu. ft. grain and 78,000 cu. ft. refrigerated.*

ESSO AUSTRIA. *The 76,750 tons d.w. turbine tanker Esso Austria was delivered to Standard Tankers, Bahamas, from the shipyard of Chantiers de l'Atlantique (Penhoet-Loire). She is one of the largest vessels to be built in a European shipyard and is the seventh tanker of over 73,000 tons d.w. to be built at St. Nazaire within the last three years. The use of the Esso sign on the side of the ship is a standard practice of the Bahamas tanker-owning subsidiary, though not of other Esso tanker companies. Other tankers of about this size handed over to Esso during 1962 were Esso Hampshire, Esso Warwickshire and the slightly larger Esso Libya and Esso Spain.*

ESSO AUSTRIA. *British.* Tanker. Built by Ch. de l'Atlantique, St. Nazaire, for Standard Tankers (Bahamas) Co. Ltd., Nassau. 48,890 tons gross, 76,750 tons d.w., 849·42 ft. l.o.a., 116·75 ft. breadth, 45·25 ft. draught, 2 Parsons grd. turbs. by shipbuilders, 24,330 s.h.p., 17 knots.

ESSO HAMPSHIRE. *British.* Tanker. Built by Verolme Dok & Schpsb., Rozenburg, for Esso Petroleum Co. Ltd., London. 48,890 tons gross, 80,000 tons d.w., 855·82 ft. l.o.a., 112·75 ft. breadth, 47 ft. draught, 2 grd. turbs. by Werkspoor, 26,000 s.h.p., 17¾ knots.

ESSO LANCASHIRE. *British.* Tanker. Built by Kockums M/V A/B, Malmö, for Esso Petroleum Co. Ltd., London. 48,899 tons gross, 80,000 tons d.w., 855·82 ft. l.o.a., 112·5 ft. breadth, 47 ft. draught, 2 De Laval grd. turbs., 26,500 s.h.p., 17¾ knots.

ESSO LIBYA. *British.* Tanker. Built by Verolme United Shipyards, Rozenburg, for Standard Tankers (Bahamas) Co. Ltd., Nassau. 53,423 tons gross, 87,200 tons d.w., 855·82 ft. l.o.a., 125·25 ft. breadth, 47 ft. draught, 2 grd. Werkspoor turbs. by 'De Schelde,' 26,500 s.h.p., 17½ knots.

ESSO LINCOLN. *British.* Tanker. Built by Nederl. Dok & Schps., Amsterdam, for Esso Petroleum Co. Ltd., London. 31,660 tons gross, 47,400 tons d.w., 740 ft. l.o.a., 102·25 ft. breadth, 37·5 ft draught, 2 grd. turbs. by the shipbuilders, 17,300 s.h.p., 17 knots.

ESSO SPAIN. *British.* Tanker. Built by Howaldtswerke Ham. A.G., Hamburg, for Standard Tankers (Bahamas) Co. Ltd., Nassau. 53,423 tons gross, 87,200 tons d.w., 855·82 ft. l.o.a., 125·25 ft. breadth, 47 ft. draught, grd. turb. by the shipbuilders, 24,400 s.h.p., 17 knots.

ESSO WARWICKSHIRE. *British.* Tanker. Built by A.G. 'Weser,' Bremen, for Esso Petroleum Co. Ltd., London. 48,890 tons gross, 80,000 tons d.w., 855·82 ft. l.o.a., 112·75 ft. breadth, 47 ft. draught, 2 grd. turbs. by the shipbuilders, 26,000 s.h.p., 17¾ knots.

EXPORT BUILDER. *American.* Refrigerated cargo. Built by National Steel & S.B. Co., San Diego, for American Export Lines Inc., New York. 11,140 tons gross, 12,600 tons d.w., 493 ft. l.o.a., 73 ft. breadth, 30·5 ft. draught, 2 grd. turbs. by G.E.C., 12,500 s.h.p., 18 knots.

EXPORT BUYER. *American.* Refrigerated cargo. Built by National Steel & S.B. Co., San Diego, for American Export Lines Inc., New York. 11,140 tons gross, 12,600 tons d.w., 493 ft. l.o.a., 73 ft. breadth, 30·5 ft. draught, 2 grd. turbs. by G.E.C., 12,500 s.h.p., 18 knots.

ESSO LANCASHIRE. *The Swedish shipbuilders Kockums Mekaniska Verstad A/B, Malmö, handed over the Esso Lancashire, 80,000 tons d.w., to her owners, Esso Petroleum Co. Ltd. This vessel is the third of five County class oil tankers; the first of the class was the Esso Pembrokeshire, built by A.G. 'Weser,' Bremen, and described in 'Merchant Ships: World Built,' Vol. X. The Esso Lancashire has the latest design of Stal-Laval steam turbine built under licence by Kockums Mek., Verstad, Malmö. The steam conditions differ from her sister ships in that the pressure is lower and the temperature higher. Back-pressure turbo-alternators are installed. The steam operating conditions are 590 p.s.i.g. (42 kg./sq. cm.) and 940 deg. F. (505 deg. C.). A fuel consumption as low as 0·487 lb./s.h.p.-hour (217 gr./s.h.p.-hour) was recorded during the official sea trial when a maximum average speed of 18·18 knots was attained.*

F

FALABA. *British.* Cargo. Built by Scotts' S.B. & Eng. Co. Ltd., Greenock, for Elder Dempster Lines Ltd., Liverpool. 7,703 tons gross, 8,139 tons d.w., 465 ft. l.o.a., 62·25 ft. breadth, 25·2 ft. draught, 5-cyl. Sulzer diesel by the shipbuilders, 7,500 b.h.p., 16 knots.

FALSTER. *Swedish.* Bulk carrier. Built by A/B Lindholmens Varv, Gothenburg, for Angbats A/B Ferm, Gothenburg. 10,450 tons gross, 16,325 tons d.w., 500 ft. l.o.a., 68·66 ft. breadth, 7-cyl. diesel by the shipbuilders, 5,800 b.h.p., 14 knots.

FENICE. *Italian.* Bulk carrier. Built by C.R.D. Adriatico, Trieste, for 'Italsider' S.p.A., Genoa. 15,982 tons gross, 24,500 tons d.w., 635·33 ft. l.o.a., 76·2 ft. breadth, 31·9 ft. draught, 8-cyl. Fiat diesel by the shipbuilders, 9,600 b.h.p., 16¾ knots.

FARSEA. *Norwegian.* Bulk carrier. Built by Haugesund M/V A/S, Haugesund, for Sverre A. Farstad & Co., Alesund. 12,808 tons gross, 18,000 tons d.w., 532 ft. l.o.a., 71·2 ft. breadth, 30 ft. draught, 6-cyl. Götaverken diesel, 7,500 b.h.p., 14½ knots.

FELIS. *Swedish.* Cargo. Built by A/S Frederikstad M/V, Frederiksstad, for Rederi A/B Jan, Gothenburg. 7,494 tons gross, 10,590 tons d.w., 450 ft. l.o.a., 61 ft. breadth, 28·5 ft. draught, 6-cyl. Götaverken diesel by the shipbuilders, 6,000 b.h.p.

FELLA HUGO STINNES. *German.* Cargo. Built by Atlas Werke A.G., Bremen, for Fella Werke G.m.b.H., Mulheim-Ruhr. 3,131 tons gross, 4,100 tons d.w., 331·42 ft. l.o.a., 47·66 ft. breadth, 20 ft. draught, 6-cyl. diesel by Mach. Kiel, 2,840 b.h.p., 13 knots.

FERDER. *Norwegian.* Car and bulk carrier. Built by Blohm & Voss, Hamburg, for A/S Antarctic, Tonsberg. 10,990 tons gross, 17,300 tons d.w., 496·42 ft. l.o.a., 70·2 ft. breadth, 33·75 ft. draught, 8-cyl. M.A.N. diesel by the shipbuilders, 7,250 b.h.p., 15 knots.

FIEPKO TEN DOORNKAAT. *German.* Cargo. Built by Jos. L. Meyer, Papenburg, for Bernhard Schulte Reederei A.G., Hamburg. 3,169 tons gross, 5,015 tons d.w., 321·25 ft. l.o.a., 46·9 ft. breadth, 22·9 ft. draught, 8-cyl. M.A.N. diesel, 2,880 b.h.p., 14½ knots.

FINNCLIPPER. *Finnish.* Refrigerated cargo. Built by Rheinstahl Nordseewerke, Emden, for Enso-Gutzeit O/Y, Helsingfors. 5,097 tons gross, 9,300 tons d.w., 445·2 ft. l.o.a., 61·75 ft. breadth, 23·82 ft. draught, 6-cyl. B. & W. diesel by Krupp, 6,500 b.h.p., 16 knots.

FINNEAGLE. *Finnish.* Refrigerated cargo. Built by Rheinstahl Nordseewerke, Emden, for Enso-Gutzeit O/Y, Helsingfors. 5,097 tons gross, 9,300 tons d.w., 445·2 ft. l.o.a., 61·75 ft. breadth, 23·82 ft. draught, 6-cyl. B. & W. diesel by Krupp, 6,500 b.h.p., 16 knots.

FLINTSHIRE. *British.* Cargo liner. Built by C. van der Giessen, Krimpen, for Glen Line Ltd., London. 12,750 tons gross, 13,000 tons d.w., 543 ft. l.o.a., 74·66 ft. breadth, 30 ft. draught, 9-cyl. diesel by Sulzer, 16,600 b.h.p., 20 knots.

FORRESBANK. *British.* Cargo liner. Built by Wm. Doxford & Sons (S.B.) Ltd., Sunderland, for Bank Line Ltd., London. 8,582 tons gross, 12,380 tons d.w., 487·75 ft. l.o.a., 62·25 ft. breadth, 29 ft. draught, 4-cyl. Doxford diesel, 6,640 b.h.p., 16¾ knots (trials).

FUTABA MARU No. 2. *Japanese.* Cargo. Built by Hitachi S.B. & E. Co. Ltd., Mukaishima, for Futaba Kaiun K.K., Tokyo. 1,913 tons gross, 2,903 tons d.w., 285·33 ft. l.o.a. 40·66 ft. breadth, 18 ft. draught, 6-cyl. diesel by Hanshin, 1,280 b.h.p., 11 knots.

FORT CREVECOEUR. *French.* Refrigerated cargo. Built by Ch. & At. de Provence, Port de Bouc, for Cie. Générale Transatlantique, Paris. 5,014 tons gross, 6,200 tons d.w., 373·5 ft. l.o.a., 51·9 ft. breadth, 21·42 ft. draught, 6-cyl. Doxford diesel by shipbuilders, 7,800 b.h.p., 17 knots.

FORT D'ORLEANS. *French.* Refrigerated cargo. Built by Ch. & At. de Provence, Port de Bouc, for Cie. Générale Transatlantique. 5,014 tons gross, 6,000 tons d.w., 373·5 ft. l.o.a., 51·9 ft. breadth, 21·42 ft. draught, 6-cyl. Doxford diesel by shipbuilders, 7,800 b.h.p., 17 knots.

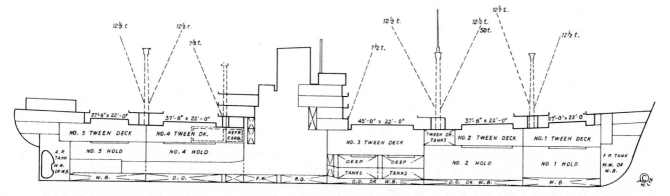

FALABA. *This vessel of 8,139 tons d.w. has been built by Scotts' Shipbuilding & Engineering Co. Ltd., Greenock, for the West African cargo service of Elder Dempster Lines Ltd., and is a sister ship of the Fourah Bay completed in 1961. The Falaba is of conventional design and has a cargo capacity of 457,889 cu. ft. bale and 501,895 cu. ft. grain. There are five cargo holds, three of them forward of the machinery space, and No. 3 tweendeck has been increased in height so as to accommodate buses. Cargo handling arrangements comprise one 50-ton, twelve 12½-ton and four 7½-ton derricks. Aluminium alloy has been used for all the superstructure above the bridge deck, including the funnel.*

FRANCOIS L.D. *French.* Ore carrier. Built by Ch. Nav. de La Ciotat, La Ciotat, for Louis Dreyfus & Cie., Paris. 15,500 tons gross, 22,500 tons d.w., 616·82 ft. l.o.a., 75 ft. breadth, 31 ft. draught, 7-cyl. Götaverken diesel, 9,000 b.h.p., 15 knots.

FREE ENTERPRISE. *British.* Ferry. Built by N.V. Werf 'Gusto,' Schiedam, for Townsend Bros. Ferries Ltd., London. 2,607 tons gross, 316·5 ft. l.o.a., 53·75 ft. breadth, 12·9 ft. draught, tw-sc. two 12-cyl. M.A.N. diesels by J. & K. Smit, 6,800 b.h.p., 20 knots.

FRIEDRICH WOLF. *East German.* Fish factory. Built by Mathias-Thesen-Werft, Halberstadt, for Vvb. der Fischwirtschaft, Halberstadt. 3,000 tons gross, 281·82 ft. l.o.a., 44·42 ft. breadth, 17·33 ft. draught, 8-cyl. diesel by Halberstadt, 2,000 b.h.p., 11½ knots.

FRIGG. *Norwegian.* Cargo. Built by A/B Falkenbergs Varv, Falkenberg, for Botvid Ohlsson, Oslo. 1,200 tons gross, 2,000 tons d.w., 251·33 ft. l.o.a., 38·66 ft. breadth, 15·66 ft. draught, 6-cyl. Polar diesel, 2,000 b.h.p., 12 knots.

FROL. *Norwegian.* Cargo. Built by A/S Trondhjems M/V, Trondheim, for A/S Turid, Trondheim. 1,948 tons gross, 3,650 tons d.w., 325·5 ft. l.o.a., 45 ft. breadth, 18·75 ft. draught, 4-cyl. M.A.N. diesel, 1,680 b.h.p., 12 knots.

F

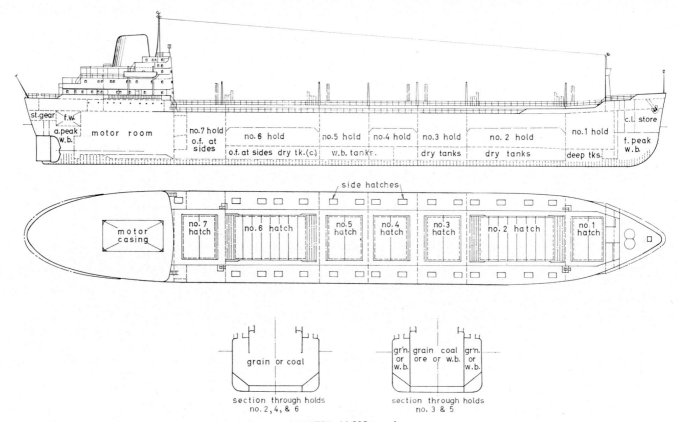

General arrangement and midship sections of the bulk carrier FALSTER, *16,325 tons d.w.*

FALSTER. *A bulk carrier of a new and interesting design was built in 1962 by A.B. Lindholmens Varv, Gothenburg, for Angbats-A.B. Ferm, Kristinehamn, a member of the Broström Group. This vessel, the* Falster *(16,325 tons d.w.) is built largely from ideas obtained from G. Procacci, a leading French expert on bulk carrier design, but the final shape was decided upon in co-operation with the owners. The object of this design is to eliminate the disadvantage of a 'stiff' vessel, which is a characteristic of conventional bulk carriers when loaded with heavy cargo, such as iron ore. Bulk carriers normally have five or six holds of equal length. Ore is carried in the bottom of each hold which results in a low centre of gravity, a short period of roll, and an uncomfortable ship prone to damage the men and material. It is not normally possible to load only a few of the holds with ore in order to obtain a lower metacentric height as this would commonly result in an unfavourable weight distribution and severe stresses in the hull, as well as bad trim. In the* Falster *the space between the collision bulkhead and the engine room has been divided into seven holds of varying length. There are two continuous bulkheads extending from the deck to the tank top in the short holds Nos. 3, 5 and 7, which are split up into centre and wing sections. The centre holds Nos. 3, 5 and 7 have been arranged for the carriage of ore, together with No. 1 hold. These four holds have been shaped so that they can be completely filled with iron ore of stowage factor of about 18 cu. ft./ton with the ship loaded to her marks. A substantial rise in the centre of gravity is thereby obtained, and the metacentric height with a full ore cargo is about 3 ft. compared with 8-10 ft. for normal types of bulk carrier. At the same time, the ore cargo holds have been distributed longitudinally in such a way that the trim of the vessel fully loaded will be correct; and bending and shearing stresses in the hull will not exceed the standard values stipulated by the Classification Societies, with a corresponding reduction of the hull scantlings. The short side holds Nos. 3, 5 and 7 can be used for light grain and also for water ballast, and their limited width allows the loading of grain in these spaces without shifting boards or bagging being necessary, even if they are only partially filled. Any surplus quantity can thus be loaded in those spaces after the other holds have been filled. In the longer holds Nos. 2, 4 and 6 the longitudinal bulkheads extend over only one-third of the depth of the hold and serve as permanent grain bulkheads. The arrangement permits a full load of grain with a stowage factor of 54 cu. ft./ton. In the* Falster *the aftermost side holds are used as deep tanks for heavy fuel oil. Since temporary shifting boards or other measures for securing the cargo are no longer required, the cost of cargo handling for this vessel is expected to be considerably lower than for the conventional type of bulk carrier. The cargo capacity grain is 800,000 cu. ft.*

F

FERDER. *This motorship, 17,300 tons d.w., affords an example of the ship which has the advantages and characteristics of a bulk carrier combined with special facilities for the carriage of motor cars. She was designed and built by Blohm & Voss A.G., Hamburg, for the Norwegian shipping company A/S Antarctic, Tonsberg, and is on charter to the Volkswagenswerk, carrying 1,220 Volkswagen cars on each voyage from Hamburg to the United States. For this purpose the ship has been fitted with housing car decks working on a novel principle, which has been developed and made by the shipbuilders. The cargo holds in the Ferder have a capacity for 1,266 vehicles, 35 per cent. buses, 65 per cent. cars. They are designed with a level tank top and hoppered wing tanks under the main deck on each side of the hatches. It has been possible to arrange four superimposed car decks in each of the six holds. Each car deck is divided into two side sections which extend from the forward bulkhead to the after bulkhead, and from the ship's side to the hatch coaming. In most cases there are also two end sections between the two side sections at the forward and after end of the hold respectively. In way of the hatches the car decks consist of portable pontoons. When in the position for carrying cars, three sides of the side section rest on fixed supports at the bulkheads and the shell. The inner side is supported by steel links, which fold back into the decks when the latter are raised, thus leaving a clear space for grab discharge. The end sections, and also the pontoons in way of the hatches, have no fixed supports. They rest on the stepped ends of the side sections. Above the car decks in each hold is a platform between the wing tanks. As it has no contact with the side sections it is held by fixed supports and link rods. After the vehicles have been unloaded the vessel is transformed into a bulk carrier by removing the pontoons from the hatchways and stowing them on deck in racks adjacent to the hatches. The end sections at the forward and aft bulkhead can then be drawn up under the main deck and secured there. This is done by one 10-ton derrick at each hatch. The side sections are first drawn together by two 10-ton derricks and then folded up against the undersides of the wing tanks, which have a slope of about 30 degrees. The decks automatically interlock in this position. When lowering the side sections the two locking hooks at the side of the hatches are released from the deck. The process of lowering the decks to the horizontal frees the interlocking device between successive decks automatically. The hold capacity is 833,000 cu. ft.*

FORT CREVECOEUR. *This refrigerated cargo liner and the Fort d'Orleans are the last two of the second series of 'Fort' ships built for Cie. General Transatlantique since the war. The four ships of this class operate between France and the West Indies in the fruit trade. These vessels were all built by the Chantiers et Ateliers de Provence, who have a further pair of slightly larger vessels on order. These latter ships are to be named Fort Josephine and Fort Trinite.*

FUTABA MARU No. 2. *This 2,903 tons d.w. cargo ship was completed by the Mukaishima shipyard of the Hitachi Shipbuilding & Engineering Co. Ltd. for Futaba Kaium K.K. The main machinery consists of a type Z-6-ZSH Hanshin diesel engine designed to develop a maximum output of 1,500 b.h.p. at 260 r.p.m. The vessel reached a speed on trials of 13·9 knots.*

GANGES MARU. *Japanese.* Cargo. Built by Usuki Ironworks, Saeki, for Daiken Shosen. 5,200 tons gross, 7,000 tons d.w., 380·33 ft. b.p., 54·33 ft. breadth, 23·67 ft. draught, M.A.N. diesel by Mitsubishi, 5,000 b.h.p., 14 knots.

GANYMEDES. *Dutch.* Cargo. Built by N.V. Schps. Gebr. Pot, Bolnes, for Koninkl. Nederl. Stoomb. Maats. N.V., Amsterdam. 5,709 tons gross, 7,062 tons d.w., 423 ft. l.o.a., 57·66 ft. breadth, 24·42 ft. draught, 7-cyl. Stork diesel, 4,900 b.h.p., 16¼ knots.

GAUTATYR. *Danish.* Cargo. Built by A/S Nakskov Skibsv., Nakskov, for Rederi A/S 'Myren,' Copenhagen. 4,846 tons gross, 8,830 tons d.w., 437·9 ft. l.o.a., 57·58 ft. breadth, 28·66 ft. draught, 7-cyl. B. & W. diesel, 4,400 b.h.p., 14¼ knots.

GEMINI. *Italian.* Bulk carrier. Built by Ansaldo S.p.A., Genoa, for 'Sidermar' S.p.A., Genoa. 23,178 tons gross, 35,000 tons d.w., 679 ft. l.o.a., 92·25 ft. breadth, 36 ft. draught, 8-cyl. Fiat diesel by Ansaldo, 16,800 b.h.p., 17 knots.

GENTILE DE FABRIANO. *Italian.* Passenger. Built by Cant. Nav. Apuania, Marina di Carrara, for Linee Marit. Dell' Adriatico, Rome, 1,800 tons gross, 312 ft. l.o.a., 41 ft. breadth, 12·42 ft. draught, two 5-cyl. Fiat diesels, 5,500 b.h.p., 18 knots.

GERMA. *Norwegian.* Cargo. Built by Kristiansands M/V A/S, Kristiansand, for A/S Gerrards Rederi, Kristiansand. 2,334 tons gross, 3,950 tons d.w., 337·2 ft. l.o.a., 47 ft. breadth, 4-cyl. B. & W. diesel by Akers, 2,400 b.h.p., 14 knots.

GERTRUD TEN DOORNKAAT. *German.* Cargo. Built by Jos. L. Mayer, Papenburg, for Bernhard Schulte, Hamburg. 3,169 tons gross, 5,015 tons d.w., 321·25 ft. l.o.a., 46·9 ft. breadth, 22·9 ft. draught, 8-cyl. M.A.N. diesel, 2,880 b.h.p., 14 knots.

GINKO MARU. *Japanese.* Tanker. Built by Ishikawajima-Harima H.I., Aioi, for Sanko Kisen K.K., Osaka. 21,000 tons gross, 34,318 tons d.w., 654·25 ft. l.o.a., 88·75 ft. breadth, 35·5 ft. draught, 6-cyl. Sulzer diesel by the shipbuilders, 16,000 b.h.p., 16 knots.

GAUTATYR. *This single-screw motorship, 8,830 tons d.w., has been delivered to the Rederi A/S 'Myren' from the Nakskov Shipyard. The new vessel is a sister ship of the Angantyr, delivered in 1960 to the same owners. The total capacity of the cargo holds is 529,900 cu. ft. grain and 481,300 cu. ft. bale.*

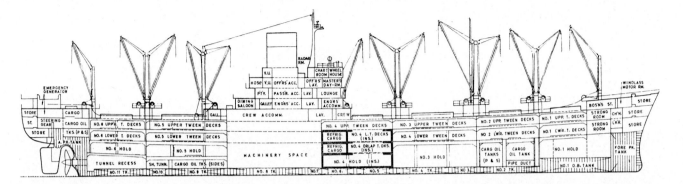

GLENOGLE. *The first of the four 13,000 tons d.w. cargo liners of the Glenlyon class ordered by the Glen Line Ltd. This vessel, the Glenogle, has been built by the Fairfield Shipbuilding & Engineering Co. Ltd. Another ship of the new class, ordered from C. Van der Giessen & Sons, Rotterdam, which was also completed in 1962, has been named Flintshire, and the Nederlandsche Dok en Scheepsbouw Maatschappij, Amsterdam, delivered the Glenlyon. The fourth, named Glenfalloch, is fitting out at Fairfields for delivery in 1963. The class has been designed by the naval architects of the Blue Funnel Line. (The Glen Line is a subsidiary of the Ocean Steam Ship Co. Ltd., which is managed by Alfred Holt & Co.). All four ships will be propelled by Sulzer 9 RD 90 diesel engines with cylinder bores of 900 mm. and a normal full speed output of 16,600 b.h.p. These engines are designed to develop 2,000 b.h.p. per cylinder. (The Sulzer engine in multiples of three cylinders, viz. three, six and nine cylinders, can develop 2,300 b.h.p. per cylinder at 119 r.p.m.) The service speed is 20 knots, which saves eight days on the Far East run compared with slower vessels which are to be withdrawn. The Glenogle has been built with a bulbous bow and a fine hull form, both features adding to her ability to maintain high speeds. She has also been fitted with a 'clear-water' type sternframe and rudder: a type which was first fitted to the Blue Funnel ship Idomeneus in 1899, and which is often referred to as a Mariner rudder and is quite mistakenly called a modern development. Unlike most of the Glen Line ships, which are of the three-island type, the Glenogle has a flush deck arrangement. The midship portion of the double bottom and decks are longitudinally framed while the holds are transversely framed throughout the length. The hulls are the first of the company's ships to be virtually all welded. The anchors are stowed into much smaller recesses than is normal but only the bases of the anchors are visible, the flukes being stowed within the recess. This has been achieved by fitting the patent 'Spek' anchor. As will be seen from the outline drawing, the ship has six holds, four forward of the engine room and two aft, and there are three liquid cargo tanks in the poop forming No. 7 hold. The cargo capacity is 636,700 cu. ft. and the refrigerated space is about 80,000 cu. ft., made up of eight lockers, the hatchway and one hold all*

GLENOGLE—*continued*

situated just forward of the engine room in No. 4 hold. Cargoes can be carried at temperatures down to −15 *deg. F. In addition to her crew of 70 persons the Glenogle has accommodation for 12 passengers, who have exclusive use of the promenade deck. Air-conditioning has been provided throughout the accommodation.*

GIOVANNI GRIMALDI. *Italian.* Bulk carrier. Built by C.R.D., Adriatico, San Marco, for Grimaldi Cia. di Nav. S.A., Palermo. 16,058 tons gross, 22,400 tons d.w., 635 ft. l.o.a., 76 ft. breadth, 30 ft. draught, 9-cyl. Fiat diesel by the shipbuilders.

GLENLYON. *British.* Refrigerated cargo. Built by Nederl. Dok & Schps., Amsterdam, for Glen Line Ltd., London. 11,950 tons gross, 13,000 tons d.w., 543·75 ft. l.o.a., 74·66 ft. breadth, 30 ft. draught, 9-cyl. Sulzer diesel, 16,600 b.h.p., 20 knots.

GLENOGLE. *British.* Refrigerated cargo. Built by Fairfield S.B. & E. Co. Ltd., Glasgow, for Glen Line Ltd., London. 11,918 tons gross, 13,000 tons d.w., 540 ft. l.o.a., 74·5 ft. breadth, 30 ft. draught, 9-cyl. Sulzer diesel by the shipbuilders, 16,600 b.h.p., 20 knots.

GLORIA. *Norwegian.* Cargo. Built by Aukra Bruk A/S, Aukra, for Gerner Mathisen Rederi A/S, Oslo. 2,100 tons gross, 2,350 tons d.w., 249·2 ft. l.o.a., 38·75 ft. breadth, 15·42 ft. draught, 9-cyl. diesel, 1,500 b.h.p., 12½ knots.

GOONAWARRA. *Swedish.* Cargo. Built by A/B Lindholmens Varv, Gothenburg, for Rederi A/B Transatlantic, Gothenburg. 8,160 tons gross, 12,350 tons d.w., 513 ft. l.o.a., 68·18 ft. breadth, 30·5 ft. draught, 8-cyl. Götaverken diesel by the shipbuilders, 10,000 b.h.p., 17¾ knots.

GORREDYK. *Dutch.* Refrigerated cargo. Built by N.V. Wilton-Fijenoord, Schiedam, for Holland-Amerika Line, Rotterdam. 7,259 tons gross, 10,200 tons d.w., 534 ft. l.o.a., 67·66 ft. breadth, 26·95 ft. draught, 8-cyl. M.A.N. diesel by the shipbuilders, 10,400 b.h.p., 17 knots.

GOSFORTH. *British.* Cargo. Built by Hall, Russell & Co. Ltd., Aberdeen, for Burnett S.S. Co. Ltd., Newcastle-upon-Tyne. 5,836 tons gross, 7,580 tons d.w., 410·25 ft. l.o.a., 56·5 ft. breadth, 23·75 ft. draught, 6-cyl. Sulzer diesel, 3,840 b.h.p., 14 knots.

GÖTA RIVER. *Liberian.* Tanker. Built by Eriksbergs M/V A/B, Gothenburg, for Cia. Atlantica Pacifica S.A., Monrovia. 22,670 tons gross, 36,950 tons d.w., 682·5 ft. l.o.a., 87·25 ft. breadth, 36·5 ft. draught, 10-cyl. B. & W. diesel by the shipbuilders, 16,600 b.h.p., 16¾ knots.

GOTHLAND. *British.* Ore carrier. Built by Lithgows Ltd., Port Glasgow, for Currie Line Ltd., Leith. 16,664 tons gross, 24,300 tons d.w., 595·2 ft. l.o.a., 74 ft. breadth, 31·95 ft. draught, 5-cyl. B. & W. diesel by Kincaid, 5,400 b.h.p., 11 knots.

GRANVILLE. *Norwegian.* Cargo. Built by Eriksbergs M/V A/B, Gothenburg, for A. F. Klaveness & Co. A/S, Oslo. 5,267 tons gross, 9,650 tons d.w., 451·75 ft. l.o.a., 58·2 ft. breadth, 25·82 ft. draught, 6-cyl. B. & W. diesel, 7,500 b.h.p., 17 knots.

GREBBEDIJK. *Dutch.* Cargo. Built by Wilton-Fijenoord Dok-en Werf Maats. N.V., Rotterdam, for Holland-Amerika Lijn, Rotterdam. 7,259 tons gross, 10,200 tons d.w., 534·58 ft. l.o.a., 67·58 ft. breadth, 26·9 ft. draught, 8-cyl. M.A.N. diesel by shipbuilders, 10,400 b.h.p., 17 knots.

GRECIAN FLAME. *Panamanian.* Ore carrier. Built by Ch. de l'Atlantique, St. Nazaire, for Cia. Roblon de Oro, Panama. 15,692 tons gross, 21,867 tons d.w., 586·9 ft. l.o.a., 74·9 ft. breadth, 31 ft. draught, 6-cyl. B. & W. diesel by the shipbuilders, 9,000 b.h.p., 15¼ knots.

GREENLAND. *British.* Collier. Built by Austin & Pickersgill Ltd., Sunderland, for Shipping & Coal Co. Ltd., London. 2,200 tons gross, 2,900 tons d.w., 285 ft. l.o.a., 42·2 ft. breadth, 18·25 ft. draught, 9-cyl. Polar diesel by Nydqvist & Holm, 4,410 b.h.p., 13½ knots.

GRIM. *Swedish.* Cargo. Built by A/B Finnboda Varf, Stockholm, for Stockholms Rederi A/B Svea, Stockholm. 1,599 tons gross, 2,400 tons d.w., 306·75 ft. l.o.a., 45·25 ft. breadth, 16·58 ft. draught, 5-cyl. diesel by Fiat, 2,420 b.h.p., 13½ knots.

GROTEDYK. *Dutch.* Refrigerated cargo. Built by Rotterdamsche D.D. Maats., Rotterdam, for N.V. Nederl.-Amerik. Stoomv. Maats. (Holland-Amerika Lijn), Rotterdam. 7,200 tons gross, 10,000 tons d.w., 534·2 ft. l.o.a., 67·58 ft. breadth, 27 ft. draught, 8-cyl. diesel by Gebr.-Stork, 10,400 b.h.p., 17 knots.

G

GOTHLAND. *An ore carrier of 24,300 tons d.w. built by Lithgows Ltd. for the Currie Line Ltd., Leith. This vessel is the third ship of this name to be built for the Currie Line, and the ninth ship of the fleet. The first Gothland (1,469 tons gross) was built by J. G. Thompson, Glasgow, in 1871, while the second ship was built by Henry Robb in 1932. The new ship is employed on a long-term time charter to the B.I.S.C. (Ore) Ltd. The Gothland is a single-decker with a single screw. All accommodation and machinery are situated aft. The grain capacity in holds is 624,348 cu. ft. and the bale capacity in holds is 623,358 cu. ft. The hull is constructed on the longitudinal system. Two longitudinal bulkheads, 19 ft. 6 in. off centreline port and starboard, divide the ship into three longitudinal compartments. These compartments are divided transversely to give five main ore holds in the centre; at the sides there are nine water ballast tanks, one main and one reserve oil fuel bunker port and starboard.*

GOSFORTH. *Built by Hall, Russell & Co. Ltd., for the Burnett Steamship Co. Ltd., of Newcastle, this motorship is a single-deck bulk carrier of moderate size by bulk carrier standards. She has a deadweight of 7,580 tons which is about 1,000 tons more than the vessel on which she was modelled, the Holmside, which went into service in 1959. Both ships have 6-cylinder Sulzer main engines of the same bore and stroke, 600 mm. by 1,040 mm. In the case of the Gosforth the engine is turbocharged, which has stepped up the power from 3,000 to 3,840 b.h.p. at 150 r.p.m. The Gosforth is a four-hold ship with a hold capacity of 365,100 cu. ft. grain and her dimensions and equipment have been tailored for navigation in the St. Lawrence Seaway and the Great Lakes.*

GUERNICA. *Spanish.* Tanker. Built by Empresa Nac. 'Bazan,' El Ferrol, for Naviera Vizcaina S.A., Bilbao. 21,700 tons gross, 32,300 tons d.w., 665 ft. l.o.a., 87·42 ft. breadth, 34·25 ft. draught, 2 grd. turbs. by Parsons, 14,000 s.h.p., 16¼ knots.

GULF DANE. *British.* Tanker. Built by Furness S.B. Co. Ltd., Haverton Hill, for Britama Tankers Ltd., London. 26,654 tons gross, 40,100 tons d.w., 714·66 ft. l.o.a., 95·58 ft. breadth, 36·33 ft. draught, 2 Brown Boveri grd. turbs. by Richardsons Westgarth, 19,000 s.h.p., 17 knots.

GULF HANSA. *Dutch.* Tanker. Built by Deutsche Werft A.G., Hamburg, for Nedgulf Tankers N.V., Rotterdam. 29,700 tons gross, 48,000 tons d.w., 743 ft. l.o.a., 101·5 ft. breadth, 37·2 ft. draught, 2 grd. turbs. by G.E.C., 19,000 s.h.p., 17 knots.

GULF ITALIAN. *Dutch.* Tanker. Built by Deutsche Werft A.G., Hamburg, for Nedgulf Tankers N.V., Rotterdam. 30,613 tons gross, 48,000 tons d.w., 743 ft. l.o.a., 101·5 ft. breadth, 37·2 ft. draught, 2 grd. turbs. by G.E.C., 19,000 s.h.p., 17 knots.

GULF SWEDE. *Dutch.* Tanker. Built by Uddevallavarvet A/B, Uddevalla, for Nedgulf Tankers N.V., Rotterdam. 26,580 tons gross, 42,400 tons d.w., 723·82 ft. l.o.a., 97·42 ft. breadth, 36·5 ft. draught, 2 grd. turbs. by G.E.C., 17,500 s.h.p., 18 knots.

GUNILLA BILLNER. *Swedish.* Tanker. Built by Kockums M/V A/B, Malmö, for Billners Rederi A/B, Gothenburg. 12,899 tons gross, 19,960 tons d.w., 557·75 ft. l.o.a., 72 ft. breadth, 31 ft. draught, 8-cyl. M.A.N. diesel by the shipbuilders, 9,000 b.h.p., 15 knots.

H

HADJI AGUS SALIM. *Indonesian.* Passenger and cargo. Built by United Polish Shipyards, Szczecin, for Indonesian Government. 6,600 tons gross, 2,300 tons d.w., 505·25 ft. l.o.a., 63·66 ft. breadth, 6-cyl. Sulzer diesel, 1,800 b.h.p., 11½ knots.

HAI ZIANG. *Nat. Chinese.* Cargo. Built by Cant. Nav. Felszegi, Trieste, for China Merchants S.N. Co. Ltd., Taipeh, Formosa. 3,800 tons gross, 5,500 tons d.w., 376·75 ft. l.o.a., 51 ft. breadth, 22·9 ft. draught, 6-cyl. diesel by Fiat, 3,150 b.h.p., 13 knots.

HAITAI. *Nat. China.* Cargo. Built by Kasado Dock Co. Ltd., Kudamatsu, for China Merchants S.N. Co. Ltd., Taipeh. 3,160 tons gross, 3,600 tons d.w., 326 ft. l.o.a., 46·75 ft. breadth, 19·2 ft. draught, 5-cyl. B. & W. diesel by Mitsui, 2,900 b.h.p., 13 knots.

HALLFAX. *Canadian.* Self-unloading bulk carrier. Built by Wm. Hamilton & Co. Ltd., Port Glasgow, for Hall Corp. of Canada. 5,230 tons gross, 9,200 tons d.w., 385·2 ft. l.o.a., 58 ft. breadth, 21·5 ft. draught, tw-sc. two 6-cyl. Polar diesels, 3,300 b.h.p., 11½ knots.

HALONIA. *French.* Ore and coal carrier. Built by At. & Ch. de Bretagne, Nantes, for Soc. Maritime National & Union Nav., Paris. 10,977 tons gross, 15,760 tons d.w., 498·66 ft. l.o.a., 65·9 ft. breadth, 30·2 ft. draught, two 9-cyl. grd. Pielstick diesels by the shipbuilders, 5,800 b.h.p., 14 knots.

HAMILTONIAN. *Canadian.* Bulk carrier. Built by Saint John S.B. & D.D. Co. Ltd., St. John, N.B., for Eastern Lake Carriers, Quebec. 18,192 tons gross, 26,100 tons d.w., 730 ft. l.o.a., 75·33 ft. breadth, 26·5 ft. draught, 2 grd. turbs. by Canadian G.E.C., 9,900 s.h.p., 17 knots.

HANKA SAWICKA. *Polish.* Cargo liner. Built by United Polish Shipyards, Szczecin, for Polish Ocean Lines. 6,904 tons gross, 10,300 tons d.w., 504·9 ft. l.o.a., 64·25 ft. breadth, 27·2 ft. draught, 6-cyl. Sulzer diesel, 7,800 b.h.p., 16½ knots.

HANS OLDENDORFF. *German.* Cargo. Built by Werft Nobiskrug, Rendsburg, for Egon Oldendorff, Lübeck. 2,983 tons gross, 4,250 tons d.w., 347·5 ft. l.o.a., 49·66 ft. breadth, 19·5 ft. draught, two 6-cyl. diesels by M.A.N., 3,000 b.h.p., 14 knots.

HANSA EXPRESS. *Finnish.* Passenger and car ferry. Built by Hanseatische Werft, Hamburg, for Merivienti O/Y, Helsingfors. 2,800 tons gross, 290 ft. l.o.a., 51 ft. breadth, 14 ft. draught, tw-sc. two Polar diesels, 5,760 b.h.p., 18½ knots.

HARRIET MARU. *Japanese.* Ore carrier. Built by Uraga Dock Co. Ltd., Yokosuka, for Osaka Shosen Kaisha, Osaka. 17,000 tons gross, 27,400 tons d.w., 585·66 ft. l.o.a., 85·5 ft. breadth, 31·9 ft. draught, 6-cyl. Sulzer diesel by the shipbuilders, 13,000 b.h.p., 15 knots.

HASSI MESSAOUD. *French.* Tanker. Built by Ch. Nav. de La Ciotat, La Ciotat, for Cie. Maritime des Chargeurs Reunis, Paris. 32,733 tons gross, 51,500 tons d.w., 758·66 ft. l.o.a., 99·66 ft. breadth, 40·58 ft. draught, 2 Parsons grd. turbs. by C.E.M., 20,200 s.h.p., 16¾ knots.

HAUKEFJELL. *Norwegian.* Cargo. Built by Kieler Howaldtswerke A.G., Kiel, for Olsen & Ugelstad, Oslo. 4,200 tons gross, 5,600 tons d.w., 355·2 ft. l.o.a., 51·2 ft. breadth, 24·65 ft. draught, 6-cyl. M.A.N. diesel, 4,000 b.h.p., 15 knots.

HAVDHEM. *Swedish.* Cargo. Built by Oresundsvarvet A/B, Landskrona, for Robert Myrsten, Slite. 6,400 tons gross, 9,300 tons d.w., 428·75 ft. l.o.a., 58·42 ft. breadth, 27·33 ft. draught, 6-cyl. Götaverken diesel, 5,000 b.h.p., 17 knots.

HAVTJELD. *Norwegian.* Cargo. Built by Oresundsvarvet A/B, Landskrona, for P. Meyer, Oslo. 9,100 tons gross, 11,300 tons d.w., 469 ft. l.b.p., 64·2 ft. breadth, 31·5 ft. draught, 8-cyl. Götaverken diesel, 11,800 b.h.p., 15½ knots.

HAWAII. *American.* Refrigerated cargo. Built by Newport News S.B. & D.D. Co., Newport News, for States Steamship Co., San Francisco. 12,700 tons gross, 12,840 tons d.w., 565 ft. l.o.a., 76·2 ft. breadth, 31·58 ft. draught, 2 grd. turbs. by the shipbuilders, 19,250 s.h.p., 20 knots.

HAVDHEM. This 9,300 tons d.w. cargo ship was delivered by Oresundsvarvet A/B, Landskrona, to a consortium led by Robert Myrsten, of Slite, Sweden. There are four cargo hatches of which Nos. 2 and 3 are unusually long at 55 ft. 9 in. The hatches are fitted with patent steel covers. There is a 30-ton heavy-lift derrick at No. 3 hatch.

HAVTJELD. This cargo liner was handed over to the Oslo owners P. Meyer by Oresundsvarvet A/B, of Landskrona, for service between West European and North American ports. Of 11,300 tons d.w., she has a very wide range of cargo handling equipment. Besides 18 derricks with 5 to 15 tons lifts, a 30-ton derrick is arranged to serve Nos. 2 and 3 holds, and two 5-ton deck cranes serve No. 4 hold. Tweendeck hatches have flush steel covers. In No. 2 hold are two built-in vegetable oil tanks, epoxy-resin coated, of about half the depth of the hold.

H

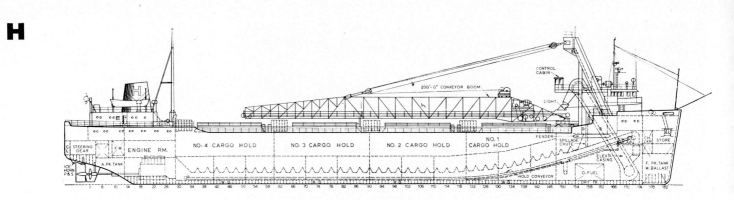

| STEERING GEAR | F.W. | ENGINE RM. | NO. 4 CARGO HOLD | NO. 3 CARGO HOLD | NO. 2 CARGO HOLD | NO. 1 CARGO HOLD | | |

200'-0" CONVEYOR BOOM

CONTROL CABIN

LIGHT

FENDER

SPILLAGE CHUTE

CH. STORE

ELEV'R CASING

HOLD CONVEYOR

F. PK. TANK
W. BALLAST

O. FUEL

ICE HORN P & S

A. PK. TANK

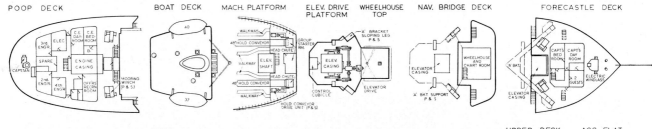

POOP DECK   BOAT DECK   MACH. PLATFORM   ELEV. DRIVE PLATFORM   WHEELHOUSE TOP   NAV. BRIDGE DECK   FORECASTLE DECK

POOP DECK: 3rd ENGR. ELEC. C.E. DAY-ROOM C.E. BED-ROOM SPARE ENGINE CASING CAPSTAN 2nd ENGR. 4th ENGR. OFFRS RECRN ROOM MOORING WINCH (P & S)

BOAT DECK: 40 — 37

MACH. PLATFORM: WALKWAY 48" HOLD CONVEYOR HEAD CHUTE GROUP STARTER RM. ELEV. SHAFT WALKWAY 48" HOLD CONVEYOR HEAD CHUTE WALKWAY HOLD CONVEYOR DRIVE UNIT (P & S)

ELEV. DRIVE PLATFORM: 'A' BRACKET SLOPING LEG P & S ELEV. CASING CONTROL CUBICLE ELEVATOR DRIVE

NAV. BRIDGE DECK: ELEVATOR CASING 'A' BKT 'A' BKT SUPPORT P & S WHEELHOUSE AND CHART ROOM

FORECASTLE DECK: CAPTS BED ROOM CAPTS DAY ROOM ELECTRIC WINDLASS 2 GUESTS ELEVATOR CASING

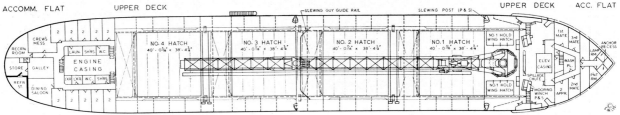

ACCOMM. FLAT   UPPER DECK   SLEWING GUY GUIDE RAIL   SLEWING POST (P & S)   UPPER DECK   ACC. FLAT

RECRN ROOM   CREW'S MESS   LAUN. SHRS W.C.   STORE   GALLEY   ENGINE CASING   LKR LKR W.C. SHRS   REER ST   DINING SALOON

NO. 4 HATCH 40'-0¾" × 38'-4¾"   NO. 3 HATCH 40'-0¾" × 38'-4¾"   NO. 2 HATCH 40'-0¾" × 38'-4¾"   NO. 1 HATCH 40'-0¾" × 38'-4¾"

1st MATE   3rd MATE   NO. 1 HOLD WING HATCH   ELEV. CASING   WASH PL.   SPILLAGE CHUTE   NO. 1 HOLD WING HATCH   MOORING WINCH P & S   2nd MATE   2 APPR.   ANCHOR RECESS   LAMP RM   PNT RM   PNT PL

HALLFAX

HALLFAX. The Hall Corporation of Canada, Montreal, took delivery in 1962 of this self-unloading bulk carrier for operation in the area between the Gulf of St. Lawrence and the Canadian Great Lakes. The vessel, 9,200 tons d.w., has been built by Wm. Hamilton & Co. Ltd., Port Glasgow, and was designed with the prime object of rapid loading, transfer and unloading of bulk cargoes such as limestone and coal. Under normal conditions, on a minimum route of 60 miles, 9,000 tons of cargo can be loaded, taken by sea, discharged, a return voyage made in ballast and a further 9,000 tons loaded within 24 hours. By means of the 200 ft. conveyor boom and special warping winches cargo can be placed on the quay at the rate of 2,000 tons an hour anywhere within a distance of 200 ft. from the ship's side. This ship is powered by twin Nydquist & Holm Polar diesel engines driving twin propellers. The service speed, fully loaded, is $11\frac{1}{2}$ knots, and the propelling machinery is fully pneumatically controlled from the bridge, which, as in most Great Lake ships, is right forward. In the Hallfax it is 300 ft. away from the engine room. Another feature of the ship is the twin Costa bulb installation fitted on the spade rudders. The hull of the Hallfax is almost entirely of welded construction. The four cargo holds are filled through four hatches having 40 ft. by 38 ft. 6 in. openings with self-trimming coamings and MacGregor steel covers. A central tunnel with access by watertight door from the engine room runs the length of the four cargo holds and permits control of the 41 air-operated bunker gates on each side, spaced between transverse peaked baffles over each of the conveyor tunnels. Each gate assembly is mounted on wheels which run on flat-bottom rails, and movement of the position is effected by means of a double-acting air-operated piston. The two 48 in. wide hold conveyors which take the material from the hoppers to the bucket elevator are 275 ft. long, and each is driven by a 75 h.p. squirrel-cage motor at a speed of approximately 500 ft./min. At the fore end of the ship these conveyors are inclined to a maximum height of about 27 ft. so that the material which is being unloaded drops into a chute feeding the bucket elevator. The elevator is of the continuous twin-chain and bucket type and is driven by a 220 h.p. wound-rotor induction motor, through a coupling and a worm-reduction gearbox, at a maximum speed of 160 ft./min. A feed chute is fitted at the head of the elevator to transfer the material from the buckets to the boom conveyor. The lower end of this chute is automatically rotated when the boom is slewed to the unload'ng position so that the material is always directed on to the belt irrespective of the boom position. A chute on the underside of the elevator casing directs any spillage on to the inclined portion of the hopper conveyors for reintroduction into the elevator. A 200 ft. boom supports the 60 in. belt conveyor and is capable of slewing through 105 degrees on either side of the centreline of the ship and of being elevated through about 62 ft. at its outboard end.

H

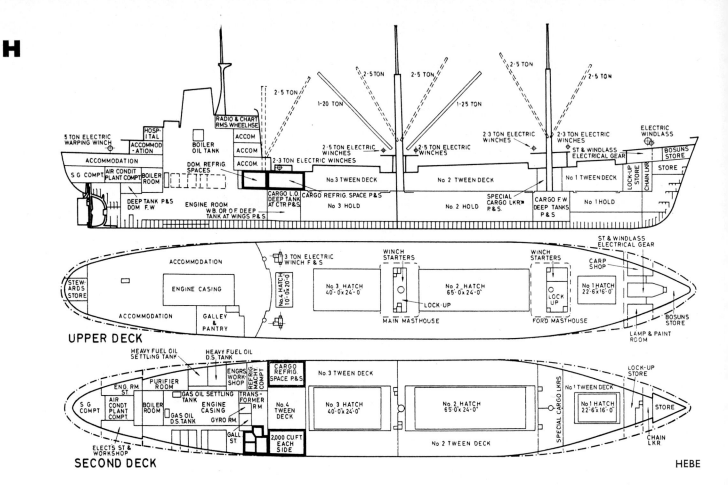

5 TON ELECTRIC WARPING WINCH

HOSPITAL

ACCOMMOD-ATION

RADIO & CHART RMS WHEELHSE

BOILER OIL TANK

ACCOM

ACCOM

2·5 TON

2·5 TON

2·5 TON

2·5 TON

2·5 TON

1·20 TON

1·25 TON

2·3 TON ELECTRIC WINCHES

2·3 TON ELECTRIC WINCHES

ELECTRIC WINDLASS

ACCOMMODATION

DOM. REFRIG. SPACES

ACCOM

2·5 TON ELECTRIC WINCHES

2·5 TON ELECTRIC WINCHES

ST & WINDLASS ELECTRICAL GEAR

BOSUNS STORE

S G COMPT

AIR CONDIT PLANT COMPT

BOILER ROOM

2·3 TON ELECTRIC WINCHES

No 3 TWEEN DECK

No 2 TWEEN DECK

No 1 TWEEN DECK

LOCK-UP STORE

CHAIN LKR

STORE

DEEP TANK P&S DOM. F.W

ENGINE ROOM

CARGO L.O DEEP TANK AT CTR P&S

CARGO REFRIG. SPACE P&S

No 3 HOLD

No 2 HOLD

SPECIAL CARGO LKR P.S

CARGO F.W DEEP TANKS P&S

No 1 HOLD

DEEP TANK P&S DOM. F.W

W.B. OR O.F. DEEP TANK AT WINGS P&S.

STEW-ARDS STORE

ACCOMMODATION

ENGINE CASING

3 TON ELECTRIC WINCH F & S

No. 4 HATCH 10'-0"x 20'-0

No 3. HATCH 40'-0"x 24'-0

WINCH STARTERS

No 2. HATCH 65'-0"x 24'-0"

LOCK-UP

WINCH STARTERS

LOCK UP

ST & WINDLASS ELECTRICAL GEAR

CARP SHOP

No 1 HATCH 22·6"x 16'-0"

ACCOMMODATION

GALLEY & PANTRY

MAIN MASTHOUSE

FORD MASTHOUSE

BOSUNS STORE

UPPER DECK

LAMP & PAINT ROOM

HEAVY FUEL OIL SETTLING TANK

HEAVY FUEL OIL D.S. TANK

ENGRS WORK SHOP

REFRIG MACHY COMPT

CARGO REFRIG. SPACE P&S

No 3 TWEEN DECK

LOCK-UP STORE

No 1 TWEEN DECK

ENG. RM. ST

PURIFIER ROOM

GAS OIL SETTLING TANK

TRANS-FORMER RM

No 4 TWEEN DECK

No 3 HATCH 40'-0"x 24'-0"

No 2 HATCH 65'-0"x 24'-0"

No 1 HATCH 22·6"x 16'-0"

STORE

S G COMPT

AIR CONDT PLANT COMPT.

BOILER ROOM

GAS OIL D.S. TANK

ENGINE CASING

GYRO RM.

GALL ST

SPECIAL CARGO LKRS

CHAIN LKR

ELECTS ST & WORKSHOP

2,000 CU FT EACH SIDE

No 2 TWEEN DECK

SECOND DECK

HEBE

82

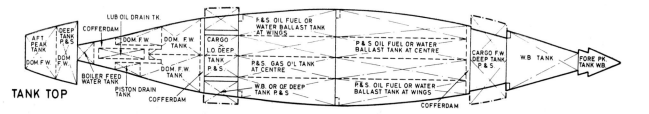

LUB OIL DRAIN TK.

DEEP TANK P&S

COFFERDAM

AFT PEAK TANK

DOM F.W

DOM. F.W

DOM F.W.

DOM. F.W. TANK

LUB OIL DRAIN TK.

F&S OIL FUEL OR WATER BALLAST TANK AT WINGS

CARGO L.O. DEEP TANK P & S

P&S OIL FUEL OR WATER BALLAST TANK AT CENTRE

CARGO FW DEEP TANK P.&S.

W.B. TANK

FORE PK. TANK W.B

BOILER FEED WATER TANK

PISTON DRAIN TANK

DOM. F.W. TANK

P&S GAS O'L TANK AT CENTRE

W.B. OR QF DEEP TANK P.&S

P&S OIL FUEL OR WATER BALLAST TANK AT WINGS

TANK TOP

COFFERDAM

COFFERDAM

HEBE. *Delivered from Henry Robb Ltd. to the British India Steam Navigation Co. Ltd., this vessel of 4,700 tons d.w. and her sister ship Bacchus have been specially designed for the carriage of cargo in containers. The Hebe has been chartered to the Admiralty for a period of 19 years for service as a Royal Fleet auxiliary. The ship has three large holds and tweendecks, all forward of the machinery space, having a total capacity of 230,000 cu. ft. Her gross tonnage is only 123 tons in excess of her deadweight and the cubic capacity is accordingly high. The holds and tweendecks spaces are served by large hatches, the largest measuring 65 ft. by 24 ft. No. 4 tweendeck, port and starboard, is insulated for the carriage of frozen cargoes at −10 deg. F. and, in addition, up to 12 refrigerated cargo containers may be carried. The main propelling machinery consists of a 5-cylinder Swan Hunter-Sulzer type turbocharged two-stroke diesel engine having cylinders of 680 mm. bore and a stroke of 1,250 mm. At 135 r.p.m. the engine output is 5,500 b.h.p. A feature of the installation is the anti-vibration coupling which has been fitted between the main engine and the first length of intermediate shafting.*

HEBE. *British.* Cargo. Built by Henry Robb Ltd., Leith, for British India S.N. Co. Ltd., London. 4,823 tons gross, 4,700 tons d.w., 379 ft. l.o.a., 55 ft. breadth, 21 ft. draught, 5-cyl. Sulzer diesel by Swan Hunter, 5,500 b.h.p., 15 knots.

HEERING ROSE. *Danish.* Cargo. Built by Elsinore S.B. & E. Co. Ltd., Elsinore, for Cherry Heering Line, Copenhagen. 4,500 tons gross, 6,075 tons d.w., 390 ft. l.o.a., 52·33 ft. breadth, 22·9 ft. draught, 6-cyl. B. & W. diesel by the shipbuilders, 4,200 b.h.p., 15 knots.

HELLE SKOU. *Danish.* Cargo. Built by Elsinore S.B. & E. Co. Ltd., Elsinore, for Ove Skou Rederi A/S, Copenhagen. 4,207 tons gross, 7,000 tons d.w., 416·33 ft. l.o.a., 56·5 ft. breadth, 24 ft. draught, 8-cyl. B. & W. diesel by the shipbuilders, 7,300 b.h.p., 17 knots.

HELLENIC LEADER. *Greek.* Refrigerated cargo. Built by Kure S.B. & E. Co. Ltd., Kure, for Transpacific Carriers Corp., Piraeus and New York. 8,730 tons gross, 10,870 tons d.w., 473 ft. l.o.a., 63·2 ft. breadth, 29 ft. draught, 6-cyl. M.A.N. diesel by Mitsubishi Yokohama, 7,800 b.h.p., 16 knots.

HELLENIC PIONEER. *Greek.* Refrigerated cargo. Built by Kure S.B. & E. Co. Ltd., Kure, for Universal Cargo Carriers Inc., New York. 8,730 tons gross, 10,870 tons d.w., 473 ft. l.o.a., 63·2 ft. breadth, 29 ft. draught, 6-cyl. diesel by Mitsubishi Nippon H.I., 7,400 b.h.p., 16 knots.

HENRIETTE MAERSK. *Danish.* Cargo. Built by Elsinore S.B. & E. Co. Ltd., Elsinore, for A. P. Möller, Copenhagen. 9,500 tons gross, 12,100 tons d.w., 495·5 ft. l.o.a., 62·66 ft. breadth, 9-cyl. B. & W. diesel by the shipbuilders, 9,800 b.h.p., 18 knots.

H

HEERING ROSE. *This cargo vessel of 6,075 tons d.w. has been built by the Elsinore Shipbuilding & Engineering Co. Ltd., Elsinore, Denmark, for the well-known liqueur manufacturing concern of Peter F. Heering, Copenhagen. Owned by a subsidiary company, the Cherry Heering Line, the new ship, Heering Rose, replaces the Christel Heering, 2,358 tons d.w., built in 1958, which has been sold to a Colombian company, while her sister ship Mille Heering is still in service. The ship is built as an open or closed shelterdecker to Lloyd's Register Class 100 A1 Ice Class 3. The cubic capacity of the holds is about 281,000 cu. ft. grain and 258,800 cu. ft. bale, including 16,000 cu. ft. of refrigerated space which can be cooled to —4 deg. F. (—20 deg. C.). The ship has four holds which are served by three hatches, of which the middle one is a large double hatch. All hatches are provided with hinged steel hatchway covers of the Elsinore shipyard's type. The holds are served by six 10-ton and two 5-ton derricks, and at the centre hatch there is a heavy derrick for lifting loads up to 35 tons. Like the two earlier ships, the Heering Rose is painted in the company's special colours and has a cherry red hull and a light green superstructure. On the promenade deck there are two double-berth cabins with separate bathrooms for passengers. The propelling machinery consists of a turbocharged 6-cylinder Elsinore-B. & W. diesel engine developing 4,200 b.h.p. and designed to give the vessel a speed of 15 knots in loaded condition as an open shelterdecker.*

HERMAEA. *This vessel and the Tyrsus (which entered service at the end of 1961) are a pair of car and rail ferries for the route between Civitavecchia (the port for Rome) and Sardinia. The two ships have a speed in service of 17 knots and do the 213 km. crossing in eight hours. They are designed to carry rail freight cars or lorries on the main train deck, with motor cars on two upper decks. The train deck can accommodate 30 railway wagons or 45 lorries, while the two car decks can take 74 cars. Passengers are taken only when accompanying their cars, and there is accommodation for a total of 350 persons, with cabin accommodation for about 90 passengers. The ships are loaded through the stern, a hydraulically operated stern door swinging upwards to give access to the train deck. Cars are moved to the car decks by means of lifts. The main engines consist of a pair of 6-cylinder Fiat diesels driving twin screws. The propellers are variable-pitch type, those in the Tyrsus being of KaMeWa design, and those in the Hermaea being of Escher-Wyss type. A bow propeller, again of KaMeWa type, is fitted in each ship.*

H

H

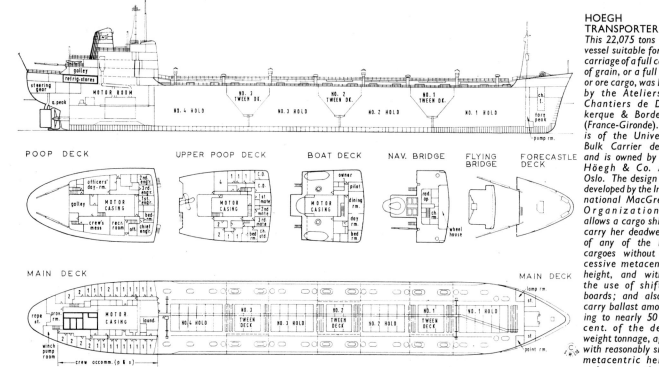

POOP DECK   UPPER POOP DECK   BOAT DECK   NAV. BRIDGE   FLYING   FORECASTLE
                                                                         BRIDGE   DECK

MAIN DECK   MAIN DECK

HOEGH TRANSPORTER

This 22,075 tons d.w. vessel suitable for the carriage of a full cargo of grain, or a full coal or ore cargo, was built by the Ateliers et Chantiers de Dunkerque & Bordeaux (France-Gironde). She is of the Universal Bulk Carrier design and is owned by Leif Höegh & Co. A/S, Oslo. The design was developed by the International MacGregor Organization. It allows a cargo ship to carry her deadweight of any of the bulk cargoes without excessive metacentric height, and without the use of shifting boards; and also to carry ballast amounting to nearly 50 per cent. of the deadweight tonnage, again with reasonably small metacentric height and consequently easy motion. The Höegh Transporter *is the first vessel to be built in France to the U.B.C. design, the basis of which is the siting of spaces between the main holds at tweendeck level. Propulsion is by diesel engine. During sea trials in very severe weather conditions with winds at gale force the ship, on account of the ballasting arrangements, had only a gentle roll and remained very steady on course. The disposition of the cargo holds, with three central tweendecks and three side tweendecks, will be noted on the accompanying drawing. A sister ship, the* Höegh Traveller *was also delivered in 1962.*

HERA. *Norwegian.* Cargo. Built by Sarpsborg M/V A/S, Greaker, for Tinfos Papirfabrik A/S, Notodden. 2,815 tons gross, 4,000 tons d.w., 300·25 ft. l.o.a., 48 ft. breadth, 19·75 ft. draught, 6-cyl. diesel by M.A.N., 2,250 b.h.p., 12 knots.

HERMAEA. *Italian.* Train ferry. Built by Cant. Nav. Riuniti, Palermo, for Italian State Railways. 4,000 tons gross, 1,200 tons d.w., 393·25 ft. l.o.a., 56·58 ft. breadth, tw-sc. two 6-cyl. Fiat diesels, 8,000 b.h.p., 17 knots.

HERMES. *Dutch.* Refrigerated cargo. Built by A. Vuijk & Zonen, Capelle, for Kon. Nederl. Stoomb. Maats. N.V., Amsterdam. 5,709 tons gross, 7,200 tons d.w., 423·9 ft. l.o.a., 57·66 ft. breadth, 24·5 ft. draught, 7-cyl. diesel by Gebr.-Stork, 4,900 b.h.p., 16 knots.

HEWELIUSZ. *Polish.* Cargo liner. Built by United Polish Shipyards, Szczecin, for Polish Ocean Lines. 5,864 tons gross, 8,200 tons d.w., 478·5 ft. l.o.a., 60·82 ft. breadth, 25 ft. draught, 6-cyl. Sulzer diesel, 7,800 b.h.p., 17 knots.

HÖEGH BANNIERE. *Norwegian.* Refrigerated cargo. Built by Drammen Slip & Verk., Drammen, for Lief Höegh & Co. A/S, Oslo. 6,100 tons gross, 8,400 tons d.w., 424·75 ft. l.o.a., 57·5 ft. breadth, 27 ft. draught, 5-cyl. Sulzer diesel, 5,500 b.h.p., 16½ knots.

HÖEGH BELLE. *Norwegian.* Refrigerated cargo. Built by Drammen Slip & Verk., Drammen, for Lief Höegh & Co. A/S, Oslo. 6,100 tons gross, 8,400 tons d.w., 424·75 ft. l.o.a., 57·66 ft. breadth, 27 ft. draught, 5-cyl. diesel by Sulzer, 5,500 b.h.p., 16½ knots.

HÖEGH DYKE. *Norwegian.* Refrigerated cargo. Built by Kieler Howaldtswerke A.G., Kiel, for Lief Höegh & Co. A/S, Oslo. 9,900 tons gross, 13,200 tons d.w., 515 ft. l.o.a., 64 ft. breadth, 29·75 ft. draught, 8-cyl. M.A.N. diesel by the shipbuilders, 9,300 b.h.p., 17 knots.

HÖEGH GANDRIA. *Norwegian.* Tanker. Built by Kieler Howaldtswerke A.G., Kiel, for Lief Höegh & Co. A/S, Oslo. 32,598 tons gross, 51,948 tons d.w., 740 ft. l.o.a., 102·2 ft. breadth, 39 ft. draught, 10-cyl. B. & W. diesel by Krupp, 19,000 b.h.p., 16¾ knots.

HÖEGH TRANSPORTER. *Norwegian.* Bulk carrier. Built by At. & Ch. de Dunkerque & Bordeaux (France-Gironde), Dunkirk, for Lief Höegh & Co. A/S, Oslo. 15,617 tons gross, 22,070 tons d.w., 584·2 ft. l.o.a., 74·82 ft. breadth, 31 ft. draught, 6-cyl. B. & W. diesel by Du Creusot, 7,400 b.h.p., 15 knots.

HÖEGH TRAVELLER. *Norwegian.* Bulk carrier. Built by At. & Ch. de Dunkerque & Bordeaux (France-Gironde), Dunkirk, for Lief Höegh & Co. A/S, Oslo. 15,616 tons gross, 22,075 tons d.w., 584·5 ft. l.o.a., 74·82 ft. breadth, 31 ft. draught, 6-cyl. B. & W. diesel by Du Creusot, 7,400 b.h.p., 15 knots.

HOKUSHU MARU. *Japanese.* Cargo. Built by Shioyama Dockyard Co. Ltd., Osaka, for Nikko Kaiji K.K., Tokyo. 2,660 tons gross, 4,237 tons d.w., 319·9 ft. l.o.a., 45·9 ft. breadth, 19·9 ft. draught, 7-cyl. diesel by Kobe Hatsudoki, 3,150 b.h.p., 13½ knots.

HOKUTO MARU. *Japanese.* Cargo. Built by Setoda S.B. Co., Setoda, for Itaya Shosen K.K., Kobe. 1,994 tons gross, 3,130 tons d.w., 294 ft. l.o.a., 42 ft. breadth, 18 ft. draught, 6-cyl. diesel by Tekko, 1,800 b.h.p., 14 knots.

HOLLANDS DREEF. *Dutch.* Cargo. Built by Boele's Schps. & Mchf., Bolnes, for N.V. Koninkl. Paketv. Maats., Amsterdam. 9,631 tons gross, 14,670 tons d.w., 500 ft. l.o.a., 63·66 ft. breadth, 29·9 ft. draught, 6-cyl. B. & W. diesel by P. Smit Jun., 5,400 b.h.p., 13 knots.

HOLMA. *Swedish.* Tanker. Built by A/B Götaverken, Gothenburg, for Rederi A/B Monacus, Kingsbacka. 21,630 tons gross, 34,650 tons d.w., 685·9 ft. l.o.a., 86·25 ft. breadth, 34·82 ft. draught, 10-cyl. diesel by the shipbuilders, 12,500 b.h.p., 16 knots.

HOLSTENAU. *German.* Cargo. Built by F. Schichau A.G., Bremerhaven, for Bugsier-Reederei-u. Bergungs A.G., Hamburg. 1,214 tons gross, 2,800 tons d.w., 269 ft. l.o.a., 39·5 ft. breadth, 8-cyl. diesel by Deutz, 2,000 b.h.p., 13 knots.

H

H

HONAN MARU. *Japanese.* Cargo. Built by Namura Shipyard Co. Ltd., Osaka, for Dai-ichi Kisen K.K., Kobe. 3,600 tons gross, 5,500 tons d.w., 328 ft. b.p., 50·2 ft. breadth, 21·2 ft. draught, U.E.T. diesel, 2,700 b.h.p., 12¼ knots.

HOUSTON CITY. *British.* Cargo. Built by Wm. Doxford & Sons (S.B.) Ltd., Sunderland, for Reardon Smith Line Ltd., Cardiff. 10,310 tons gross, 14,400 tons d.w., 499·5 ft. l.o.a., 67·25 ft. breadth, 30·58 ft. draught, 4-cyl. diesel by the shipbuilders, 6,000 b.h.p., 14½ knots.

HOWA MARU. *Japanese.* Cargo. Built by Kure S.B. & E. Co., Kure, for Nitto Shosen K.K., Tokyo. 9,358 tons gross, 13,000 tons d.w., 511·82 ft. l.o.a., 64·5 ft. breadth, 29·5 ft. draught, 6-cyl. Sulzer diesel by Ishikawajima H.I., 9,000 b.h.p., 16¼ knots.

HOZUI MARU. *Japanese.* Cargo. Built by Ishikawajima-Harima H.I., Tokyo, for Nippon Yusen Kaisha & Hachiuma, Tokyo. 8,318 tons gross, 11,384 tons d.w., 460·5 ft. l.o.a., 62·5 ft. breadth, 27·25 ft. draught, 6-cyl. Sulzer diesel by the shipbuilders, 5,610 b.h.p., 14 knots.

HUDSON TRANSPORT. *Canadian.* Tanker. Built by Davie S.B. Ltd., Levis, for Hall Corp. of Canada, Montreal. 4,076 tons gross, 6,400 tons d.w., 355·5 ft. l.o.a., 46 ft. breadth, 22·75 ft. draught, tw-sc. two 10-cyl. diesels by Fairbanks-Morse, 3,200 b.h.p., 12½ knots.

I

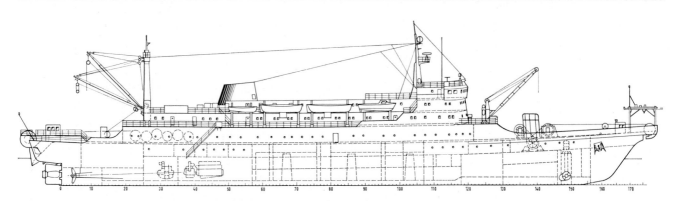

INGUL. *This cable laying and repair ship and her sister ship the Jana, which will be delivered in 1963, were ordered by the U.S.S.R. from the Wartsila-Koncernen A/B of Helsinki. In addition to a bow propulsion unit the Ingul is fitted with an active rudder, and is the first cable-layer to be so fitted, and thus has particularly good manoeuvrability at low speeds. The propelling machinery is diesel-electric, having D.C. propulsion motors, while the auxiliary supply is A.C.*

IDRIJA. *Yugoslav.* Bulk carrier. Built by Brodogradiliste Uljanik, Pula, for Yugoslavenska Tankerska Plovidba, Zadar. 13,152 tons gross, 18,400 tons d.w., 569·42 ft. l.o.a., 72·75 ft. breadth, 29·58 ft. draught, 6-cyl. B. & W. diesel by the shipbuilders, 8,300 b.h.p., 15 knots.

IGARKALES. *Russian.* Cargo. Built by Valmet O/Y Pansio Telakka, Abo, for U.S.S.R. 2,842 tons gross, 3,400 tons d.w., 334·75 ft. l.o.a., 46 ft. breadth, 19·2 ft. draught, 5-cyl. B. & W. diesel by the shipbuilders, 2,900 b.h.p., 13½ knots.

ILLIRIA. *Italian.* Passenger and cargo. Built by Cant. Nav. Pellegrino, Naples for 'Adriatica' S.p.A. di Nav., Venice. 3,780 tons gross, 332·66 ft. l.o.a., 48 ft. breadth, 15·5 ft. draught, tw-sc. two 6-cyl. Fiat diesels, 5,800 b.h.p., 18¾ knots.

IMAM. *Russian.* Cargo. Built by Neptun-Werft, Rostock, for U.S.S.R. 3,455 tons gross, 4,735 tons d.w., 341·9 ft. l.o.a., 47·33 ft. breadth, 20·75 ft. draught, 6-cyl. diesel by M.A.N., 3,250 b.h.p., 15 knots.

INGUL. *Russian.* [Cable Ship. Built by Wärtsilä Kon. Sandvikens Skepps, Helsingfors, for U.S.S.R. 5,900 tons gross, 3,400 tons d.w., 426·66 ft. l.o.a., 52·42 ft. breadth, 17 ft. draught, tw-sc. diesel-electric, two 6-cyl. Sulzer diesels by the shipbuilders, 4,300 s.h.p., 14 knots.

INKURLES. *Russian.* Cargo. Built by Valmet O/Y Pansio Telekka, Abo, for U.S.S.R. 2,842 tons gross, 3,400 tons d.w., 334·75 ft. l.o.a., 46 ft. breadth, 19·2 ft. draught, 5-cyl. B. & W. diesel, 2,900 b.h.p., 13½ knots.

INVERBANK. *British.* Cargo liner. Built by Wm. Doxford & Sons (S.B.) Ltd., Sunderland, for Bank Line Ltd., London. 6,313 tons gross, 10,355 tons d.w., 487 ft. l.o.a., 62·25 ft. breadth, 26 ft. draught, 4-cyl. Doxford diesel, 6,640 b.h.p., 14 knots.

IRBITLES. *Russian.* Cargo. Built by Valmet O/Y Pansio Telakka, Abo, for U.S.S.R. 2,842 tons gross, 3,400 tons d.w., 334·75 ft. l.o.a., 46 ft. breadth, 19·2 ft. draught, 5-cyl. B. & W. diesel by the shipbuilders, 2,900 b.h.p., 13½ knots.

IRISH CEDAR. *Irish Republic.* Bulk carrier. Built by Verolme United Shipyards, Heusden, for Irish Shipping Ltd., Dublin. 10,477 tons gross, 15,123 tons d.w., 504·25 ft. l.o.a., 67·58 ft. breadth, 28·58 ft. draught, 8-cyl. M.A.N. diesel by the shipbuilders, 7,250 b.h.p., 15 knots.

IRISH ROWAN. *Irish Republic.* Bulk carrier. Built by Verolme Cork Dockyard Ltd., Cork, for Irish Shipping Ltd., Dublin. 12,600 tons gross, 14,900 tons d.w., 499·5 ft. l.o.a., 67·25 ft. breadth, 30 ft. draught, 6-cyl. Doxford diesel by Hawthorn Leslie, 6,800 b.h.p., 15 knots.

IRSHALES. *Russian.* Cargo. Built by Valmet O/Y Pansio Telakka, Abo, for U.S.S.R. 2,842 tons gross, 3,400 tons d.w., 334·75 ft. l.o.a., 46 ft. breadth, 19·2 ft. draught, 5-cyl. B. & W. diesel by the shipbuilders, 2,900 b.h.p., 13½ knots.

ISE MARU. *Japanese.* Tanker. Built by Kure S.B. & E. Co., Kure, for Terukuni Kaiun K.K., Tokyo. 38,900 tons gross, 774·33 ft. l.o.a., 111 ft. breadth, 45·25 ft. draught, 9-cyl. Sulzer diesel by Ishikawajima-Harima H.I., 19,800 b.h.p., 15½ knots.

ISONZO. *Italian.* Refrigerated cargo. Built by Cant. Nav. Breda, Venice, for Lloyd Triestino S.p.A. di Nav., Trieste. 7,300 tons gross, 10,000 tons d.w., 450·2 ft. l.o.a., 60·9 ft. breadth, 24·5 ft. draught, 7-cyl. diesel by Fiat, 8,400 b.h.p., 18½ knots (trials).

IZHMALES. *Russian.* Cargo. Built by Valmet O/Y Helsingin Telakka, Helsingfors, for U.S.S.R. 2,842 tons gross, 3,400 tons d.w., 334·75 ft. l.o.a., 46 ft. breadth, 19·2 ft. draught, 5-cyl. B. & W. diesel by the shipbuilders, 2,900 b.h.p., 13½ knots.

IRISH ROWAN. *The first ship to be completed by the new Verolme shipyard in Southern Ireland, Verolme Cork Dockyard Ltd., Rushbrooke, County Cork, was delivered in 1962 to her owners, Irish Shipping Ltd., Dublin. This vessel, 14,900 tons d.w., is the second of a pair of ships built during the past few months for these owners. The first of these, the Irish Sycamore, was delivered in 1961 by Wm. Gray & Co. Ltd. (see 'Merchant Ships: World Built,' Vol. X). Both ships are powered by Doxford diesel engines. The Irish Rowan is the largest vessel ever built in the Republic of Ireland. She was constructed by men who, in practically every case, were completely new to shipbuilding. Under the supervision of about 30 Dutch technical staff and foremen the 1,250 employees at Rushbrooke launched their second ship in 1962 and a third ship—a bulk carrier of 30,000 tons d.w.—was laid down almost immediately. The Irish Rowan has been completed as a closed shelterdeck general cargo vessel, with full provision for the carriage of grain, but quick conversion into the open condition can be effected if required. The cargo capacity is grain 742,610 cu. ft., bale 691,560 cu. ft. Five cargo holds (the after three of which have hopper sides) are served by weather-deck hatchways fitted with MacGregor single-pull steel hatch covers, operated by Laurence Scott electric cargo winches. The accommodation, arranged aft, is fully air-conditioned. Every cabin is a single-berth room, except those for cadets and deck boys.*

JAG SHANTI. *Indian.* Cargo. Built by Hitachi S.B. & E. Co. Ltd., Innoshima, for Great Eastern Shipping Co. Ltd., Bombay. 6,514 tons gross, 10,650 tons d.w., 489·66 ft. l.o.a., 61·82 ft. breadth, 26·25 ft. draught, 6-cyl. B. & W. diesel by the shipbuilders, 5,400 b.h.p., 14¼ knots.

JAG VIJAY. *Indian.* Cargo. Built by Hitachi S.B. & E. Co. Ltd., Innoshima, for Great Eastern Shipping Co. Ltd., Bombay. 6,514 tons gross, 10,650 tons d.w., 489·58 ft. l.o.a., 61·82 ft. breadth, 26·25 ft. draught, 6-cyl. B. & W. diesel by the shipbuilders, 5,400 b.h.p., 14½ knots.

JAGARDA. *Norwegian.* Tanker. Built by Kieler Howaldtswerke A.G., Kiel, for Anders Jahre, Sandefjord. 32,455 tons gross, 51,850 tons d.w., 740 ft. l.o.a., 102·2 ft. breadth, 38·9 ft. draught, 2 grd. turbs. by the shipbuilders, 16,500 s.h.p., 16¾ knots.

JAMAICA PRODUCER. *British.* Refrigerated cargo. Built by Lithgows Ltd., Port Glasgow, for Jamaica Banana Producers S.S. Co. Ltd., Kingston. 5,781 tons gross, 4,900 tons d.w., 397 ft. l.o.a., 56·25 ft. breadth, 24·2 ft. draught, 6-cyl. Sulzer diesel by Rowan, 9,000 b.h.p., 17 knots.

JAN KOCHANOWSKY. *Polish.* Cargo. Built by Brodogradiliste 3 Maj, Rijeka, for Polish Ocean Lines. 7,200 tons gross, 8,500 tons d.w., 488·2 ft. l.o.a., 62·33 ft. breadth, 28·33 ft. draught, 6-cyl. Sulzer diesel by the shipbuilders, 7,800 b.h.p., 16½ knots.

JAN TEN DOORNKAAT. *German.* Cargo. Built by Jos. L. Meyer, Papenburg, for Reederei Bernhard Schulte A.G., Hamburg. 1,918 tons gross, 4,300 tons d.w., 309·58 ft. l.o.a., 46·25 ft. breadth, 22·25 ft. draught, 6-cyl. M.A.N. diesel, 2,250 b.h.p., 13 knots.

JAN ZIZKA. *Polish.* Cargo. Built by United Polish Shipyards, Szczecin, for Polish Ocean Lines. 3,381 tons gross, 5,283 tons d.w., 407·82 ft. l.o.a., 54·25 ft. breadth, 20·82 ft. draught, 9-cyl. Sulzer diesel, 5,000 b.h.p., 15½ knots.

JAPAN MAIL. *American.* Refrigerated cargo. Built by Todd Shipyards Corp., San Pedro, Cal., for American Mail Line Ltd., Seattle. 12,712 tons gross, 14,900 tons d.w., 563·66 ft. l.o.a., 76·33 ft. breadth, 31·58 ft. draught, 2 grd. turbs. by G.E.C., 20,000 s.h.p., 20 knots.

JARICHA. *Norwegian.* Tanker. Built by Kieler Howaldtswerke A.G., Kiel, for Anders Jahre, Sandefjord. 32,878 tons gross, 52,203 tons d.w., 740 ft. l.o.a., 102·2 ft. breadth, 39 ft. draught, 2 grd. turbs. by the shipbuilders, 16,500 s.h.p., 16½ knots.

JAVARA. *Norwegian.* Bulk carrier. Built by Kieler Howaldtswerke A.G., Kiel, for A/S Kosmos, Sandefjord. 10,434 tons gross, 15,000 tons d.w., 496 ft. l.o.a., 65·6 ft. breadth, 29·42 ft. draught, 8-cyl. M.A.N. diesel by the shipbuilders, 6,500 b.h.p., 14¾ knots.

JAWACHTA. *Norwegian.* Tanker. Built by Kieler Howaldtswerke A.G., Kiel, for Anders Jahre, Sandefjord. 32,500 tons gross, 53,200 tons d.w., 740 ft. l.o.a., 102·2 ft. breadth, 31·33 ft. draught, 2 grd. turbs. by Howaldtswerke Ham., 13,000 s.h.p.

JESPER MAERSK. *Danish.* Bulk carrier. Built by Nippon Kokan K.K., Tsurumi, for A. P. Möller, Copenhagen. 23,539 tons gross, 35,280 tons d.w., 669·66 ft. l.o.a., 90·25 ft. breadth, 35 ft. draught, 8-cyl. B. & W. diesel by Mitsui, 11,550 b.h.p., 16 knots.

JETTA DAN. *Danish.* Tanker. Built by Odense Staalskibs A/S, Odense, for J. Lauritzen, Copenhagen. 24,500 tons gross, 38,800 tons d.w., 695·82 ft. l.o.a., 91·25 ft. breadth, 37 ft. draught, 9-cyl. diesel by B. & W., 13,500 b.h.p., 16 knots.

JOHAN WESSEL. *Norwegian.* Cargo. Built by A/B Ekensbergs Varv, Stockholm, for J. H. Wessels Kulforretning A/S, Drammen. 2,800 tons gross, 5,900 tons d.w., 375·33 ft. l.o.a., 50·58 ft. breadth, 20·25 ft. draught, 6-cyl. diesel by B. & W., 3,750 b.h.p., 15 knots.

JOHANN CHRISTIAN SCHULTE. *German.* Cargo. Built by P. Lindenau, Kiel, for Reederei Bernhard Schulte A.G., Hamburg. 2,020 tons gross, 4,300 tons d.w., 309 ft. l.o.a., 46 ft. breadth, 17·9 ft. draught, 6-cyl. diesel by M.A.N., 2,250 b.h.p., 13¼ knots.

J

J

JAMAICA PRODUCER. *This refrigerated banana/cargo vessel delivered to the Jamaica Banana Producers Steamship Co. Ltd., for service between the West Indies and the U.K., represents a change for these owners from steam turbine to diesel propulsion. The new vessel, built by Lithgows Ltd., Port Glasgow, has a deadweight of 4,900 tons and carries about 1,900 tons of bananas. The Jamaica Planter, 5,360 tons d.w., built by Lithgows in 1959 (see 'Merchant Ships: World Built,' Vol. VIII), was also designed to carry the same quantity of bananas. The new ship is slightly smaller than the Jamaica Planter, which is powered by steam turbine machinery of 7,000 s.h.p., and she has one diesel engine of 9,000 b.h.p. output. A noticeable feature of the new ship is the very prominent bulbous bow. The insulated bin*

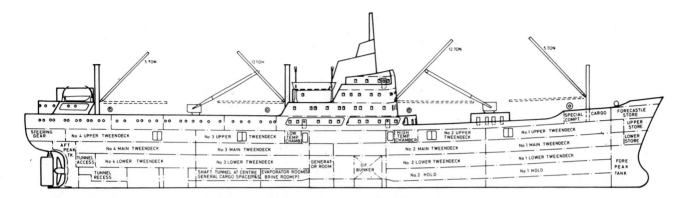

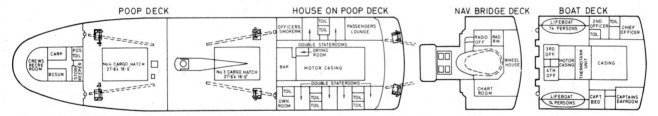

| POOP DECK | HOUSE ON POOP DECK | NAV. BRIDGE DECK | BOAT DECK |

JAMAICA PRODUCER—continued

capacity is 214,000 cu. ft. Of the four insulated holds, Nos. 1 and 2 are subdivided horizontally for the carriage of citrus fruits and bananas; each space being served by coolers. The banana cargo is loaded through side doors to port and starboard. The spaces have been specially designed so that the bananas will reach their destination with the minimum of bruising or damage. Bulkheads in contact with the fruit are of resin-bonded gaboon plywood, coated with special paint, and extra care has been taken to produce a smooth finish. The vessel has two high temperature compartments for the carriage of such exotic tropical fruits as mangoes, pawpaws, etc. Two low temperature compartments are also provided for the carriage of frozen cargoes to Jamaica and to bring back such cargoes as frozen turtles. Twelve passengers are carried. During sea trials a maximum speed of 19 knots was attained.

J

JARICHA. An oil tanker of 52,203 tons d.w. built by Kieler Howaldtswerke A.G. for the Norwegian shipowner Anders Jahre, Sandefjord. This vessel is powered by steam turbine machinery, a method of propulsion which is becoming more popular in Norway where, as in the other Scandinavian countries, it has been usual in the past to have diesel engine propulsion wherever possible. The Jaricha has geared turbines of 16,500 s.h.p. normal output at 103·5 r.p.m. and 17,500 s.h.p. maximum output at 105·7 r.p.m. In place of the conventional squat funnel this ship has a tall thin funnel through which the exhaust gases are led. As an aid to navigation the Jaricha has a television camera mounted on the cross-piece between the two forward king posts, enabling anyone on the bridge to obtain a clear picture of what is immediately ahead of the ship. This is of considerable advantage in a ship of over 740 ft. overall length with the navigating bridge arranged aft. Steam is supplied by two watertube boilers having a normal rating of 28 tons/hour (42 tons/hour maximum) each. The boilers are of the latest type and are side-fired, an arrangement which Kieler Howaldtswerke has employed for some few years. K.H. boilers are made in handed pairs and have a centreline firing aisle designed to permit quick operation of the burners, which are in easy reach of the fireman on duty. After the boilers have been constructed and assembled in the shop, they can be separated into two for ease of entry into the boiler space on board ship. The economizers or air heaters are fitted after the boilers have been erected on board. The more important parts such as headers, downcomers, steam exhaust pipes, etc., are located behind the boiler shell, but are easily accessible by the removal of metal coverplates which are secured to the boiler shell by means of wedges. The boiler itself is completely gastight, which prevents flue gases from escaping into the engine room even when the furnace pressure becomes excessive.

JUNELLA. *This stern trawler is a step forward in the British trawler fleet as she is the first British trawler to freeze the whole of her catch. She is also unusual, though not unique, in being a British-flag stern trawler. The first British stern trawlers were of course the Fairtry class ships of Chr. Salvesen & Co. Ltd. They are factory trawlers, far larger than the normal distant-water trawler, and process their catch before freezing it. The Lord Nelson, completed in Germany for British owners, is a stern trawler but freezes only part of her catch, the remainder being stored in wet ice as is customary. The Junella freezes the whole of her catch as whole fish. She has been built by Hall, Russell & Co. Ltd., Aberdeen, for J. Marr & Son Ltd., Hull. Comprehensive fish preservation plant includes special plate freezers and refrigerating machinery and cooling equipment for the storage hold. All of the fish caught is gutted and washed under cover of the tweendecks, after which it is frozen whole in the vertical plate freezers. The 70-lb. blocks of frozen fish are then stored at −20 deg. F. in the large refrigerated hold located amidships. A large number of electronic navigational aids are carried which include Marconi Mark IVA radar, Lodestar automatic direction finder, Globespan W/T and R/T transmitters, two Atalanta receivers, Kestrel R/T equipment for the skipper's use, Fishgraph echometer for fish finding, and internal communications equipment incorporating a tape-recorder. Redifon VHF R/T equipment and a Loran navigational aid are fitted, and also a Decca Navigator. The vessel carries Kelvin-Hughes radar, and also the first production model of the Kelvin Hughes 'Humber' fish finder. Specially designed for deep water bottom trawling, this equipment has an exceptionally high-powered transmitter of 8 kw. output, a concentrated narrow sound beam, and a retractable 30 k/cs. transducer which can be lowered 2 ft. below the hull. Fish echoes are presented simultaneously on two 'sea-bed locked' displays, one of these being a bright, continuous 6½ in. C.R.T. scale expander (viewing unit) and the other a recording scale expander with 6 in. dry-paper 'white line' record chart. A conventional type dry-paper recorder with 'white line' record chart is also included.*

The scale expansion facilities of the equipment are such that echoes from the sea-bed and the two or four fathoms immediately above it are displayed across the full width of the C.R.T. viewing unit, while the recording scale expander provides, on dry paper, a permanent record, over complete tows, of the seabed and the four fathoms immediately above it. The position of the fish can be correlated with time marks, and hence with the ship's position. Diesel-electric propelling machinery manufactured by the English Electric Co. Ltd. has been installed. This provides a total of 2,700 b.h.p. for all conditions of operation, including sailing to and from the fishing grounds at maximum speed with all three generators running, and operating on the fishing grounds with only two generators.

J

JOHANNES FRITZEN. *German.* Ore carrier. Built by A.G. 'Weser,' Bremen, for Johs. Fritzen & Sohn, Emden. 24,636 tons gross, 36,000 tons d.w., 703·2 ft. l.o.a., 90 ft. breadth, 43·9 ft. draught, grd. turb. by the shipbuilders, 12,700 s.h.p., 15¾ knots.

JOHANNES R. BECHER. *East German.* Fish factory. Built by Mathias-Thesen-Werft, Wismar, for Fischkombinat Rostock, Rostock. 3,000 tons gross, 281·82 ft. l.o.a., 44·25 ft. breadth, 17·33 ft. draught, 8-cyl. diesel by Halberstadt, 1,800 b.h.p., 11 knots.

JULLE. *Danish.* Passenger and car ferry. Built by Adler Werft, Bremen, for Juelsminde-Kalundborg Lines A/S, Copenhagen. 2,301 tons gross, 289 ft. l.o.a., 53·25 ft. breadth, 13 ft. draught, tw-sc. four 9-cyl. grd. diesels by M.A.N., 5,200 b.h.p., 18 knots.

14 JULY. *Iraqi.* Cargo. Built by Hitachi S.B. & E. Co. Ltd., Osaka, for Iraqi Maritime Transport Co. Ltd., Basra. 5,701 tons gross, 7,959 tons d.w., 415 ft. l.o.a., 56 ft. breadth, 25·75 ft. draught, 6-cyl. B. & W. diesel by the shipbuilders, 5,400 b.h.p., 17 knots (trials).

JUMNA. *British.* Cargo. Built by C. Connell & Co. Ltd., Glasgow, for James Nourse Ltd., London. 7,800 tons gross, 13,900 tons d.w., 508·25 ft. l.o.a., 65·25 ft. breadth, 30 ft. draught, 5-cyl. Sulzer diesel by Barclay Curle, 7,500 b.h.p., 16 knots.

JUNELLA. *British.* Refrigerated stern trawler. Built by Hall, Russell & Co. Ltd., Aberdeen, for J. Marr & Sons Ltd., Hull. 1,450 tons gross, 238·5 ft. l.o.a., 38·58 ft. breadth, diesel-electric, three 8-cyl. G.E.C. diesels, 2,700 s.h.p.

K

KRISTINE MAERSK. *This 42,650 tons d.w. steam tanker was built by Odense Staalskibsvaerft A/S for the A. P. Möller group, and is the largest ship in this owners' fleet, being somewhat larger than the two sister ships Caroline Maersk and Katrine Maersk, also turbine driven tankers, delivered by the same shipyard in 1960 and 1961 respectively. The propelling machinery in the Kristine Maersk consists of double-reduction geared turbines driving a single screw and developing 12,500 s.h.p. normal power and 13,750 s.h.p. maximum. This power installation is similar to those supplied for the other large tankers mentioned, and like them comes from the General Electric Co. of the U.S.A.*

KAISA DAN. *Danish.* Polar cargo. Built by Bijker's Aannemings, Gorinchem, for J. Lauritzen, Copenhagen. 1,859 tons gross, 2,325 tons d.w., 268·42 ft. l.o.a., 40·42 ft. breadth, 18 ft. draught, 10-cyl. Smit-Bolnes diesel, 1,700 b.h.p., 12½ knots.

KALLE. *Danish.* Ferry. Built by Adler Werft G.m.b.H., Bremen, for Juelsminde-Kalundborg Linien A/S, Copenhagen. 2,310 tons gross, 289 ft. l.o.a., 53·25 ft. breadth, 13 ft. draught, tw-sc. four 9-cyl. grd. diesels by M.A.N., 5,240 b.h.p., 17 knots.

KAMCHATSKLES. *Russian.* Timber carrier. Built by Nystads Varv, Nystad, for U.S.S.R. 2,925 tons gross, 3,400 tons d.w., 335 ft. l.o.a., 46 ft. breadth, 18·75 ft. draught, 5-cyl. diesel by B. & W., 2,900 b.h.p., 13½ knots.

KAMOGWA MARU No. 11. *Japanese.* Cargo. Built by Kasado Dock Co. Ltd., Kudamatsu, for Shimosaki Kisen K.K., Kobe. 1,595 tons gross, 2,550 tons d.w., 272·25 ft. l.o.a., 39·5 ft. breadth, 16·82 ft. draught, 6-cyl. diesel by Ito Tekko, 1,800 b.h.p., 12¼ knots.

KANGAROO. *Australian.* Cargo and passenger. Built by Evans, Deakin & Co. Pty. Ltd., Brisbane, for Government of Western Australia. 4,129 tons gross, 2,450 tons d.w., 323·82 ft. l.o.a., 50·42 ft. breadth, 18 ft. draught, two 7-cyl. grd. diesels by British Polar, 2,620 b.h.p., 13 knots.

KARACHAYEVSK. *Russian.* Cargo. Built by Wärtsilä Kon. Crichton-Vulcan, Abo, for U.S.S.R. 9,250 tons gross, 12,200 tons d.w., 482·33 ft. l.o.a., 64·82 ft. breadth, 30 ft. draught, 6-cyl. Sulzer diesel by the shipbuilders, 9,000 b.h.p., 17 knots.

KASIMOV. *Russian.* Cargo. Built by Wärtsilä Kon. Crichton-Vulcan, Abo, for U.S.S.R. 9,250 tons gross, 12,200 tons d.w., 482·33 ft. l.o.a., 64·82 ft. breadth, 30 ft. draught, 6-cyl. Sulzer diesel by the shipbuilders, 9,000 b.h.p., 17 knots.

KASSIM. *Iraqi.* Cargo. Built by Hitachi S.B. & E. Co. Ltd., Osaka, for Iraqi Maritime Transport Co. Ltd., Basra. 3,832 tons gross, 5,850 tons d.w., 415 ft. l.o.a., 56 ft. breadth, 25·75 ft. draught, 6-cyl. B. & W. diesel by the shipbuilders, 5,400 b.h.p., 17 knots.

KASUGASAN MARU. *Japanese.* Refrigerated cargo. Built by Mitsui S.B. Co. Ltd., Tamano, for Mitsui Sempaku K.K., Tokyo. 8,410 tons gross, 9,695 tons d.w., 492 ft. l.o.a., 63·58 ft. breadth, 28 ft. draught, 8-cyl. B. & W. diesel by the shipbuilders, 12,000 b.h.p., 18 knots.

KEIKO MARU. *Japanese.* Cargo. Built by Onomichi S.B. Co., Onomichi, for Sanko Kaiun K.K., Amagasaki. 1,200 tons gross, 2,000 tons d.w., 6-cyl. diesel by Hanshin, 1,300 b.h.p., 13 knots.

KEIYO MARU. *Japanese.* Fish carrier. Built by Hayashikane S.B. & E. Co., Shimonoseki, for Hokkaido Gyogyo Kosha K.K., Tokyo. 3,700 tons gross, 4,400 tons d.w., 362 ft. l.o.a., 50 ft. breadth, 20·58 ft. draught, 6-cyl. diesel by the shipbuilders, 3,800 b.h.p., 13½ knots.

KENKON MARU. *Japanese.* Cargo. Built by Sanoyasu Dockyard Co. Ltd., Osaka, for Inui Kisen K.K., Kobe. 4,535 tons gross, 7,420 tons d.w., 383·33 ft. l.o.a., 53·5 ft. breadth, 22·82 ft. draught, 5-cyl. M.A.N. diesel by Kawasaki, 3,800 b.h.p., 14 knots.

KENSINGTON. *British.* Cargo. Built by A/B Ekensbergs Varv, Stockholm, for Woodside Shipping Co. Ltd., Glasgow. 8,900 tons gross, 12,800 tons d.w., 485·42 ft. l.o.a., 61·66 ft. breadth, 30 ft. draught, 7-cyl. diesel by B. & W., 7,600 b.h.p., 15½ knots.

KIBI MARU. *Japanese.* Tanker. Built by Setoda S.B. Co., Setoda, for Satokuni Kisen K.K., Kobe. 1,804 tons gross, 2,912 tons d.w., 274·75 ft. l.o.a., 41·5 ft. breadth, 17·82 ft. draught, 8-cyl. diesel by Niigata, 1,800 b.h.p., 12½ knots.

KIMOVSK. *Russian.* Cargo. Built by Wärtsilä Kon. Crichton-Vulcan, Abo, for U.S.S.R. 9,250 tons gross, 12,200 tons d.w., 482·33 ft. l.o.a., 64·82 ft. breadth, 30 ft. draught, 6-cyl. Sulzer diesel by the shipbuilders, 9,000 b.h.p., 17 knots.

K

K

KINDVIK. *Norwegian.* Tanker. Built by Moss Vaerft & Dokk A/S, Moss, for A. C. Olsen, Sandefjord. 8,730 tons gross, 13,000 tons d.w., 500 ft. l.o.a., 61 ft. breadth, 27 ft. draught, 6-cyl. B. & W. diesel, 6,500 b.h.p., 14½ knots.

KINSEI MARU. *Japanese.* Chemical tanker. Built by Sanoyasu Dockyard Co. Ltd., Osaka, for Tabuchi Kaiun K.K., Osaka. 1,550 tons gross, 2,387 tons d.w., 17·33 ft. breadth, 6-cyl. diesel by Niigata, 1,500 b.h.p., 12½ knots.

KIROVSKLES. *Russian.* Cargo. Built by Nystads Varv A/B, Nystad, Finland, for U.S.S.R. 2,700 tons gross, 3,400 tons d.w., 335 ft. l.o.a., 46 ft. breadth, 18·75 ft. draught, 5-cyl. B. & W. diesel, 2,900 b.h.p.

KOEI MARU. *Japanese.* Tanker. Built by Ishikawajima-Harima H.I., Aioi, for Kyoei Tanker K.K., Kobe. 30,684 tons gross, 51,000 tons d.w., 730 ft. l.o.a., 100·2 ft. breadth, 39·42 ft. draught, 9-cyl. Sulzer diesel by the shipbuilders, 15,300 b.h.p., 15¾ knots.

KONINGEN FABIOLA. *Belgian.* Passenger and car ferry. Built by J. Boel & Fils, Tamise, for Belgian Government. 3,057 tons gross, 384·82 ft. l.o.a., 52·42 ft. breadth, 12·5 ft. draught, tw-sc. two 12-cyl. Sulzer diesels, 9,600 b.h.p., 22 knots.

KOTOURA MARU. *Japanese.* Ore carrier. Built by Hitachi S.B. & E. Co., Innoshima, for Yamashita Kisen K.K., Tokyo. 15,800 tons gross, 25,679 tons d.w., 32·2 ft. draught, 7-cyl. B. & W. diesel by the shipbuilders, 7,600 b.h.p., 13 knots.

KOVROV. *Russian.* Cargo. Built by Wärtsilä Kon. Cricton-Vulcan, Abo, for U.S.S.R. 9,250 tons gross, 12,200 tons d.w., 482·33 ft. l.o.a., 64·82 ft. breadth, 30 ft. draught, 6-cyl. Sulzer diesel by the shipbuilders, 9,000 b.h.p., 17 knots.

KOWA MARU. *Japanese.* Collier. Built by Hakodate Dock Co. Ltd., Hakodate, for Kowa Kaiun K.K., Kobe. 2,750 tons gross, 4,350 tons d.w., 320·33 ft. l.o.a., 47·66 ft. breadth, 20·5 ft. draught, 5-cyl. diesel by Ito Tekko, 2,800 b.h.p., 12½ knots.

KOWA MARU No. 2. *Japanese.* Cargo. Built by Hitachi S.B. & E. Co. Ltd., Mukaishima, for Kyowa Sangyo Kaiun K.K., Osaka. 2,000 tons gross, 2,700 tons d.w., 249·2 ft. b.p., 40·66 ft. breadth, 18 ft. draught, 8-cyl. diesel by Niigata, 1,800 b.h.p., 11½ knots.

KRATOS. *Swedish.* Ore carrier. Built by A/B Götaverken, Gothenburg, for Rederi A/B Transoil, Gothenburg. 18,150 tons gross, 26,100 tons d.w., 584·42 ft. l.o.a., 78·2 ft. breadth, 34·58 ft. draught, 7-cyl. Götaverken diesel, 8,750 b.h.p., 15 knots.

KREMSERTOR. *German.* Cargo. Built by A.G. 'Weser,' Bremen, for Ister Reederei G.m.b.H., Bremen. 12,000 tons gross, 18,100 tons d.w., 544 ft. l.o.a., 71 ft. breadth, 31 ft. draught, 7-cyl. B. & W. diesel by Krupp, 7,600 b.h.p., 15½ knots.

KRISTINE MAERSK. *Danish.* Tanker. Built by Odense Staalskibs. A/S, Odense, for A. P. Möller, Copenhagen. 26,636 tons gross, 42,650 tons d.w., 708·2 ft. l.o.a., 93·75 ft. breadth, 36·58 ft. draught, 2 grd. turbs. by G.E.C., 12,500 b.h.p., 15½ knots.

KRUGERLAND. *German.* Cargo liner. Built by Flensburger Schiffs. Ges., Flensburg, for Globus-Reederei G.m.b.H., Hamburg. 6,203 tons gross, 11,390 tons d.w., 486·75 ft. l.o.a., 64·42 ft. breadth, 25·82 ft. draught, 8-cyl. diesel by M.A.N., 9,300 b.h.p., 17½ knots.

KUDAMATSU MARU. *Japanese.* Tanker. Built by Mitsubishi S.B. & E. Co. Ltd., Nagasaki, for Tokyo Tanker K.K., Tokyo. 28,823 tons gross, 46,000 tons d.w., 736 ft. l.o.a., 100·25 ft. breadth, 37·5 ft. draught, grd. turb. by the shipbuilders, 17,600 s.h.p.

KULPAWN RIVER. *British.* Cargo. Built by N.V. Kon. Maats. 'De Schelde,' Flushing, for Black Star Line Ltd., Accra. 5,315 tons gross, 6,800 tons d.w., 460·9 ft. l.o.a., 60·2 ft. breadth, 23·25 ft. draught, 5-cyl. Sulzer diesel by the shipbuilders, 4,500 b.h.p., 15 knots.

LSCO KABIBI. *Philippine.* Tanker. Built by Osaka S.B. Co. Ltd., Osaka, for Luzon Stevedoring Corp., Manila. 1,820 tons gross, 2,800 tons d.w., 275·25 ft. l.o.a., 40·66 ft. breadth, 17·82 ft. draught, 6-cyl. B. & W. diesel by Hitachi, 1,680 b.h.p., 11½ knots.

LSCO TABANGAO. *Philippine.* Tanker. Built by Osaka S.B. Co., Osaka, for Luzon Stevedoring Corp., Manila. 2,860 tons gross, 4,300 tons d.w., 330 ft. l.o.a., 46·58 ft. breadth, 20 ft. draught, 7-cyl. B. & W. diesel by Hitachi, 1,960 b.h.p., 11¼ knots.

LSCO TACLOBO. *Philippine.* Tanker. Built by Osaka S.B. Co., Osaka, for Luzon Stevedoring Corp., Manila. 1,470 tons gross, 2,000 tons d.w., 241 ft. l.o.a., 38·25 ft. breadth, 16 ft. draught, 8-cyl. B. & W. diesel by Hitachi, 1,380 b.h.p., 11 knots.

LAGO LACAR. *Argentine.* Cargo liner. Built by Brodogradiliste Split, for Empresa Lineas Marit. Argentinas, Buenos Aires. 8,486 tons gross, 10,500 tons d.w., 515·82 ft. l.o.a., 73·2 ft. breadth, 26·9 ft. draught, 9-cyl. diesel by Fiat, 10,300 b.h.p., 17 knots.

LANDVARD. *Norwegian.* Tanker. Built by A/S Akers M/V, Oslo. for Klosters Rederi A/S, Oslo. 12,978 tons gross, 19,780 tons d.w., 557 ft. l.o.a., 72 ft. breadth, 30·82 ft. draught, 8-cyl. B. & W. diesel by the shipbuilders, 9,300 b.h.p., 16 knots.

LAPPONIA. *Finnish.* Cargo. Built by Wärtsilä Kon. Crichton-Vulcan, Abo, for Finska Angfartygs A/B, Helsingfors. 1,471 tons gross, 2,200 tons d.w., 294·75 ft. l.o.a., 43 ft. breadth, 16·75 ft. draught, 6-cyl. Sulzer diesel by the shipbuilders, 2,400 b.h.p., 13½ knots.

LAWRENDOC. *Canadian.* Bulk carrier. Built by Collingwood Shipyards Ltd., Collingwood, Ont., for Canada Steamship Lines Ltd., Montreal. 2,497 tons gross, 3,750 tons d.w., 291 ft. l.o.a., 45·25 ft. breadth, 19·33 ft. draught, two 6-cyl. grd. diesels by Canadian Fairbanks Morse, 2,000 b.h.p., 14 knots.

LEANDROS. *Greek.* Cargo. Built by Brodogradiliste 3 Maj, Rijeka, for Costa de Marfil Cia. Nav. S.A., London. 10,200 tons gross, 14,400 tons d.w., 485·58 ft. l.o.a., 65·9 ft. breadth, 6-cyl. Sulzer diesel by the shipbuilders, 7,800 b.h.p., 16 knots.

LEBEDIN. *Russian.* Tanker. Built by Mitsubishi S.B. & E. Co. Ltd., Hiroshima, for U.S.S.R. 22,226 tons gross, 35,000 tons d.w., 679·2 ft. l.o.a., 88·9 ft. breadth, 35 ft. draught, 9-cyl. Sulzer diesel by the shipbuilders, 18,000 b.h.p., 17¼ knots.

LENA CHRISTINA BRODIN. *Swedish.* Cargo. Built by Oresundsvarvet A/B, Landskroner, for Rederi A/B Disa, Stockholm. 8,600 tons gross, 11,000 tons d.w., 463 ft. l.o.a., 63·25 ft. breadth, 28·9 ft. draught, 8-cyl. Götaverken diesel, 7,500 b.h.p., 16½ knots.

LENINSKY PUT. *Russian.* Tanker. Built by Nosenko Shipyards, Nicolaiev, for U.S.S.R. 22,500 tons d.w.

LENKORAN. *Russian.* Tanker. Built by Ishikawajima-Harima H.I., Aioi, for U.S.S.R. 23,158 tons gross, 35,000 tons d.w., 679 ft. l.o.a., 88·82 ft. breadth, 9-cyl. Sulzer diesel by the shipbuilders, 18,000 b.h.p., 17 knots.

LESLIE LYKES. *American.* Cargo. Built by Bethlehem Steel Co., Sparrows Point, for Lykes Bros. S.S. Co. Inc., New Orleans. 9,891 tons gross, 11,100 tons d.w., 495 ft. l.o.a., 69·2 ft. breadth, 29·58 ft. draught, 2 grd. turbs by G.E.C., 9,900 s.h.p., 17 knots.

LINDOS. *Greek.* Cargo. Built by Osaka S.B. Co., Osaka, for Torres Cia. Nav. S.A., Andros and Panama. 10,300 tons gross, 15,000 tons d.w., 505·25 ft. l.o.a., 66·58 ft. breadth, 30·42 ft. draught, 6-cyl. diesel by Iino, 9,000 b.h.p., 15¼ knots.

L

L

LIS FRELLSEN. *Danish.* Cargo. Built by Zaanlandse Schps. Maats., Zaandam, for O.E.M. Frellsen, Roskilde. 1,474 tons gross, 2,150 tons d.w., 259·42 ft. l.o.a., 39·42 ft. breadth, 16 ft. draught, 7-cyl. diesel by Werkspoor, 1,630 b.h.p., 12 knots.

LISICHANSK. *Russian.* Tanker. Built by Ishikawajima-Harima H.I., Aioi, for U.S.S.R. 23,153 tons gross, 35,000 tons d.w., 679 ft. l.o.a., 88·9 ft. breadth, 35 ft. draught, 9-cyl. Sulzer diesel by the shipbuilders.

LIVANITA. *Norwegian.* Ore carrier. Built by Smith's Dock Co. Ltd., Middlesbrough, for A/S Uglands Rederi, Grimstad. 18,736 tons gross, 26,700 tons d.w., 604·25 ft. l.o.a., 79·25 ft. breadth, 32·33 ft. draught, 4-cyl. Doxford diesel by Hawthorn Leslie, 6,640 b.h.p., 13 knots.

LIVNY. *Russian.* Tanker. Built by Ishikawajima-Harima H.I., Aioi, for U.S.S.R. 23,150 tons gross, 34,655 tons d.w., 679·2 ft. l.o.a., 88·9 ft. breadth, 9-cyl. Sulzer diesel by the shipbuilders, 18,000 b.h.p., 17 knots.

LJUBOTIN. *Russian.* Tanker. Built by Ishikawajima-Harima H.I., Aioi, for U.S.S.R. 22,100 tons gross, 35,000 tons d.w., 679 ft. l.o.a., 88·82 ft. breadth, 34·95 ft. draught, 9-cyl. Sulzer diesel by the shipbuilders, 18,000 b.h.p., 17 knots.

LLANWERN. *British.* Cargo. Built by Bartram & Sons Ltd., Sunderland, for Evan Thomas Radcliffe & Co. Ltd., Cardiff. 9,229 tons gross, 11,150 tons d.w., 498·25 ft. l.o.a., 63·2 ft. breadth, 28·5 ft. draught, 6-cyl. Sulzer diesel by Geo. Clark, 6,600 b.h.p., 16½ knots (trials).

LONDON CONFIDENCE. *British.* Tanker. Built by N.V. Kon. Maats. 'De Schelde,' Flushing, for London & Overseas Freighters Ltd., London. 21,668 tons gross, 32,000 tons d.w., 664·75 ft. l.o.a., 88·2 ft. breadth, 34·25 ft. draught, 9-cyl. Sulzer diesel by the shipbuilders, 16,000 b.h.p., 16½ knots.

LOUISIANA MARU. *Japanese.* Refrigerated cargo. Built by Kawasaki Dockyard Co. Ltd., Kobe, for Kawasaki Kisen K.K., Kobe. 9,200 tons gross, 11,900 tons d.w., 514 ft. l.o.a., 63·82 ft. breadth, 28·5 ft. draught, 9-cyl. diesel by the shipbuilders, 9,000 b.h.p., 16¼ knots.

LOUSSA. *Swedish.* Bulk carrier. Built by A/B Götaverken, Gothenburg, for Trafik A/B Grängesberg-Oxelösund, Stockholm. 17,500 tons gross, 25,850 tons d.w., 584·2 ft. l.o.a., 78·2 ft. breadth, 34·58 ft. draught, 6-cyl. Götaverken diesel, 7,300 b.h.p., 14¼ knots.

LÖVLAND. *Norwegian.* Cargo. Built by Marinens Hovedverft, Horten, for Samuelsens Rederi, Farsund. 4,156 tons gross, 6,100 tons d.w., 369·25 ft. l.o.a., 50·58 ft. breadth, 24·2 ft. draught, 8-cyl. Götaverken diesel, 4,000 b.h.p., 15½ knots.

LUBERTSY. *Russian.* Tanker. Built by Rauma-Repola O/Y, Rauma, Finland, for U.S.S.R. 3,300 tons gross, 4,000 tons d.w., 344·82 ft. l.o.a., 48·58 ft. breadth, 20·42 ft. draught, 5-cyl. B. & W. diesel, 2,000 b.h.p., 14 knots.

LUCIGEN. *British.* Tanker. Built by Smith's Dock Co. Ltd., Middlesbrough, for H. E. Moss & Co., Liverpool. 12,800 tons gross, 19,320 tons d.w., 559·25 ft. l.o.a., 71·5 ft. breadth, 30 ft. draught, 6-cyl. Doxford diesel by Hawthorn Leslie, 9,000 b.h.p., 16¼ knots (trials).

LUGANSK. *Russian.* Tanker. Built by Mitsubishi S.B. & E. Co. Ltd., Hiroshima, for U.S.S.R. 22,262 tons gross, 35,000 tons d.w., 679·2 ft. l.o.a., 88·9 ft. breadth, 35 ft. draught, 9-cyl. Sulzer diesel by the shipbuilders, 18,000 b.h.p., 17½ knots.

LUNE FISHER. *British.* Coaster. Built by N.V. Schps. 'Foxhol,' Foxhol, for Seaway Coasters Ltd., London. 1,012 tons gross, 1,296 tons d.w., 217·82 ft. l.o.a., 33·82 ft. breadth, 6-cyl. diesel by Deutz, 1,250 b.h.p., 13 knots.

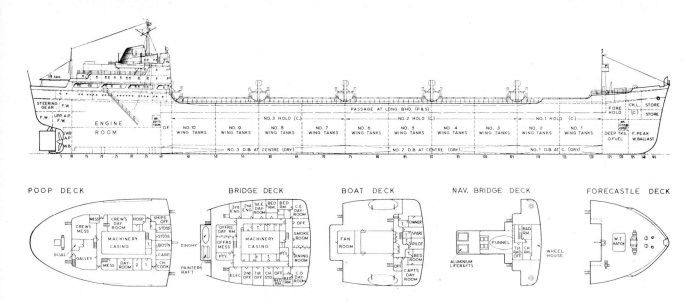

LIVANITA. *The first of two ore carriers of 26,700 tons d.w. ordered from Smith's Dock Co. Ltd., South Bank, Middlesbrough, was handed over to her owners, A/S Ugland Rederi, Grimstad, Norway, early in 1962. This vessel, the Livanita, is on charter to the British Iron & Steel Corporation Ltd. (BISCO) for 15 years. Other vessels of similar tonnage are on order for Ugland Rederi at Nakskov Shipyard and Oresundsvarvet, Sweden. The Livanata is powered by a Doxford 'P' type oil engine and has a contract speed of 13 knots. An interesting feature of this new ship is the ballast system, which is entirely operated from a small control panel in the engine room. The Livanita has been built to the requirements of Lloyd's Register for the carriage of iron ore, and stiffening for navigation in ice has been incorporated. She complies with the latest Norwegian Sea Control requirements. There are three main cargo holds and five main cargo hatches of the Velle type measuring 61 ft. by 28 ft. 4 in. Two longitudinal bulkheads are arranged 17 ft. 6 in. to port and starboard of the centreline of the holds, dividing the ore holds at the centre from the 10 side tanks situated to port and starboard. The vessel is of welded construction throughout, and has a rounded gunwale. Electricity is supplied at 440 volts, 3-phase, 50 cycles A.C. by three diesel driven alternators.*

M

M. M. DANT. *American.* Cargo and passenger. Built by National Steel & S.B. Co., San Diego, for States Steamship Co., San Francisco. 12,700 tons gross, 14,320 tons d.w., 565 ft. l.o.a., 76·2 ft. breadth, 31·58 ft. draught, 2 grd. turbs. by G.E.C., 19,250 s.h.p., 20 knots.

MADS SKOU. *Danish.* Cargo. Built by Elsinore S.B. Co. & Msk., Elsinore, for Ove Skou Rederi A/S, Copenhagen. 4,207 tons gross, 7,000 tons d.w., 416·33 ft. l.o.a., 56·5 ft. breadth, 24 ft. draught, 8-cyl. B. & W. diesel by the shipbuilders, 6,550 b.h.p., 17 knots.

MAIN LLOYD. *Dutch.* Cargo. Built by Rotterdamsche D.D. Maats., Rotterdam, for Koninkl. Rotterdamsche Lloyd N.V., Rotterdam. 9,733 tons gross, 11,550 tons d.w., 528·33 ft. l.o.a., 66·25 ft. breadth, 29 ft. draught, 9-cyl. Stork diesel, 10,500 b.h.p., 18 knots.

MAK HUGO STINNES. *German.* Cargo. Built by Rheinstahl Nordseewerke, Emden, for Hugo Stinnes, Hamburg. 3,118 tons gross, 4,096 tons d.w., 331·42 ft. l.o.a., 47·42 ft. breadth, 20 ft. draught, tw-sc. two 6-cyl. M.A.K. diesels, 2,840 b.h.p., 12½ knots.

MANHATTAN. *American.* Tanker. Built by Bethlehem Steel Co., Quincy, for Manhattan Tankers Co. Inc., New Jersey. 65,740 tons gross, 106,568 tons d.w., 940·42 ft. l.o.a., 132·5 ft. breadth, 49·33 ft. draught, tw-sc. 4 grd. turbs by the shipbuilders, 39,000 s.h.p., 17¾ knots.

MANSFIELD. *East German.* Ore carrier. Built by Warnowwerft, Warnemünde, for Deutsche Seereederei, Rostock. 8,609 tons gross, 11,350 tons d.w., 498 ft. l.o.a., 63·2 ft. breadth, 27·25 ft. draught, 7-cyl. diesel by D.M.R., 5,850 b.h.p., 15 knots.

MANX MAID. *British.* Passenger and car ferry. Built by Cammell Laird & Co. (S.B. & Eng.) Ltd., Birkenhead, for Isle of Man Steam Packet Co. Ltd., Douglas. 2,725 tons gross, 343·9 ft. l.o.a., 52·9 ft. breadth, tw-sc. 2 grd. turbs by the shipbuilders, 9,500 s.h.p., 21 knots.

MARATHA ENDEAVOUR. *British.* Cargo. Built by Howaldtswerke Ham. A.G., Hamburg, for Chowgule Steamships (Bahamas) Ltd., Nassau. 11,211 tons gross, 15,380 tons d.w., 520 ft. l.o.a., 70·75 ft. breadth, 29 ft. draught, 7-cyl. M.A.N. diesel, 6,130 b.h.p., 14 knots.

MARCHON ENTERPRISE. *British.* Cargo. Built by Clelands S.B. Co. Ltd., Wallsend-on-Tyne, for Marchon Products Ltd., Hull. 1,599 tons gross, 2,445 tons d.w., 260·2 ft. l.o.a., 39·25 ft. breadth, 16·75 ft. draught, 8-cyl. Deutz diesel, 1,800 b.h.p., 12½ knots.

MARCHON VENTURER. *British.* Cargo. Built by Clelands S.B. Co. Ltd., Wallsend-on-Tyne, for Marchon Products Ltd., Hull. 1,595 tons gross, 2,445 tons d.w., 260·33 ft. l.o.a., 39·25 ft. breadth, 16·66 ft. draught, 8-cyl. Deutz diesel, 1,800 b.h.p., 12½ knots.

MARGO. *Liberian.* Cargo. Built by Burntisland S.B. Co. Ltd., Burntisland, for Panaviero S.A., Panama. 9,150 tons gross, 13,000 tons d.w., 483 ft. l.o.a., 62·25 ft. breadth, 29·2 ft. draught, 5-cyl. Götaverken diesel, 6,300 b.h.p.

MARIA AMELIA LOLLI GHETTI. *Italian.* Bulk carrier. Built by Ansaldo S.p.A., Spezia, for 'Carbocoke' Soc. di Nav. S.p.A., Palermo 23,180 tons gross, 35,000 tons d.w., 679 ft. l.o.a., 92·25 ft. breadth, 36 ft. draught, 8-cyl. Fiat diesel, 16,800 b.h.p., 17 knots.

MARIA LUISA VELASCO. *Spanish.* Cargo. Built by Empresa Nacl. 'Bazan.' Cartegena, for Naviera Castellana S.A. 5,228 tons gross, 7,000 tons d.w., 412·25 ft. l.o.a., 54·75 ft. breadth, 24·25 ft. draught, 8-cyl. Sulzer diesel by the shipbuilders, 4,000 b.h.p., 14 knots.

MARIE MAERSK. *Danish.* Tanker. Built by Odense Staalskibs. A/S, Odense, for A. P. Möller, Copenhagen. 21,628 tons gross, 33,800 tons d.w., 686·2 ft. l.o.a., 83·82 ft. breadth, 35·2 ft. draught, 8-cyl. B. & W. diesel, 11,500 b.h.p., 16½ knots.

MARIE SKOU. *Danish.* Cargo. Built by Elsinore S.B. & E. Ltd., Elsinore, for Ove Skou, Copenhagen. 4,200 tons gross, 7,400 tons d.w., 416·33 ft. l.o.a., 56·5 ft. breadth, 8-cyl. B. & W. diesel by the shipbuilders, 6,550 b.h.p., 17 knots.

MARIO Z. (ex *Ursa Major*). *Italian.* Bulk carrier. Built by Cant. Riuniti dell Adriatico, Monfalcone, for S.A. Sarda di Armamento. 23,206 tons gross, 35,000 tons d.w. 670·2 ft. l.o.a., 92·33 ft. breadth, 35·95 ft. draught, 8-cyl. Fiat diesel by the shipbuilders 16,800 b.h.p., 17 knots.

MANX MAID. *Built by Cammell Laird & Co. (Shipbuilders & Engineers) Ltd., Birkenhead, for the Isle of Man Steam Packet Co. Ltd., this twin-screw car and passenger ferry, 2,725 tons gross, is the island's first car ferry. She is equipped with Denny-Brown stabilizers for passenger comfort, and with a speed of 21 knots can make the trip from Liverpool to Douglas in about four hours. Provision has been made for the carriage of 1,400 passengers and 60 to 70 cars. Electro-hydraulic steering gear is of ample power for operating the streamlined rudder. A bow rudder, also operated by an electric hydraulic gear, is fitted to enable the vessel to navigate stern first. A 14 ft. diameter turntable is fitted at the forward end of the main deck to assist the easy handling of vehicles. At the after end of the main deck there is a spiral arrangement of ramps, unique on ships, leading up to the promenade deck. The propelling machinery in the Manx Maid is generally similar to that fitted in the Manxman (built for the Isle of Man S.P. Co. Ltd. by the same builders in 1955), the main difference being the higher power (9.000 s.h.p. maximum in Manxman), and the Babcock integral furnace type boilers installed with trunked forced draught instead of the header type in a closed stokehold.*

MARATHA ENDEAVOUR. *This vessel, built by Howaldtswerke Hamburg A.G. for Chowgule Steamships (Bahamas) Ltd., 15,380 tons d.w. as a closed shelterdecker, has been designed to operate either as an open or closed shelterdeck ship and has a heavy-lift derrick capable of lifting 160 tons. With somewhat more beam than most vessels of her size, she draws very little water—only 26 ft. as an open shelterdeck vessel—and is therefore able to enter ports with heavy cargoes where ships of similar tonnage but normal draught would be prevented from operating. The ship has been designed to carry ore, grain, bulk, general or other cargoes with equal facility. The 160-ton lift derrick will enable her to carry barges, transformers, locomotives and other heavy cargoes, and her decks have been strengthened accordingly. It is most unusual to find a modern tramp ship with a heavy-lift derrick of such high capacity. The cargo capacity is grain 854,760 cu. ft., bale 780,941 cu. ft. There are six holds with half-height deep tanks in Nos. 1 and 4 holds which can be used for cargo if required. The hatches, with the exception of No. 1 hatch which is 31 ft. 5½ in. by 26 ft. 3 in., are of a large size measuring 39 ft. 4 in. by 29 ft. 6 in. and give easy access to the lower holds and tweendecks for the rapid loading and discharge of cargo. Cargo handling equipment includes ten 5-ton derricks at Nos. 1, 2, 3, 5 and 6 hatches, two 5/10-ton derricks at No. 4 hatch, and the 160-ton heavy-lift derrick at the after end of No. 3 hatch. A feature of the stern is the bulbous bossing which is combined with some fining of the stern lines in way of the upper part of the propeller aperture.*

MANHATTAN. *This tanker of 106,568 tons d.w. entered service in 1962 under the United States flag after delivery to the Manhattan Tankers Co. of New York. The 940 ft. twin-screw vessel was constructed by the Bethlehem Steel Co. in the giant three-position building basin at its Quincy, Massachusetts, yard. The dimensions of the Manhattan make her larger, in all respects but length, than the largest merchant ship previously built in the U.S.A., the passenger liner United States. When ordered, she was the world's largest tanker, but has since been exceeded by two vessels completed in Japan, as well as by others now building. However, her twin-screw propulsion and power give her a speed and manoeuvrability believed to exceed those of any supertanker of comparable size. She exceeded 19 knots on her speed trials in loaded condition. The Manhattan is propelled by double-reduction geared turbines designed and built by her builders at the Quincy yard. These deliver a normal shaft horse-power of 39,000 with a maximum continuous output at 115 r.p.m. of 43,000 s.h.p. Power is transmitted to two five-bladed nickel-manganese bronze propellers, each 22 ft. in diameter and weighing 31¼ tons. Her service speed is 17¾ knots. The Manhattan has 45 separate cargo tanks, each 67 ft. deep, giving an aggregate liquid cargo capacity of 38,220,000 gallons.*

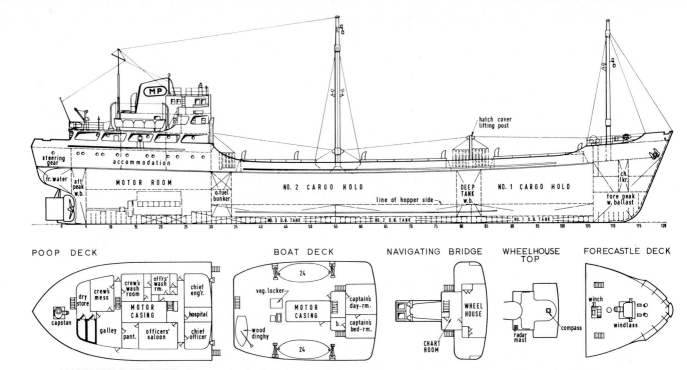

M

MP

steering
gear

accommodation

fr. water

aft
peak
w.b.

MOTOR ROOM

o-fuel
bunker

NO. 2 CARGO HOLD

line of hopper side

DEEP
TANK
w.b.

NO. 1 CARGO HOLD

hatch cover
lifting post

ch.
lkr.

fore peak
w. ballast

NO. 3 D.B. TANK   NO. 2 D.B. TANK   NO. 1 D.B. TANK

POOP DECK

dry
store

crew's
mess

crew's
wash
room

offr's
wash
rm.

chief
eng'r.

capstan

MOTOR
CASING

hospital

galley

pant.

officers'
saloon

chief
officer

BOAT DECK

veg. locker

MOTOR
CASING

24

captain's
day-rm.

b.

captain's
bed-rm.

wood
dinghy

24

NAVIGATING BRIDGE

WHEEL
HOUSE

CHART
ROOM

**WHEELHOUSE
TOP**

radar
mast

compass

FORECASTLE DECK

winch

windlass

MARCHON ENTERPRISE. *This vessel is the first of two small ships specially designed for the carriage of phosphate rock. She has been built by Clelands Shipbuilding Co. Ltd. for Marchon Products Ltd., a member of the Allbright & Wilson group of chemical companies. This vessel, 2,445 tons d.w., will carry phosphate rock from Casablanca to Whitehaven, where the owners have their large chemical plant. The new ship, together with the Marchon Trader (built in 1957) and the Marchon Venturer, will carry almost all the phosphate requirements of the Whitehaven plant. The second vessel, the Marchon Venturer (which also entered service in 1962) is fitted with a Costa propulsion bulb built into her rudder with a view to giving her an increase in speed over her sister ship, which has a rudder of conventional design. The Marchon Enterprise has a cargo capacity of bale 97,390 cu. ft., grain 94,333 cu. ft.*

MARIA LUISA VELASCO. *This 7,000 tons d.w. cargo ship has been delivered to the Naviera Castellana from the Cartagena shipyard of Empresa Nacional Bazan. The vessel is of the two-deck type and the hold capacity is 335,000 cu. ft. The vessel operates on the liner service from Piraeus and other Mediterranean ports to the West Coast of U.S.A. and Canada via the Gulf of Mexico.*

MARITA. *Norwegian.* Bulk carrier. Built by Kaldnes M/V A/S, Tönsberg, for A/S Tanktransport, Tönsberg. 10,100 tons gross, 15,250 tons d.w., 500·33 ft. l.o.a., 65·2 ft. breadth, 28·58 ft. draught, 6-cyl. M.A.N. diesel by Kockums, 5,200 b.h.p., 14½ knots (trials).

MARJORIE LYKES. *American.* Cargo liner. Built by Bethlehem Steel Co., Sparrows Point, for Lykes Bros. S.S. Co. Inc., New Orleans. 10,200 tons gross, 10,960 tons d.w., 495 ft. l.o.a., 69·2 ft. breadth, 29·58 ft. draught, 2 grd. turbs. by G.E.C., 11,000 s.h.p., 18 knots.

MATKO LAGINJA. *Yugoslav.* Refrigerated cargo. Built by Brodogradiliste Titovo, Kraljevica, for Yugoslav Lines, Rijeka. 2,308 tons gross, 3,000 tons d.w., 348·5 ft. l.o.a., 46·82 ft. breadth, 18·58 ft. draught, 6-cyl. Sulzer diesel by Jugoturbina, 3,000 b.h.p., 14½ knots.

MEGANTIC. *British.* Refrigerated cargo. Built by Swan, Hunter & Wigham Richardson Ltd., Newcastle-upon-Tyne, for Shaw Savill & Albion Co. Ltd., London. 13,100 tons gross, 12,400 tons d.w., 537·75 ft. l.o.a., 71·42 ft. breadth, 32·25 ft. draught, tw-sc. two 7-cyl. B. & W. diesels by Harland & Wolff, 16,000 b.h.p., 18 knots.

MEIHOHSAN MARU. *Japanese.* Cargo. Built by Fujinagata S.B. Co. Ltd., Osaka, for Meiji Kaiun K.K., Kobe. 6,452 tons gross, 9,500 tons d.w., 436·5 ft. l.o.a., 58·25 ft. breadth, 27 ft. draught, 6-cyl. diesel by Mitsui, 6,500 b.h.p., 14½ knots.

MEISHUSAN MARU. *Japanese.* Cargo. Built by Fujinagata S.B. & E. Co. Ltd., Osaka, for Meiji Kaiun K.K., Kobe. 6,452 tons gross, 9,750 tons d.w., 436·42 ft. l.o.a., 58·2 ft. breadth, 27 ft. draught, 6-cyl. B. & W. diesel by Mitsui, 6,500 b.h.p., 14½ knots.

MEKAMBO. *French.* Ore carrier. Built by At. & Ch. de Dunkerque & Bordeaux (France-Gironde), Bordeaux, for Cie. Marit. des Chargeurs Réunis, Paris. 21,687 tons gross, 29,000 tons d.w., 647·42 ft. l.o.a., 84·2 ft. breadth, 34·5 ft. draught, 8-cyl. B. & W. diesel by Du Creusot, 10,000 b.h.p., 14½ knots.

M

MEGANTIC. *This twin-screw motorship, built by Swan, Hunter & Wigham Richardson Ltd., is the first of a new class of refrigerated ships ordered by the Shaw Savill Line, and a sister ship, Medic, is to be launched in 1963. The cargo capacity of the Megantic is 580,000 cu. ft. refrigerated, 83,000 cu. ft. general. Innovations include an extended poop deck, two sets of deck cranes, built-in deep tanks and machinery partially aft. Service speed is 18 knots.*

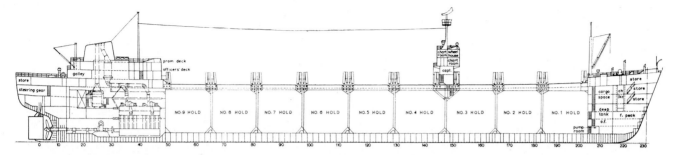

MEKAMBO. *Built at the Bordeaux shipyard of the Ateliers et Chantiers de Dunkerque et Bordeaux (France-Gironde) for the Compagnie Maritime de Transport Pondéreux, this ore carrier, 29,000 tons d.w., will be managed by the Compagne Maritimes des Chargeurs Reunis, Paris. The company's fleet has hitherto consisted of passenger vessels, cargo vessels and banana carriers. A steam pipeline has been run either side of the hatch coamings with flanges so that hoses can be attached for supplying steam to the shore for de-icing in some parts of the world where the ore is stockpiled in snow and ice. (The ship is probably the only ore carrier afloat to have this feature.) This has influenced the owners to have boilers fitted of sufficient capacity to operate two steam turbo-alternators. A feature of the ship is the arrangement of propeller-shaft driven D.C. generator and A.C. alternators. These operate on the Neufville-Trottier system—a system which has been operating satisfactorily in French ships for some years. It was originally introduced with the intention of overcoming the problem occurring when attempting to parallel shaft driven A.C. or D.C. generators with separately driven generators with the main engine running at varying speeds. There are nine cargo holds, hoppered at the top and bottom, and capable of holding about 1,168,220 cu. ft. of ore, with ballast tanks on either side having a total capacity of about 376,870 cu. ft. of sea water.*

MENIER CONSOL. *Canadian.* Cargo. Built by Davie S.B. Ltd., Levis, for Anticosti Shipping Co., Quebec. 2,575 tons gross, 3,100 tons d.w., 304·58 ft. l.o.a., 49·5 ft. breadth, 15·25 ft. draught, two 10-cyl. diesels by Fairbanks-Morse, 2,880 b.h.p., 13 knots.

MERCURY. *British.* Cable ship. Built by Cammell Laird & Co. (S.B. & Eng.) Ltd., Birkenhead, for Cable & Wireless Ltd., London. 8,962 tons gross, 6,375 tons d.w., 483·82 ft. l.o.a., 58·58 ft. breadth, 24 ft. draught, tw-sc. diesel-electric, four 8-cyl. motors by English Electric, 6,000 b.h.p., 16 knots.

MIGOLINA. *Swedish.* Bulk carrier. Built by Bremer Vulkan, Vegesack, for Rederi A/B Dalen, Gothenburg. 11,082 tons gross, 15,240 tons d.w., 509·9 ft. l.o.a., 66·75 ft. breadth, 28·5 ft. draught, 6-cyl. M.A.N. diesel, 6,120 b.h.p., 15 knots.

MILORA. *Norwegian.* Bulk carrier. Built by Rheinstahl Nordseewerke, Emden, for Yngvar Hvistendahl, Tönsberg. 12,230 tons gross, 17,100 tons d.w., 522·82 ft. l.o.a., 70·58 ft. breadth, 30·66 ft. draught, 5-cyl. B. & W. diesel by Krupp, 7,500 b.h.p., 15½ knots.

MOBIL ENDURANCE. *British.* Tanker. Built by Eriksbergs M/V A/B, Gothenburg, for Mobil Tankships Ltd., London. 31,456 tons gross, 50,700 tons d.w., 735·42 ft. l.o.a., 104·42 ft. breadth, 38·58 ft. draught, 2 grd. turbs. by De Laval, 18,000 s.h.p., 16¾ knots.

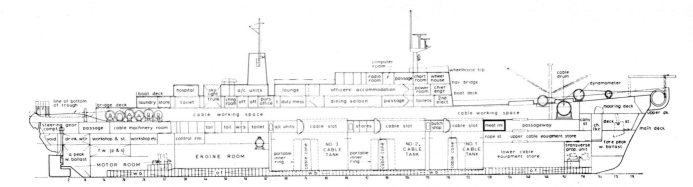

MERCURY. *This cable ship, the second largest to fly the British flag, has been built by Cammell Laird & Co. (Shipbuilders & Engineers) Ltd., Birkenhead, for Cable & Wireless Ltd., London. The vessel, 8,962 tons gross, with a speed of 16 knots, is claimed to be the fastest cable layer in the world. During sea trials a speed of $17\frac{1}{2}$ knots was attained. She is powered by diesel-electric machinery and has a transverse propulsion unit in the bow. A feature of the new vessel is the twin funnel arrangement which allows the extensive cable working spaces to run through the superstructure without obstruction, so that cable work can be carried out either at the bow or at the stern. She can carry 1,200 miles of lightweight cable and 48 repeaters. Her steaming range is 8,000 miles and her sea endurance 80 days. The Mercury has been designed to Lloyd's Class +100 Al, for cable ships. She is almost entirely of welded construction, seams and butts of the shell being flush. The hull has been specially strengthened for navigation in ice. A cellular double bottom is fitted throughout, forming water ballast, fresh water and oil tanks. Oil fuel bunkers are fitted forward of the motor room and around No. 1 cable tank, and water ballast and fresh water tanks around Nos. 2 and 3 cable tanks respectively. The capacity of tanks is sufficient to give the vessel 60 days' supply of fuel and water while continuously at sea. To give the vessel the high degree of manoeuvrability desirable for cable-laying operations a Voith-Schneider transverse propulsion unit giving a side thrust of 6 tons is fitted immediately abaft the forward peak tank. Special consideration has been given to the trim of the vessel when laying cables, and to obtain the best balance possible the diesel engine room is aft of amidships and the electric propulsion motor room is as far aft as possible, while three cable tanks are fitted forward of the engine and propulsion motor rooms. The coiling capacity of the cable tanks is over 99,000 cu. ft., equivalent to about 1,200 miles of lightweight cable. The cable machinery is arranged on the upper and bridge decks. The after machinery is of the five-sheave type for handling cable with rigid repeaters, and is electro-hydraulically operated. The forward cable machinery is situated forward of the bridge front for picking up cable for repair, and laying armoured cable in shallow water at speeds up to 8 knots, and can withstand a pull of 30 tons. Cable is drawn from the cable tanks through large cable slots in the decks and passed along the working alleyway on the upper deck to the forward cable machinery. The after cable machinery has been arranged on the upper deck at the after end of the cable working space and is capable of paying out cable at 8 knots and sustaining a load of 6 tons. It is also capable of picking up a cable at one knot against a pull of 10 tons and withstanding a surge load of 20 tons. The cable is drawn from the cable tanks and payed out over a stern chute via the cable machinery. Because of the duties of the vessel, accommodation is provided for 159 persons.*

MOBIL ENERGY. *British.* Tanker. Built by Eriksbergs M/V A/B, Gothenburg, for Mobil Tankships Ltd., London. 31,450 tons gross, 50,700 tons d.w., 735·42 ft. l.o.a., 104·42 ft. breadth, 38·75 ft. draught, 2 grd. turbs. by De Laval, 18,000 s.h.p., 16¾ knots.

MOL. *Belgian.* Cargo. Built by N.V. Kon. Maats. 'De Schelde,' Flushing, for Cie. Maritime Belge (Lloyd Royal) S.A., Antwerp. 9,095 tons gross, 11,880 tons d.w., 482·82 ft. l.o.a., 62·2 ft. breadth, 29 ft. draught, 5-cyl. Sulzer diesel by the shipbuilders, 5,875 b.h.p., 14 knots.

MONDOC. *Canadian.* Bulk carrier. Built by Collingwood Shipyards Ltd., Collingwood, Ont., for Canada Steamship Lines Ltd., Montreal. 2,497 tons gross, 3,750 tons d.w., 291 ft. l.o.a., 45·25 ft. breadth, 19·33 ft. draught, two 6-cyl. grd. diesels by Canadian Fairbanks Morse, 2,000 b.h.p., 14 knots.

MONTPELIER VICTORY. *American.* Tanker. Built by Bethlehem Steel Co., Quincy, Mass., for Victory Carriers Inc., New York. 27,797 tons gross, 47,000 tons d.w., 736 ft. l.o.a., 102·25 ft. breadth, 38 ft. draught, 2 grd. turbs. by the shipbuilders, 21,500 s.h.p., 17½ knots.

MONTREALAIS (ex *Montrealer*). *Canadian.* Bulk carrier. Built by Canadian Vickers Ltd., Montreal, for Papachristidis Co. Ltd., Montreal. 18,192 tons gross, 26,100 tons d.w., 730 ft. l.o.a., 75·33 ft. breadth, 26·5 ft. draught, 2 grd. turbs. by Canadian G.E.C., 9,900 s.h.p., 17 knots.

MORMACTRADE. *American.* Cargo. Built by Sun S.B. & D.D. Co., Chester, Pa., for Moore-McCormack Lines Inc., New York. 9,324 tons gross, 12,480 tons d.w., 483·25 ft. l.o.a., 68·2 ft. breadth, 31·42 ft. draught, 2 grd. turbs. by G.E.C., 12,100 s.h.p., 19 knots.

MONTREALAIS. *Canadian Vickers Ltd. delivered this large bulk carrier of 26,100 tons d.w. to the Papachristidis Co. Ltd., Montreal. As in the case of previous vessels of this type built by Canadian Vickers, she was constructed in two parts; but in this instance a separate sub-contract was placed for the construction of the bow section with the Quebec firm of Geo. T. Davie & Sons Ltd. When the two sections had been completed the stern portion was towed from Canadian Vickers yard to the Champlain dry dock at Quebec, where it was joined to the bow portion built by Geo. T. Davie & Sons Ltd. The Montrealais has five cargo holds, cargo hold capacity 1,162,000 cu. ft.*

N

N. A. COMEAU. *Canadian.* Ferry. Built by G. Brown & Co. (Marine) Ltd., Greenock, for Traverse Matane Godbout Ltd., Quebec. 1,200 tons gross, 187 ft. l.o.a., 40·33 ft. breadth, 6-cyl. diesel by British Polar, 1,650 b.h.p.

NAESS CAVALIER. *British.* Bulk carrier. Built by Mitsubishi S.B. & E. Co. Ltd., Nagasaki, for Anglo-Pacific Shipping Co. Ltd., London. 23,811 tons gross, 35,500 tons d.w., 669·33 ft. l.o.a., 90·5 ft. breadth, 35 ft. draught, 9-cyl. U.E.C. diesel by the shipbuilders, 12,000 b.h.p., 15½ knots.

NAESS CHAMPION. *British.* Tanker. Built by Mitsubishi S.B. & E. Co. Ltd., Nagasaki, for Anglo-American Shipping Co. Ltd., London. 54,700 tons gross, 88,500 tons d.w., 874·82 ft. l.o.a., 122 ft. breadth, 47·42 ft. draught, 2 grd. turbs. by shipbuilders, 22,000 s.h.p., 16 knots·

NAESS CLARION. *British.* Bulk carrier. Built by Hitachi S.B. & E. Co. Ltd., Innoshima, for Anglo-Pacific Shipping Co. Ltd., London. 23,352 tons gross, 35,500 tons d.w., 669·33 ft. l.o.a., 90·5 ft. breadth, 35 ft. draught, 8-cyl. B. & W. diesel by shipbuilders, 12,000 b.h.p., 15½ knots.

NAESS COMET. *Norwegian.* Bulk carrier. Built by Kieler Howaldtswerke A.G., Kiel, for Herness Shipping Co. A/S, Oslo. 23,811 tons gross, 35,500 tons d.w., 669·33 ft. l.o.a., 90·5 ft. breadth, 35 ft. draught, 6-cyl. Götaverken diesel by shipbuilders, 12,000 b.h.p., 15½ knots.

NAMIK KEMAL. *Turkish.* Cargo. Built by Nipponkai H.I., Toyama, for D. B. Deniz Nakliyati T.A.S., Istanbul. 5,615 tons gross, 7,900 tons d.w., 408·2 ft. l.o.a., 54·58 ft. breadth, 21·5 ft. draught, 7-cyl. Sulzer diesel by Uraga, 4,480 b.h.p., 14 knots.

NAMINOUE MARU. *Japanese.* Passenger and cargo. Built by Sanoyasu Dockyard Co. Ltd., Osaka, for Ohshima Unyu K.K., Naze. 2,244 tons gross, 42 ft. breadth, 14·75 ft. draught, 9-cyl. diesel by Hatsudoki, 4,050 b.h.p., 17 knots.

NANIWA MARU No. 37. *Japanese.* Tanker. Built by Hashihama S.B. Co., Imabari, for Naniwa Unyu K.K., Osaka. 1,489 tons gross, 2,417 tons d.w., 17·75 ft. draught, 6-cyl. diesel by Nippon Hatsudoki, 1,650 b.h.p., 11½ knots.

NASIA RIVER. *British.* Cargo. Built by Orenstein-Koppel & Lbcr. Masch., Lübeck, for Black Star Line Ltd., Accra. 5,217 tons gross, 7,143 tons d.w., 460·9 ft. l.o.a., 60·2 ft. breadth, 23·25 ft. draught, three 5-cyl. Sulzer grd. diesels by 'De Schelde,' 4,500 b.h.p., 15 knots.

NEDER RIJN. *Dutch.* Cargo. Built by Howaldtswerke Hamburg A.G., for Stoomvaart Maatschappij 'Nederland,' Amsterdam. 10,300 tons gross, 11,700 tons d.w., 537·2 ft. l.o.a., 69 ft. breadth, 30 ft. draught, 8-cyl. Stork diesel, 15,000 s.h.p., 20 knots.

NEGROS MARU. *Japanese.* Tanker. Built by Kasado Dock Co. Ltd., Kudamatsu, for Nissin Kaiun Kaisha, Tokyo. 3,450 tons gross, 5,500 tons d.w., 342·75 ft. l.o.a., 50 ft. breadth, 21·33 ft. draught, 6-cyl. diesel by Hatsudoki, 2,700 b.h.p., 12 knots.

NEPTUN. *German.* Cable ship. Built by Lübecker Flender-Werke A.G., Lübeck, for Union Kabellegungs-und Schiffs. G.m.b.H., Nordenham. 8,909 tons gross, 12,000 tons d.w., 493·82 ft. l.o.a., 61·66 ft. breadth, 29·33 ft. draught, tw-sc. diesel-electric, four 12-cyl. M.A.N. diesels, 5,960 b.h.p., 14 knots.

NEPTUN. *Polish.* Stern trawling factory ship. Built by United Polish Shipyards, Gdansk, for Polish Government. 2,890 tons gross, 1,250 tons d.w., 278·82 ft. l.o.a., 45·33 ft. breadth, 17 ft. draught, 8-cyl. Sulzer diesel, 2,400 b.h.p., 12½ knots.

NGAKUTA. *New Zealand.* Newsprint Carrier. Built by Caledon S.B. & E. Co. Ltd., Dundee, for Union S.S. Co. of New Zealand Ltd., Wellington. 4,576 tons gross, 5,980 tons d.w., 367 ft. l.o.a., 53·42 ft. breadth, 23·5 ft. draught, 6-cyl. Sulzer diesel by Denny, 3,000 b.h.p., 12½ knots.

NAESS CHAMPION. *This is the second of the two 88,500 tons d.w. tankers delivered by the Mitsubishi Shipbuilding & Engineering Co. Ltd., Nagasaki, to the Anglo-American Shipping Co. Ltd., which is the principal shipowning company in the Naess group. The first of the two ships was the Naess Sovereign, described in 'Merchant Ships: World Built,' Vol. IX. Like the Naess Sovereign, the Naess Champion has been chartered for 15 years to Standard-Vacuum Tankers Ltd., Bermuda, and is expected to trade primarily between the Persian Gulf, Australia and the Philippines. As with other present Anglo-American vessels, the ship is manned by British officers with an Indian crew, and is managed by Naess, Denholm & Co. Ltd., London and Glasgow. Three 35,000 tons d.w. bulk carriers also entered into service with the Naess group during 1962.*

NGATORO. *New Zealand.* Newsprint carrier. Built by Caledon S.B. & E. Co. Ltd., Dundee, for Union S.S. Co. of New Zealand, Wellington. 4,576 tons gross, 5,780 tons d.w., 367 ft. l.o.a., 53·42 ft. breadth, 23·5 ft. draught, 6-cyl. Sulzer diesel by A. Stephen, 3,000 b.h.p., 12½ knots.

NICHIHO MARU. *Japanese.* Ore carrier. Built by Nippon Kokan, Yokohama, for Nissan Kisen K.K., Tokyo. 29,578 tons gross, 48,735 tons d.w., 703·75 ft. l.o.a., 98·5 ft. breadth, 37·75 ft. draught, 9-cyl. Sulzer diesel by Uraga, 13,500 b.h.p., 14½ knots.

NICHIWA MARU. *Japanese.* Cargo. Built by Shikoku Dock Co., Takamatsu, for Nissho Kisen K.K., Tokyo. 2,300 tons gross, 3,500 tons d.w., 21·33 ft. draught, 7-cyl. diesel by Ito Tekko, 2,450 b.h.p., 12 knots.

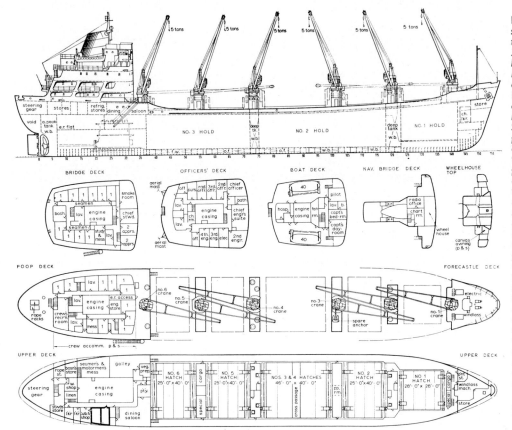

N

BRIDGE DECK · OFFICERS' DECK · BOAT DECK · NAV. BRIDGE DECK · WHEELHOUSE TOP

POOP DECK · FORECASTLE DECK

UPPER DECK · UPPER DECK

NGAKUTA. The first of two sister ships of 5,980 tons d.w. delivered to the Union Steam Ship Co. of New Zealand Ltd. by The Caledon Ship-building & Engineering Co. Ltd., of Dundee. The second ship, also completed in 1962, is named Ngatoro. The Ngakuta has been designed with the newsprint trade between Tauranga (N.Z.) and Sydney and Melbourne (Australia) primarily in view. The bale capacity is 270,000 cu. ft. The three cargo holds are clear of pillars and other obstructions. The cargo holds are mechanically ven-tilated, and to expedite loading and unloading of newsprint and other special cargoes, the main hatches are exceptionally wide. Except for No. 1 hatch, all hatches are 40 ft. wide, giving a hatch area which is probaly unique for a British-built vessel of this size. All the hatch-ways are fitted with hydraulically operated MacGregor watertight steel covers, and are served by six A.S.E.A. cranes. These electrically driven slewing and luffing deck cranes are each suitable for a safe working load of 5 tons. Propulsion of the Ngakuta and the Ngatoro is by a 6-cylinder Sulzer 6SD60 diesel engine of the latest type. It develops 3,000 b.h.p. at 150 r.p.m. The propeller is a four-bladed Heliston type of 13 ft. diameter, 9 ft. 9½ in. pitch and 67 sq. ft. area.

NEDER RIJN. *The first of two fast cargo liners ordered from Howaldtswerke Hamburg A.G. by N.V. Stoomvaart Maatschappij 'Nederland,' Amsterdam, was delivered in 1962. This vessel, the Neder Rijn, 11,700 tons d.w., is powered by the first large-bore diesel engine to be built in the Netherlands. This is an 8-cylinder 850 mm. bore and 1,800 mm. stroke single-acting two-stroke Stork engine fitted with exhaust gas driven turbochargers. The Neder Rijn has a service speed of 20 knots. The sister ship Neder Rhone, also being built by Howaldtswerke Hamburg A.G., will be powered by an 8-cylinder Sulzer diesel engine of 900 mm. bore and 1,550 mm. stroke. The engine in each ship is rated at 15,000 s.h.p. The two new ships will be running between Continental ports and the Far East. There are five cargo holds, three forward and two aft of the machinery space, with a total bale capacity of 618,990 cu. ft. and 12,191 cu. ft. of space in the open forecastle. Eight refrigerated cargo compartments are provided, and there are 11 deep tanks for the carriage of edible oil or latex having a total capacity of 63,982 cu. ft. arranged in Nos. 1 and 4 holds. The comprehensive cargo handling gear includes 21 derricks, of which three are for 80-ton lifts. The two heavy-lift derricks at the foremast can be coupled together so that a weight of 160 tons can be lifted.*

NILS HOLGERSSON. *German.* Ferry. Built by Hanseatische Werft, Hamburg, for Travemünde-Trelleborg Linie, Lübeck. 3,529 tons gross, 360·9 ft. l.o.a., 50 ft. breadth, 14·58 ft. draught, tw-sc. two 12-cyl. diesels by Ottensener Eisenwerke, 7,200 b.h.p., 19 knots.

NINA BORTHEN. *Norwegian.* Tanker. Built by Marinens Hovedverft, Horten, for Harry Borthen & Co. A/S, Oslo. 12,750 tons gross, 19,450 tons d.w., 560 ft. l.o.a., 72 ft. breadth, 30·66 ft. draught, 6-cyl. Doxford diesel by the shipbuilders, 8,000 b.h.p., 15½ knots.

NINI. *Greek.* Bulk carrier. Built by Kawasaki Dockyard Co. Ltd., Kobe, for Oak Shipping Co. S.A., Piraeus and New York. 28,651 tons gross, 44,000 tons d.w., 746 ft. l.o.a., 100·6 ft. breadth, 37·8 ft. draught, 2 grd. turbs. by the shipbuilders, 20,260 s.h.p., 16½ knots.

NIPPI MARU. *Japanese.* Cargo. Built by Hashihama S.B. Co., Imabari, for Nippi Boeki K.K., & Shonan Kisen K.K., Osaka. 2,750 tons gross, 4,100 tons d.w., 319·2 ft. l.o.a., 45·2 ft. breadth, 20 ft. draught, 6-cyl. diesel by Hanshin, 2,100 b.h.p., 11 knots.

NIPPON. *Swedish.* Refrigerated cargo. Built by Nederl. Dok & Schps., Amsterdam, for A/B Svenska Ostasiatiska Kompaniet, Gothenburg. 10,310 tons gross, 10,660 tons d.w., 520·5 ft. l.o.a., 67·75 ft. breadth, 27·5 ft. draught, 8-cyl. Götaverken diesel, 10,000 b.h.p., 17½ knots.

NISSHO MARU. *Japanese.* Tanker. Built by Sasebo H.I. Ltd., Sasebo, for Idemitsu Kosan K.K., Tokyo. 74,869 tons gross, 132,334 tons d.w., 954·66 ft. l.o.a., 141·33 ft. breadth, 54 ft. draught, 2 grd. turbs. by Ishikawajima-Harima H.I., 25,500 s.h.p., 16 knots.

NORBEGA. *Norwegian.* Bulk carrier. Built by Akers Mek. Verksted, Oslo, for I/S Sverdco, Oslo. 12,148 tons gross, 18,805 tons d.w., 523·75 ft. l.o.a., 69·33 ft. breadth 32·2 ft. draught 5-cyl. B. & W. diesel by Akers 8,390 b.h.p. 16¾ knots.

NORDFONN. *Norwegian.* L.P.G. carrier. Built by Ch. Nav. de La Ciotat, La Ciotat, for Sigval Bergesen, Stavanger. 4,137 tons gross, 5,000 tons d.w., 360·58 ft. l.o.a., 50·25 ft. breadth, 21·66 ft. draught, 6-cyl. B. & W. diesel by Creusot, 3,200 b.h.p., 13¾ knots.

NILS HOLGERSSON. *This passenger and car ferry of the TT-Linie was completed by the Hanseatische Werft G.m.b.H., Hamburg. The new vessel has a gross tonnage of 3,529 tons and has accommodation for 900 passengers and 120 cars. The vessel has a speed of 19 knots, which enables her to complete the journey in 6½ hours. Loading and unloading is effected through a stern door and side doors. Cars are arranged on two decks, the upper of which can be raised to accommodate buses and other vehicles.*

NIPPON. *The second of a series of four cargo vessels ordered from the Netherlands Dock & Shipbuilding Co. Ltd. by the Swedish East Asia Co., Gothenburg, one of the Broström group of shipping companies. This vessel, 10,660 tons d.w., like the Stureholm ('Merchant Ships: World Built,' Vol. VI), owned by the Swedish America Line of the Broström group, has been built as a training ship with accommodation and equipment for 12 deck and 12 engine room apprentices, with two instructors, in addition to the normal ship's complement. In addition to elementary courses for beginners, continuation courses are held for the more competent apprentices. In the Nippon, as well as in the Albatross (also owned by the Broström group) and the Stureholm, the object of the elementary courses is to give the apprentices a basic practical and theoretical knowledge, before continuing their practice at sea and studies at navigation school. The continuation courses are intended to give specially selected apprentices and other members of Broström fleet crews a wider practical and theoretical education. Each course on board is calculated to last for about 4½ months, which corresponds to the time taken to complete a voyage from Sweden to Japan and back.*

NICHIHO MARU. *This ore carrier of 48,735 tons d.w. has been built at the Tsurumi shipyard of Nippon Kokan Kabushiki Kaisha, Yokohama, for Nissan Kisen Kabushiki Kaisha, and is the largest ore carrier yet built for a Japanese owner. For economic reasons ore carriers are becoming steadily larger, and accordingly harbour and ore handling facilities at loading and discharging points are being improved, while at the same time overseas mines are also being developed. Following this trend, ore handling wharves are being prepared at Ohgihsima, Kawasaki City, for these vessels. The basic idea of the design of the Nichiho Maru was to achieve maximum economy by*

NICHIHO MARU—*continued*

increasing the carrying capacity while maintaining a moderately low speed (14½ knots fully loaded) so that freight charges are reduced. In order to reduce the number of crew, automatic and remote controls were adopted to some extent for the main engine and other auxiliaries. Because of the nature of the cargo the engine is arranged aft, while the bridge is amidships for reasons of navigational convenience. In fixing the dimensions of the vessel the draught was made 37 ft. 8⅝ in. (11·5 m.) in view of the depth at loading harbours. Cargo freeboard was adopted rather than tanker freeboard, on account of the following advantages: (a) convenience in using bulldozers in ore loading and discharging, due to the reduced number of hold partitions; (b) reduction of the material weight of the ship and simplification of the piping, through the reduction in the number of wing deep tanks; (c) reduction of hull weight and simplification of structure through eliminating the passage tunnel under the upper deck between amidships and aft; (d) shipboard comfort through longer rolling period; (e) better seaworthiness due to higher freeboard than tanker freeboard. In order to increase the rate of service attention has been given to improving the loading and discharging efficiency and also the propulsion efficiency by adoption of the cylindrical bow, the performance of which has been proved at N.K.K. in similar vessels. The ore hold space (capacity 1,004,285 cu. ft.) is separated into two sections by a deep tank located under the bridge amidships.

NORDIA. *Finnish.* Passenger and car ferry. Built by Wärtsilä Kon. Sandvikens Skepps., Helsingfors, for A/B Siljarederiet, Abo. 3,631 tons gross, 333·33 ft. l.o.a., 60·75 ft. breadth, 13·25 ft. draught, tw-sc. two 9-cyl. Sulzer diesels by Wärtsilä, 6,600 b.h.p., 18 knots.

NORSE CORAL (ex *Totem Star*). *British.* Cargo. Built by Soc. des Forges de la Mediterranée, La Seyne, for Fulcrum Shipping Co. Ltd., Nassau. 12,227 tons gross, 15,240 tons d.w., 525·58 ft. l.o.a., 66·75 ft. breadth, 31 ft. draught, 6-cyl. Götaverken diesel by the shipbuilders, 7,600 b.h.p., 15½ knots.

NORSE REEF. *British.* Cargo. Built by Soc. des Forg de la Mediterranée, La Seyne, for Fulcrum Shipping Co. Ltd., Nassau. 12,200 tons gross, 15,000 tons d.w., 525·58 ft. l.o.a., 66·75 ft. breadth, 6-cyl. Götaverken diesel by the shipbuilders, 7,600 b.h.p., 15½ knots.

NORTH HIGHNESS. *Greek.* Bulk carrier. Built by Ishikawajima-Harima H.I., Aioi, for Principe Cia. Naviera S.A., Piraeus. 15,110 tons gross, 21,000 tons d.w., 580·75 ft. l.o.a., 74·5 ft. breadth, 30·82 ft. draught, 6-cyl. Sulzer diesel by the shipbuilders, 9,000 b.h.p., 15 knots.

NORTHERN STAR. *British.* Passenger liner. Built by Vickers-Armstrongs (S.B.) Ltd., Newcastle-upon-Tyne, for Shaw, Savill & Albion Co. Ltd., London. 24,733 tons gross, 650 ft. l.o.a., 83·66 ft. breadth, 26 ft. draught, tw-sc. 4 grd. Parsons turbs. 22,000 s.h.p., 22 knots.

NORTHLAND. *Norwegian.* Refrigerated cargo. Built by A/B Götaverken, Gothenburg, for A/S Atlas, Haugesund. 6,434 tons gross, 4,560 tons d.w., 430 ft. l.o.a., 57 ft. breadth, 23·2 ft. draught, 8-cyl. Götaverken diesel, 7,500 b.h.p., 18 knots.

NOWOWIEJSKI. *Polish.* Refrigerated cargo. Built by Brodogradiliste Split, Split, for Polish Government. 7,100 tons gross, 12,800 tons d.w., 501·25 ft. l.o.a., 61·82 ft. breadth, 29·5 ft. draught, 6-cyl. diesel by Fiat, 6,000 b.h.p., 15 knots.

NTINA J. PATERA. *Greek.* Bulk carrier. Built by J. Boel & Fils, Tamise, for The Archontonisos Shipping Corp., Piraeus. 14,520 tons gross, 21,860 tons d.w., 597·9 ft. l.o.a., 74·5 ft. breadth, 7-cyl. diesel by Sulzer, 10,500 b.h.p., 15½ knots.

No. I NIKKEI MARU. *Japanese.* Bauxite carrier. Built by Japan Steel & Tube Co. Ltd., Tsurumi, for Tamai Shosen Kaisha, Kobe. 10,500 tons gross, 16,550 tons d.w., 472·25 ft. b.p., 66·9 ft. breadth, 29·5 ft. draught, 7-cyl. U.E.C. diesel by Mitsubishi Nagasaki, 6,450 b.h.p., 16¼ knots.

NISSHO MARU. *The first of the two oil tankers of 132,334 tons d.w. ordered by Idemitsu Kosan Co. Ltd., Japan, was delivered in 1962. Built by Sasebo Heavy Industries Ltd., in their building dock, this gigantic ship is the largest of her kind in the world. The sister ship is on order at Ishikawajima-Harima Heavy Industries Co. Ltd., Aioi. Final figures show that the new tanker is a little larger than was originally estimated, and her cargo carrying capacity has increased slightly from the original estimated figure of 185,400 cu. m. to 186,475 cu. m. Also, the deadweight tonnage has been increased by 2,284 tons from 130,050 to 132,334 tons, and the gross tonnage by 1,869 tons from 73,000 to 74,869 tons. The net tonnage of the tanker is 56,432 and the displacement tonnage 163,360. The Idemitsu Oil Co. imports about seven million tons of crude oil annually, of which 5·5 million tons comes from the Middle East and 1·5 million tons from Russia. The company has to supply its own tankers only for that oil coming from the Middle East, i.e. 5·5 million tons. The Nissho Maru will carry 1·1 million tons of this and the Universe Apollo and Universe Daphne one million tons each—convincing proof of the potentialities of these mammoth vessels. The general arrangement drawing shows that the Nissho Maru has a long forecastle, midships bridge and poop—in effect looking like an enlarged version of the Universe Daphne and Universe Apollo. But instead of the usual tank subdivision in three rows with centre tanks of about 12 m. and wing tanks of 24 m. in length, the vessel has four rows of tanks. Each of the two inner rows consists of 13 centre tanks and each of the two outer rows of seven wing tanks, making 26 centre tanks and 14 wing tanks, or a total of 40. The main pump room is between the engine room and the cargo oil tanks, the auxiliary pump room between the fore deep tanks and the cargo oil tanks, and the main boiler room forward of the engine room. There are four sets of main cargo oil pumps, each with a discharging capacity of 1,640 cu. m./hour. The propelling machinery in the Nissho Maru consists of a set of double-reduction*

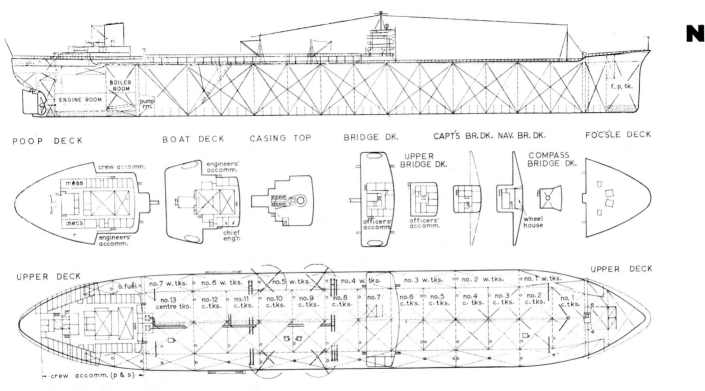

POOP DECK   BOAT DECK   CASING TOP   BRIDGE DK.   CAPT'S BR. DK. NAV. BR. DK.   FO'C'SLE DECK

NISSHO MARU—*continued*

geared cross-compound impulse steam turbines, comprising one h.p. and l.p. stage, having a maximum continuous output of 28,000 s.h.p. at 105 r.p.m. and a normal service output of 25,500 s.h.p. at 101·5 r.p.m. Steam conditions at the turbine inlet are 810 p.s.i.g. (57 kg./sq. cm.) and 878 deg. F. (470 deg. C.) with a vacuum at the condenser top of 28·5 Hg. (722 mm. Hg.).

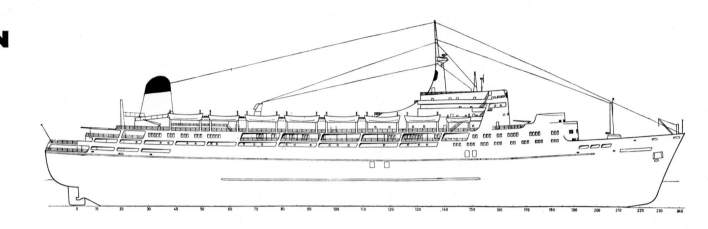

NORTHERN STAR. *The passenger liner Northern Star, built on the Tyne by Vickers-Armstrongs (Shipbuilders) Ltd. for the Shaw Savill & Albion Co. Ltd., has joined the Southern Cross on voyages round the world, the two ships going in opposite directions and each making four round voyages a year.*

COMPARATIVE DETAILS

	Northern Star	Southern Cross			Northern Star	Southern Cross
Gross tonnage	24,733 tons	20,203 tons	Draught		26 ft.	24 ft. 9 in.
Length o.a.	650 ft.	604 ft.	Complement: Passengers ...		1,412	1,160
Length q.p.	595 ft.	560 ft.	Crew		490	411
Breadth	83·66 ft.	78 ft.	Horse-power		22,000 s.h.p.	20,000 s.h.p.
Depth	46 ft. 3 in.	45 ft. 3 in.	Speed		22 knots	20 knots

Comparative details of the Northern Star and Southern Cross (described in 'Merchant Ships: World Built,' Vol. IV) are given in the table. It will be seen that the dimensions are larger all over, though the increase in depth has been restricted to one foot. The increase in draught is slightly more than this, which reflects the fact that the Northern Star has one additional deck worked in. It is this that makes it possible for the later ship to have a passenger capacity more than 30 per cent. greater. Incidentally, the economic advantage of the larger ship is shown by the fact that the crew goes up only by 20 per cent. and the fuel consumption (assuming equal efficiency) by 10 per cent. The main difference in the passenger spaces is the abolition in the later ship of the Southern Cross's internal swimming pool, and the moving of the external swimming pool to the after part of the ship. The

NORTHERN STAR—*continued*

propelling machinery in the Northern Star consists of a twin-screw arrangement of double-reduction geared steam turbines of Pametrada design, built by the Parsons Marine Turbine Co. Ltd. There are three Yarrow type boilers in the Southern Cross, while the Northern Star has only two boilers, which are of Babcock & Wilcox type. Each main propulsion turbine unit consists of an all-impulse h.p. ahead turbine working in series with an l.p. ahead turbine of single-flow mixed impulse and reaction design.

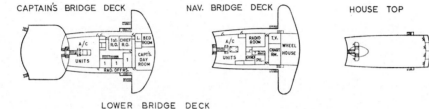

CAPTAIN'S BRIDGE DECK   NAV. BRIDGE DECK   HOUSE TOP

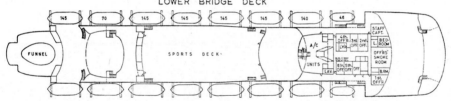

LOWER BRIDGE DECK

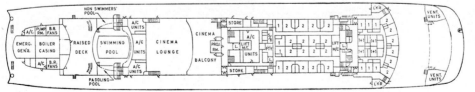

SUN DECK

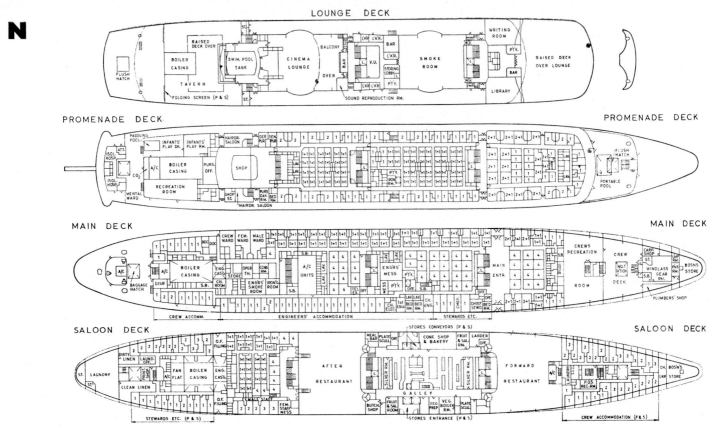

N

NORTHERN STAR

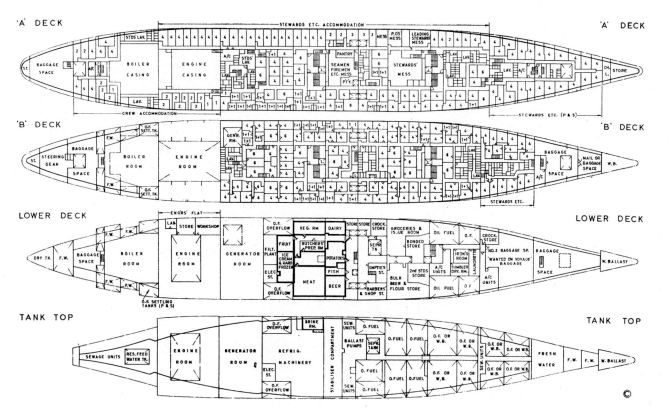

NORTHERN STAR

N

NORBEGA. *This bulk carrier, 18,805 tons d.w., has been delivered to Interessentakapet Sverdco, of Oslo, by Akers Mek. Verksted. Like most of the vessels ordered from Akers, the hull was built at one of the yards by a subsidiary company, in this case A/S Stord Verft.*

NORDIA. *This car and passenger ferry was built by Wartsila-Koncernen A.J.B. Sandvikens Skeppsdocka for A/B Silja-rederiet of Abo. She is designed for a travelling time of about 10 hours and has a speed of 18 knots. Amenities include a cinema, hairdressing shops, Finnish steam baths, a nursery and playroom. Cars are carried at two levels and are driven through the ship, there being electrically operated doors fore and aft. Lorries and buses are also carried. Two 9-cylinder Wartsila-Sulzer diesel engines supply power to variable-pitch propellers of KaMeWa design. The carrying capacity of the Nordia, which has a gross tonnage of 3,631 tons, is 175 cars and 1,140 passengers.*

NORTHLAND. *The Norwegian shipowners A/S Atlas (Christian Haaland, Haugesund) took delivery in 1962 of this new refrigerated cargo vessel from A.B. Götaverken, Sweden. The vessel, 4,560 tons d.w., is of interest as she has a very high cubic capacity—278,000 cu. ft. bale—for a ship of her size. She has been designed for the carriage of fruit or chilled meat and similar cargoes and has a service speed of 18 knots. The Northland has been built with two holds forward and two aft of the engine room and with upper and lower tweendeck spaces. In addition there is an orlop tweendeck forward of the engine room. Cargo is handled by eight derricks, four capable of 5-ton lifts and the remainder for lifts of 12 tons. There are eight electric winches for 5-ton lifts. The insulated cargo space has been divided into six insulated compartments, four forward and two aft of the engine room. In addition there are two refrigerated chambers arranged on the port side of the engine casing in the upper tweendeck. The accommodation is of a high standard, and it includes provision for 10 passengers.*

O

OCEAN TRANSPORT. *British.* Bulk carrier. Built by Hawthorn Leslie (S.B.) Ltd., Newcastle-upon-Tyne, for British Empire S.N. Co. Ltd., and Empire Transport Co. Ltd., London. 8,608 tons gross, 12,600 tons d.w., 462·75 ft. l.o.a., 63·2 ft. breadth, 28·82 ft. draught, 4-cyl. Doxford diesel by the shipbuilders, 6,640 b.h.p., 14½ knots.

ODENSHOLM. *Swedish.* Refrigerated cargo. Built by Wärtsilä Kon. Crichton-Vulcan, Abo, for A/B Svenska Amerika Linien, Gothenburg. 6,922 tons gross, 7,800 tons d.w., 441·9 ft. l.o.a., 57·9 ft. breadth, 26·2 ft. draught. 7-cyl. Götaverken diesel, 5,800 b.h.p., 15 knots.

OIHONNA. *Finnish.* Cargo. Built by Wärtsilä Kon. Crichton-Vulcan, Abo, for Finska Angfartygs A/B, Helsingfors. 1,471 tons gross, 2,200 tons d.w., 294·75 ft. l.o.a., 43 ft. breadth, 16·9 ft. draught, 6-cyl. Sulzer diesel by the shipbuilders, 2,400 b.h.p., 13½ knots.

OKHOTSK. *Russian.* Cargo. Built by Hitachi S.B. & E. Co. Ltd., Osaka, for U.S.S.R. 11,106 tons gross, 12,000 tons d.w., 517·58 ft. l.o.a., 69·2 ft. draught, 8-cyl. B. & W. diesel, 12,000 b.h.p., 17 knots.

OKITSU MARU. *Japanese.* Ore carrier. Built by Yokohama S.B. Co. Ltd., Yokohama, for Nippon Yusen Kaisha, Tokyo. 29,600 tons gross, 50,618 tons d.w., 715·75 ft. l.o.a., 102 ft. breadth, 37·42 ft. draught, 9-cyl. M.A.N. diesel by the shipbuilders, 13,000 b.h.p., 16¾ knots (trials).

OKLAHOMA. *Swedish.* Tanker. Built by Eriksbergs M/V A/B, Gothenburg, for Sveriges Oljekonsumenters Riksförbund, Stockholm. 25,672 tons gross, 41,700 tons d.w., 704·82 ft. l.o.a., 95·2 ft. breadth, 36·58 ft. draught, 9-cyl. B. & W. diesel by shipbuilders, 15,000 b.h.p., 16 knots.

OLIVEBANK. *British.* Cargo. Built by Harland & Wolff Ltd., Belfast, for Bank Line Ltd., London. 6,461 tons gross, 10,162 tons d.w., 483·33 ft. l.o.a., 62·75 ft. breadth, 26 ft. draught, 6-cyl. B. & W. diesel by the shipbuilders, 5,800 b.h.p., 15 knots.

OLYMP. *Norwegian.* Tanker. Built by Tangen Verft, Kragero, for A/S Olymp, Oslo. 13,089 tons gross, 19,500 tons d.w., 556·82 ft. l.o.a., 72 ft. breadth, 30·75 ft. draught, 6-cyl. B. & W. diesel by Akers M/V, 9,300 b.h.p., 15¾ knots.

ONOBA. *Dutch.* Tanker. Built by Rotterdamsche D.D. Maats., Rotterdam, for Shell Tankers N.V., Rotterdam. 31,340 tons gross, 49,000 tons d.w., 748 ft. l.o.a., 102·75 ft. breadth, 38 ft. draught, 2 grd. turbs. by the shipbuilders, 16,000 s.h.p., 16¼ knots.

OREGON. *American.* Refrigerated cargo. Built by Newport News S.B. & D.D. Co., Newport News, for States Steamship Co., San Francisco. 12,691 tons gross, 12,840 tons d.w., 565 ft. l.o.a., 76·2 ft. breadth, 31·58 ft. draught, 2 grd. turbs. by shipbuilders, 19,250 s.h.p., 20 knots.

ORENBURG. *Russian.* Cargo. Built by Hitachi S.B. & E. Co. Ltd., Osaka, for U.S.S.R. 11,058 tons gross, 12,011 tons d.w., 517·58 ft. l.o.a., 69·2 ft. breadth, 30·66 ft. draught, 8-cyl. B. & W. diesel by the shipbuilders, 12,000 b.h.p., 17½ knots.

ORION MARU. *Japanese.* Tanker. Built by Mitsubishi H.I.R., Kobe, for Osaka Shosen Kaisha. 27,800 tons gross, 48,000 tons d.w., 707·75 ft. l.o.a., 100 ft. breadth, 38·66 ft. draught, 2 grd. turbs. by the shipbuilders, 18,500 s.h.p., 16¾ knots.

ORNEN. *Danish.* Ferry. Built by Aalborg Vaerft A/S, Aalborg, for A/S D/S Oresund, Copenhagen. 2,100 tons gross, 258·82 ft. l.o.a., 44·82 ft. breadth, 13·2 ft. draught, tw-sc. two 7-cyl. B. & W. diesels, 4,400 b.h.p., 15 knots.

ORNETA. *Polish.* Cargo. Built by United Polish Shipyards, Szczecin, for Polish Ocean Lines. 3,021 tons gross, 4,252 tons d.w., 374·66 ft. l.o.a., 48·33 ft. breadth, 20·82 ft. draught, 8-cyl. diesel by M.A.N., 4,150 b.h.p., 15 knots.

OSTFRIESLAND. *German.* Refrigerated cargo. Built by Howaldtswerke Ham. A.G., Hamburg, for Bugsier-Reederei u. Bergungs A.G., Hamburg. 9,950 tons gross, 12,300 tons d.w., 532·82 ft. l.o.a., 65·25 ft. breadth, 29·67 ft. draught, 9-cyl. Fiat diesel by Borsig, 10,000 b.h.p., 18½ knots.

OCEAN TRANSPORT. *This vessel, 12,600 tons d.w., has been built by Hawthorn Leslie (Shipbuilders) Ltd., Hepburn-on-Tyne, and is owned 32/64th by the British Empire Steam Navigation Co. Ltd. and 32/64th by the Empire Transport Co. Ltd. Designed for the carriage of grain, the ship has Nos. 2 and 4 lower holds arranged for the carriage of water ballast and fitted with specially designed pontoon type watertight tweendeck hatch covers. The cargo capacity is 654,670 cu. ft. grain, 584,640 cu. ft. bale. Cargo can be carried in five lower holds and five tweendecks, all of them equipped with permanent fittings for the carriage of grain which do not interfere with the carriage of other types of cargoes. There are no centreline divisions or other obstacles which would interfere with the carriage of cargo in Nos. 2 and 4 lower holds. Cargo is handled by means of 16 electrically driven totally enclosed winches.*

OTINA. *British.* Tanker. Built by Cammell Laird & Co. (S.B. & Eng.) Ltd., Birkenhead, for Shell Tankers Ltd., London. 32,221 tons gross, 48,740 tons d.w., 748·2 ft. l.o.a., 102·5 ft. breadth, 38 ft. draught, 2 grd. turbs. by the shipbuilders, 16,000 s.h.p., 16 knots.

OVERSEAS AMBASSADOR. *British.* Tanker. Built by Uddevallavarvet A/B, Uddevalla, for London & Overseas Tankers Ltd., Bermuda. 22,650 tons gross, 34,080 tons d.w., 698·33 ft. l.o.a., 88·25 ft. breadth, 35·25 ft. draught, tw-sc. two 8-cyl. Götaverken diesels by the shipbuilders, 7,500 b.h.p., 16¾ knots.

OVERSEAS DISCOVERER. *British.* Tanker. Built by Uddevallavarvet A/B, Uddevalla, for London & Overseas Tankers Ltd., Bermuda. 22,643 tons gross, 34,230 tons d.w., 698·33 ft. l.o.a., 88·25 ft. breadth, 35·5 ft. draught, tw-sc. two 8-cyl. Götaverken diesels by the shipbuilders, 15,000 b.h.p., 17 knots.

OTINA. *This ship is the first large crude oil carrier to be built for Shell Tankers Ltd. with her navigating bridge and all the accommodation aft. The Otina and a sister ship, Oscilla, were ordered from Cammell Laird & Co. (Shipbuilders) Ltd. A prominent feature on deck is the flying bridge of Shell's modernized design which runs 510 ft. from poop front to forecastle head. On the streamlined foremast there is a comfortable enclosed crow's nest fitted with heaters and a telephone.*

PALLADIO. *Italian.* Tanker. Built by Cant. Nav. Riuniti, Ancona, for Adriatica S.p.A., Venice. 2,800 tons gross, 4,200 tons d.w., 329·6 ft. b.p., 49·25 ft. breadth, diesel by Fiat, 5,720 b.h.p.

P. J. ADAMS. *Australian.* Tanker. Built by Broken Hill Pty. Co. Ltd., Wyalla, for Ampol Petroleum Ltd., Sydney. 22,334 tons gross, 32,250 tons d.w., 665·25 ft. l.o.a., 87·5 ft. breadth, 34·5 ft. draught, 2 grd. turbs. by Parsons, 12,500 s.h.p., 15½ knots.

PARRAKOOLA. *Swedish.* Cargo. Built by A/B Götaverken, Gothenburg, for Rederi A/B Transatlantic, Gothenburg. 8,160 tons gross, 10,980 tons d.w., 512·82 ft. l.o.a., 68·2 ft. breadth, 28·66 ft. draught, 8-cyl. Götaverken diesel, 10,000 b.h.p., 17¾ knots (trials).

PATIGNIES. *Belgian.* Ore carrier. Built by J. Boel & Fils, Tamise, for Cie. Belge d'Armement S.A., Antwerp. 15,000 tons gross, 21,400 tons d.w., 600·25 ft. l.o.a., 75·42 ft. breadth, 30·58 ft. draught, 6-cyl. B. & W. diesel by Cockerill-Ougrée, 9,000 b.h.p., 15 knots.

PEARL TRADER. *Greek.* Cargo. Built by Wm. Doxford & Sons (S.B.) Ltd., Sunderland, for Monrovia Shipping Co. Ltd. of Liberia, London. 10,122 tons gross, 15,100 tons d.w., 509·25 ft. l.o.a., 67·33 ft. breadth, 30·33 ft. draught, 4-cyl. Doxford diesel, 6,000 b.h.p., 14½ knots.

PETER RICKMERS. *German.* Cargo. Built by Rickmers Werft, Bremerhaven, for Rickmers-Linie G.m.b.H., Hamburg. 10,223 tons gross, 13,100 tons d.w., 524 ft. l.o.a., 67·2 ft. breadth, 30·75 ft. draught, 6-cyl. M.A.N. diesel, 8,000 b.h.p., 17½ knots.

PHILIPPINE BEAR. *American.* Cargo. Built by Bethlehem Steel Co., San Francisco, for Pacific Far East Line Inc., San Francisco. 12,799 tons gross, 14,925 tons d.w., 565 ft. l.o.a., 76·25 ft. breadth, 31·58 ft. draught, 2 grd. turbs. by Westinghouse, 17,500 s.h.p., 20 knots.

PHILIPPINE MAIL. *Philippine.* Refrigerated cargo. Built by Todd Shipyards Corp., San Perdo, for American Mail Line Ltd., Seattle. 12,600 tons gross, 14,925 tons d.w., 563·66 ft. l.o.a., 76 ft. breadth, 31·5 ft. draught, 2 grd. turbs. by G.E.C., 17,500 s.h.p., 20 knots.

PIAKO. *British.* Cargo. Built by Alex. Stephen & Sons Ltd., Glasgow, for New Zealand Shipping Co. Ltd., London. 9,459 tons gross, 9,750 tons d.w., 487 ft. l.o.a., 66·33 ft. breadth, 30·33 ft. draught, 8-cyl. Sulzer diesel by the shipbuilders, 9,750 b.h.p., 16½ knots.

PICOVERDE. *Spanish.* Cargo. Built by Ast. del Cadagua, Bilbao, for Mino S.A., Bilbao. 2,200 tons gross, 3,500 tons d.w., 321·58 ft. l.o.a., 45·2 ft. breadth, 6-cyl. Götaverken diesel by 'Elcano,' 3,000 b.h.p., 13½ knots.

PIERRE L.D. *French.* Ore carrier. Built by Soc. des Forges de la Méditerranée, La Seyne, for Louis Dreyfus & Cie., Paris. 21,500 tons gross, 32,500 tons d.w., 652·9 ft. l.o.a., 87·2 ft. breadth, 35 ft. draught, 8-cyl. Götaverken diesel by the shipbuilders, 10,140 b.h.p., 14 knots.

PINJA. *Finnish.* Cargo. Built by Valmet O/Y Pansio Telakka, Abo, for O/Y Tank-tonnage A/B, Helsingfors. 1,900 tons gross, 2,300 tons d.w., 282 ft. l.o.a., 42·2 ft. breadth, 17·25 ft. draught, 8-cyl. diesel by Deutz, 2,000 b.h.p., 12½ knots.

PIONEER MOON. See former name *American Challenger.*

PIRJO. *Finnish.* Cargo. Built by Valmet O/Y Pansio Telakka, Abo, for A/B O/Y Henry Nielson, Helsingfors. 1,924 tons gross, 2,300 tons d.w., 281·5 ft. l.o.a., 40·82 ft. breadth, 17·75 ft. draught, 8-cyl. diesel by Deutz 2,000 b.h.p., 12½ knots.

POLINNIA. *Italian.* Bulk carrier. Built by Cant. Nav. Breda, Venice, for Polinnia-Soc. di Nav. p.A., Palermo. 17,298 tons gross, 23,400 tons d.w., 630 ft. l.o.a., 79·5 ft. breadth, 30·5 ft. draught, 9-cyl. diesel by Fiat, 12,600 b.h.p., 16 knots.

POLJARNY. *Russian.* Cargo. Built by Neptun Werft, Rostock, for U.S.S.R. 3,455 tons gross, 4,375 tons d.w., 341·82 ft. l.o.a., 47·33 ft. breadth, 6-cyl. diesel by M.A.N., 3,250 b.h.p., 15 knots.

POLYDOROS. *Greek.* Cargo. Built by A.G. 'Weser' Werk Seebeeck, Bremerhaven, for Nava Strovili Cia. Nav. S.A., London. 11,500 tons gross, 15,702 tons d.w., 531 ft. l.o.a., 68·2 ft. breadth, 8-cyl. diesel by M.A.N., 7,600 b.h.p., 15½ knots.

P

P. J. ADAMS. *The largest vessel built in Australia up to 1963 was handed over to Ampol Petroleum Ltd., New South Wales. This vessel, the tanker P. J. Adams, of 32,250 tons d.w., was built by the Broken Hill Proprietary Co. Ltd., and has been constructed almost entirely of Australian materials. The Australian Shipbuilding Act enabled the Federal Government to subsidize the construction of the P. J. Adams. The amount involved is believed to be about £A1,000,000. The new ship is mainly of welded construction and has two longitudinal bulkheads which, together with the transverse bulkheads, divide the hull into 30 compartments having a total capacity of 30,000 tons of crude oil. Three cargo pumps, each having a capacity of 1,000 tons/hour and driven by a steam turbine, will handle the loading and discharge of the cargo. The propelling machinery consists of a set of Parsons double-reduction geared steam turbines capable of developing a service power of 12,500 s.h.p. continuously at 100 r.p.m. of the propeller, and designed to give a maximum continuous overload output of 13,200 s.h.p. at about 103 r.p.m.*

PEARL TRADER. *This cargo vessel, 15,100 tons d.w., was delivered to Mr. N. G. Livanos by William Doxford & Sons (Shipbuilders) Ltd. She is of closed shelterdeck type. Cargo handling is effected by eight 5-ton, two 10-ton and four 3-ton derricks serving the six main hatches.*

PETER RICKMERS. *This cargo motor-ship, 13,100 tons d.w., has been delivered to the Partenreeder Rickmers-Linie, of Hamburg, from the Bremerhaven shipyard of Rickmers Werft. She is noteworthy for her particularly heavy cargo handling equipment. This comprises two heavy-lift derricks each with a capacity of 130 tons. in addition she has 12 derricks of 10 tons and six of 5 tons capacity. The cargo capacity is 756,458 cu. ft. grain and 678,372 cu. ft. bale.*

P

PIAKO. A new diesel vessel of 9,750 tons d.w. was delivered in 1962 to the New Zealand Shipping Co. Ltd. for service between the United Kingdom and New Zealand or Australia. Built by Alexander Stephen & Sons Ltd., Linthouse, she is the first British built ship to be fitted with a Velle Shipshape crane. A similar ship, the Somerset, equipped with Velle Shipshape cranes was completed in 1962 by John Brown (Clydebank) Ltd. for the Federal Steam Navigation Co. Ltd. The Shipshape crane, although looking like and having the simplicity of a derrick, operates as a high-speed crane.

PORT NICHOLSON. *Port Line Ltd. took delivery in 1962 of this fast refrigerated diesel-powered cargo liner from Harland & Wolff Ltd., Belfast, who last year completed two smaller vessels of 9,000 tons gross for the same owners. This vessel, 13,847 tons d.w., is the largest ship in the Port Line fleet, and one of the largest refrigerated vessels in the world. She is of conventional design with bridge and machinery amidships and carries 12 passengers. Propulsion is by twin Harland & Wolff-B. & W. diesel engines driving two screws. She has an A.C. electrical installation.*

POLYSTAR. *Norwegian.* Tanker. Built by Eriksbergs M/V A/B, Gothenburg, for Einar Rasmussen, Kristiansand. 12,755 tons gross, 20,250 tons d.w., 559·82 ft. l.o.a., 71·9 ft. breadth, 30·66 ft. draught, 7-cyl. B. & W. diesel by the shipbuilders, 9,800 b.h.p., 15¾ knots.

PORT NICHOLSON. *British.* Refrigerated cargo. Built by Harland & Wolff Ltd., Belfast, for Port Line Ltd. 14,000 tons gross, 13,847 tons d.w., 573·5 ft. l.o.a., 75·9 ft. breadth, 30 ft. draught, tw-sc. two 6-cyl. B. & W. diesels by the shipbuilders, 17,000 b.h.p., 18½ knots.

POSJET. *Russian.* Cargo. Built by Neptun Werft, Rostock, for U.S.S.R. 3,455 tons gross, 4,375 tons d.w., 341·82 ft. l.o.a., 47·33 ft. breadth, 6-cyl. diesel by M.A.N., 3,250 b.h.p., 15 knots.

PRINCESA ISABEL. *Brazilian.* Passenger. Built by Soc. Española de Const. Nav., Bilbao, for Cia. Nacional de Nav. Costeira Autarquia Federal, Rio de Janeiro. 9,698 tons gross, 3,890 tons d.w., 483 ft. l.o.a., 64·25 ft. breadth, 18 ft. draught, tw-sc. two 8-cyl. B. & W. diesels by the shipbuilders, 9,200 b.h.p., 17½ knots (trials).

PRINCESA LEOPOLDINA. *Brazilian.* Passenger. Built by Cia. Euskalduna, Bilbao, for Cia. Nacional de Nav. Costeira Autarquia Federal, Rio de Janeiro. 9,698 tons gross, 3,890 tons d.w., 483 ft. l.o.a., 64·25 ft. breadth, 17·9 ft. draught, tw-sc. two 8-cyl. B. & W. diesels by the shipbuilders, 9,200 b.h.p., 17½ knots (trials).

P

PROA EUROPA. *Spanish.* Cargo. Built by Ast. de T. Ruiz de Velasco, Bilbao, for Naviera Proa, Bilbao. 1,686 tons gross, 2,850 tons d.w., 261·66 ft. l.o.a., 38·82 ft. breadth, 19·66 ft. draught, 8-cyl. B. & W. diesel by Maquinista, 2,240 b.h.p., 12½ knots.

PROFESSOR M. T. HUBER. *Polish.* Tanker. Built by United Polish Shipyards, Gdansk, for Polish Government. 12,866 tons gross, 19,000 tons d.w., 580·42 ft. l.o.a., 77·66 ft. breadth, 30·33 ft. draught, 6-cyl. Sulzer diesel by Cegielski, 9,000 b.h.p., 16 knots.

PRINCESA LEOPOLDINA. *This passenger liner is one of a pair of sister ships completed in Spain for the Cia. Nacional de Navegacao Costeira of Brazil. This vessel was built by the Cia. Euskalduna, Bilbao, while the second ship, Princesa Isabel, was built by the Soc. Espanola de Construccion Naval. Each has a gross tonnage of about 9,500 tons and accommodation for 530 passengers, in three classes. They have been built for service between Rio de la Plata, the Atlantic ports of Brazil and the Amazon ports as far up as Manaos. Each ship has two cargo holds forward, with a total capacity of 72,526 cu. ft. They are powered by diesel machinery and have stabilizers. Their range is 8,200 miles.*

RAFFAELE CAFIERO. *Italian.* Tanker. Built by 'Navalmeccanica' Cant. Nav., Castellammare, for 'Elios' S.p.A. di Nav., Palermo. 24,415 tons gross, 38,500 tons d.w., 670·58 ft. l.o.a., 93·75 ft. breadth, 36 ft. draught, 9-cyl. Fiat diesel, 18,900 b.h.p., 17 knots.

RAILA DAN. *Danish.* Cargo. Built by Bijker's Aannemings, Gorinchem, for J. Lauritzen, Copenhagen. 1,859 tons gross, 2,325 tons d.w., 268·42 ft. l.o.a., 40·42 ft. breadth, 18 ft. draught, 10-cyl. diesel by Smit-Bolnes, 1,700 b.h.p., 12½ knots.

RAKWERE. *Russian.* Cargo. Built by Neptun Werft, Rostock, for U.S.S.R. 3,455 tons gross, 4,735 tons d.w., 341·9 ft. l.o.a., 47·33 ft. breadth, 20·75 ft. draught, 6-cyl. diesel by M.A.N., 3,250 b.h.p., 15 knots.

RAVNAAS. *Norwegian.* Cargo. Built by Eriksbergs M/V A/B, Gothenburg, for Agdesidens Rederi A/S, Arendal. 8,970 tons gross, 13,000 tons d.w., 475·66 ft. l.o.a., 62·2 ft. breadth, 29·25 ft. draught, 5-cyl. B. & W. diesel by the shipbuilders, 6,250 b.h.p., 15¼ knots.

REGENT LIVERPOOL. *British.* Tanker. Built by Harland & Wolff Ltd., Belfast, for Regent Petroleum Tankship Co. Ltd., London. 30,550 tons gross, 49,300 tons d.w., 746·25 ft. l.o.a., 98·33 ft. breadth, 39·25 ft. draught, 2 grd. turbs. by the shipbuilders, 16,500 s.h.p., 16 knots.

RENE SIEGFRIED. *French.* Dredger. Built by At. & Ch. de Bretagne, Nantes, for Pont & Chaussées de la Loire Atlantique, Nantes. 2,400 tons gross, 306·66 ft. l.o.a., 49·2 ft. breadth, 13·33 ft. draught, 9-cyl. Pielstick diesel by the shipbuilders, 3,195 b.h.p., 12 knots.

RENI. *Russian.* Cargo. Built by Neptun Werft, Rostock, for U.S.S.R. 3,455 tons gross, 4,375 tons d.w., 341·82 ft. l.o.a., 47·33 ft. breadth, 6-cyl. diesel by M.A.N., 3,250 b.h.p., 15 knots.

RICHMOND MARU. *Japanese.* Cargo. Built by Mitsubishi S.B. & E. Co. Ltd., Nagasaki, for Daido Kaiun Kaisha, Kobe. 9,570 tons gross, 12,400 tons d.w., 523·9 ft. l.o.a., 67·42 ft. breadth, 30·33 ft. draught, 9-cyl. U.E.C. diesel by the shipbuilders, 13,000 b.h.p., 18 knots.

RINGWOOD. *Norwegian.* Bulk carrier. Built by Harland & Wolff Ltd., Glasgow, for Olav Ringdal, Oslo. 10,500 tons gross, 15,170 tons d.w., 535 ft. l.o.a., 65·66 ft. breadth, 28·5 ft. draught, 6-cyl. B. & W. diesel by the shipbuilders, 6,000 b.h.p., 14¾ knots.

RIO CARCARANA. *Argentine.* Cargo liner. Built by Brodogradiliste 3 Maj, Rijeka, for Empresa Lineas Marit. Argentinas, Buenos Aires. 7,400 tons gross, 10,500 tons d.w., 516·25 ft. l.o.a., 66·75 ft. breadth, 26·82 ft. draught, 9-cyl. diesel by Deutz, 10,300 b.h.p., 17½ knots.

RIO COLORADO. *Argentine.* Cargo/passenger. Built by Brodogradiliste 3 Maj, Rijeka, for Empresa Lineas Maritimas Argentinas, Buenos Aires. 7,400 tons gross, 10,500 tons d.w., 516·25 ft. l.o.a., 66·75 ft. breadth, 26·82 ft. draught, 9-cyl. diesel by Fiat, 10,300 b.h.p., 18 knots.

RIYO MARU. *Japanese.* Tanker. Built by Sasebo H.I. Ltd., Sasebo, for Taiyo Shosen Kaisha, Tokyo. 28,452 tons gross, 47,000 tons d.w., 726·33 ft. l.o.a., 100·42 ft. breadth, 37·66 ft. draught, 9-cyl. Sulzer by Mitsubishi H.I.R., 18,000 b.h.p., 16¼ knots.

ROGN. *Norwegian.* Tanker. Built by A/B Ekensbergs Varv, Stockholm, for A/S Rederiet Odfjell, Bergen. 4,563 tons gross, 6,350 tons d.w., 389·66 ft. l.o.a., 54·25 ft. breadth, 21·75 ft. draught, 6-cyl. Götaverken diesel by Uddevallavarvet, 5,900 b.h.p., 14¼ knots.

RONACASTLE. *Norwegian.* Bulk carrier. Built by Uddevallavarvet A/B, Uddevalla, for Skibs A/S Agnes, Mandal. 12,743 tons gross, 18,160 tons d.w., 555 ft. l.o.a., 70·2 ft. breadth, 30 ft. draught, 7-cyl. Götaverken diesel by the shipbuilders, 8,750 b.h.p., 15¾ knots.

ROSA DA FONSECA. *Brazilian.* Passenger. Built by Brodogradiliste Split, for Commissao da Marinha Mercante, Rio de Janeiro. 10,450 tons gross, 492·2 ft. l.o.a., 65·58 ft. breadth, 16·33 ft. draught, tw-sc. two 7-cyl. B. & W. diesels by Krupp, 17½ knots.

ROSS CAPE. *Norwegian.* Bulk carrier. Built by Mitsubishi S.B. & E. Co. Ltd., Nagasaki, for Hvalfanger A/S Rosshavet, Sandefjord. 28,000 tons gross, 42,000 tons d.w., 712·25 ft. l.o.a., 97·33 ft. breadth, 34·33 ft. draught, 6-cyl. Sulzer diesel by Uraga, 13,000 b.h.p., 16½ knots.

R

RAFFAELE CAFIERO. This completion by the Italian shipyard Navalmeccanica S.p.A., Castellammare di Stabia, is for the Elios S.p.A. di Navigazione, of Palermo, which is one of the companies controlled by the Italian owner Achille Lauro. The Raffaele Cafiero is a motor tanker of 38,500 tons d.w., propelled by a Fiat diesel engine developing 18,900 b.h.p. in service and at the date of completion was the largest motor tanker yet built in Italy. A number of larger motor tankers are on order from Italian yards, including the series of 48,000 tons d.w. vessels for Russian ownership being built by Ansaldo. The usual two longitudinal bulkheads are fitted, and transverse bulkheads divide the cargo space into 11 centre tanks and a total of 12 wing tanks. Two side tanks and one centre tank are void spaces under all conditions and are therefore connected neither to the cargo piping nor the ballast piping system. The main engine of the Raffaele Cafiero is the first 9-cylinder large-bore engine which Fiat have built. The output at normal rating on trials was just over 19,000 b.h.p. at a speed of 122·7 r.p.m., while at the overload rating an output of 26,100 b.h.p. was achieved at 131·4 r.p.m.

ROSS MOUNT. *Norwegian.* Cargo. Built by A/S Framnaes M/V, Sandefjord, for Hvalfanger A/S Rosshavet, Sandefjord. 11,500 tons gross, 16,282 tons d.w., 522·82 ft. l.o.a., 67·2 ft. breadth, 29·5 ft. draught, 5-cyl. diesel by Götaverken, 6,300 b.h.p., 16½ knots.

RU YUNG. *Nat. Chinese.* Passenger and cargo. Built by Uraga Dock Co., Yokosuka, for Chinese Maritime Trust Ltd., Taipeh. 10,343 tons gross, 12,500 tons d.w., 518·42 ft. l.o.a., 66·5 ft. breadth, 29·66 ft. draught, 8-cyl. Sulzer diesel by Uraga, 10,200 b.h.p., 18 knots.

REGENT LIVERPOOL. *This turbine tanker, 49,300 tons d.w., has been completed at the Belfast yard of Harland & Wolff Ltd. for the Regent Petroleum Tankship Co. Ltd. She is the largest tanker to be built for these owners and is a crude oil carrier, as opposed to previous vessels of the fleet which have been refined products carriers. It is of interest to compare the photograph of this Regent tanker with the one of Otina of similar size, built by Cammell Laird's for Shell, which has her bridge and all accommodation aft. The Regent Liverpool will carry crude oil to the Regent refinery at Milford Haven. The vessel is of conventional three-island type. The hull is divided by longitudinal and transverse bulkheads into 25 tanks, four of which are for water ballast only. Water ballast can also be carried in the fore and aft peak tanks, deep tanks forward and double bottom tanks in the engine room. Fuel bunkers are arranged immediately forward and aft of the cargo tanks. Fresh water is carried in tanks built aft of the machinery space on the steering gear flat, and also in a tank in the tonnage space amidships. The steam turbine propelling machinery, which is of Pametrada type, was built by Harland & Wolff Ltd.*

RINGWOOD. *This 15,170 tons d.w. cargo ship was built by Harland & Wolff, Govan, for Ringdals Rederi A/S, Oslo. This is another example of a new vessel fitted with Velle cranes throughout, six being installed.*

S

SADOHARU MARU. *Japanese.* Refrigerated cargo. Built by Hitachi S.B. & E. Co. Ltd., Innoshima, for Shinnihon Kisen K.K., Kobe. 8,950 tons gross, 12,052 tons d.w., 505·33 ft. l.o.a., 65·82 ft. breadth, 30·2 ft. draught, 7-cyl. B. & W. diesel by shipbuilders, 10,500 b.h.p., 20 knots.

SAHEL II. *French.* Wine carrier. Built by S.A. des Anc. Ch. Dubigeon, Nantes, for Soc. Anon de Gerance & d'Armement, Paris. 2,448 tons gross, 2,930 tons d.w., 295·2 ft. l.o.a., 45·33 ft. breadth, 7-cyl. diesel by M.A.N., 2,520 b.h.p., 13½ knots.

SAFINA-E-ARAB. *Pakistan.* Pilgrim ship. Built by Soc. Espanola de Const. Nav., Cadiz, for Pan-Islamic S.S. Co. Ltd., Karachi. 8,477 tons gross, 459·33 ft. l.o.a., 60·25 ft. breadth, 23 ft. draught, 5-cyl. Sulzer diesel by the shipbuilders, 6,500 b.h.p., 15 knots.

SAIMA DAN. *Danish.* Cargo. Built by Bijker's Aannemings, Gorinchem, for J. Lauritzen, Copenhagen. 3,065 tons gross, 3,700 tons d.w., 323·33 ft. l.o.a., 46·42 ft. breadth, 21·75 ft. draught, 5-cyl. B. & W. diesel, 3,250 b.h.p., 14 knots.

SAINT FRANCOIS. *French.* Cargo. Built by At. & Ch. de la Seine Maritime, Le Trait, for Cie. de Navigation Denis Fréres, Paris. 3,300 tons gross, 5,500 tons d.w., 426·5 ft. l.o.a., 55 ft. breadth, 24·58 ft. draught, B. & W. diesel, 5,750 b.h.p., 16 knots.

SAINT-MATTHIEU. *French.* Refrigerated cargo. Built by Ch. & At. de Provence, Port de Bouc, for Soc. Anon. de Gérance & d'Armement, Paris. 7,700 tons gross, 10,100 tons d.w., 440·42 ft. l.o.a., 60·82 ft. breadth, 27·9 ft. draught, 4-cyl. Doxford diesel by the shipbuilders, 4,200 b.h.p., 15 knots.

SAN JUAN PIONEER. *Liberian.* Ore/oil carrier. Built by Tsurumi Dock Co. Ltd., Yokohama, for San Juan Carriers Ltd., Peru. 46,300 tons gross, 67,500 tons d.w., 835 ft. l.o.a., 106·33 ft. breadth, 44 ft. draught, 2 grd. turbs. by Ishikawajima-Harima, 22,500 s.h.p., 16¼ knots.

SAN JUAN PROSPECTOR. *Liberian.* Ore/oil carrier. Built by Mitsui S.B. & E. Co. Ltd., Tamano, for San Juan Carriers Ltd., Monrovia and San Francisco. 44,300 tons gross, 67,500 tons d.w., 835 ft. l.o.a., 106·42 ft. breadth, 44 ft. draught, 2 grd. turbs. by Ishikawajima-Harima, 22,500 s.h.p., 16¼ knots.

SANTA MAGDALENA. *American.* Passenger and cargo. Built by Bethlehem Steel Co., Sparrows Point, for Grace Line Inc., New York. 14,100 tons gross, 7,790 tons d.w., 545 ft. l.o.a., 79 ft. breadth, 29 ft. draught, 2 grd. turbs. by G.E.C., 18,000 s.h.p., 20 knots.

SAKURA MARU. *Japanese.* Floating fair and passenger. Built by Mitsubishi H.I.R., Kobe, for Japan Industry Floating Fair Assn. 12,200 tons gross, 4,800 tons d.w., 515·2 ft. l.o.a., 69 ft. breadth, 21·67 ft. draught, 7-cyl. U.E.C. diesel by the shipbuilders, 9,800 b.h.p., 17½ knots.

SAM RATULANGI. *Indonesian.* Passenger and cargo. Built by United Polish Shipyards, Szczecin, for Djakarta Lloyd, Djkarta. 6,630 tons gross, 503·25 ft. l.o.a., 63·66 ft. breadth, 27·33 ft. draught, 6-cyl. Sulzer diesel by Cegielski, 7,800 b.h.p., 16½ knots.

SANDVIKEN. *Norwegian.* Cargo. Built by A/B Oskarshamns Varv, Oskarshamn, for Wallen, Steckmest & Co. A/S, Bergen. 8,700 tons gross, 12,850 tons d.w., 485 ft. l.o.a., 61·66 ft. breadth, 30 ft. draught, 7-cyl. diesel by Götaverken, 5,800 b.h.p., 15 knots.

SANTA ISABEL MARU. *Japanese.* Bulk carrier. Built by Nagasaki S.B. & E. Co. Ltd., Nagasaki, for Chiyoda Koseki Yuso K.K., Tokyo. 30,000 tons gross, 51,000 tons d.w., 740·5 ft. l.o.a., 101·33 ft. breadth, 37·82 ft. draught, 9-cyl. U.E.C. diesel by the shipbuilders, 13,600 b.h.p., 14 knots.

SAPHIR. *Norwegian.* Tanker. Built by A/S Stord Verft, Lervik, for Edvin Endresen, Stavanger. 3,914 tons gross, 5,300 tons d.w., 374·95 ft. l.o.a., 48·9 ft. breadth, 21·2 ft. draught, 4-cyl. B. & W. diesel by A/S Akers M/V, 3,180 b.h.p., 14 knots.

SADOHARU MARU. *This cargo liner is claimed to be the most highly automated ship so far built in Japan, and was constructed by Hitachi Zosen for the Japan-Gulf of Mexico service of Shinnihon Kisen K.K. Automation promises to offset rising crew costs to some extent. This vessel needs a crew of only 41 compared with the 49 usually employed in ships of similar type and size. Features include remote control of the main engine from a console in the wheelhouse, automation of fuel oil, lubricating oil, fresh water, sea water, refrigeration and other systems, grouping of engine room gauges, meters and controls in a soundproof booth, a circular wheelhouse, and chromium-plated cylinder liners in the main engine to minimize wear and reduce maintenance.*

SAFINA E ARAB. *This ship is a combined cargo and passenger vessel built at the Matagorda yard of the Sociedad Espanola de Construcction Naval for the Pan Islamic Steamship Co. of Pakistan, and is specially equipped for carrying pilgrims.*

S

SAVANNAH. *American.* Cargo and passenger. Nuclear. Built by New York Shipbuilding Co., Camden, N.J., for U.S. Maritime Administration. 12,220 tons gross, 9,990 tons d.w., 595·5 ft. l.o.a., 78·2 ft. breadth, 29·5 ft. draught, grd. turb. De Laval, 22,000 s.h.p., 20 knots.

SCANIA. *Swedish.* Cargo. Built by A/B Lindholmens Varv, Gothenburg, for Rederi A/B Svenska Lloyd, Gothenburg. 3,760 tons gross, 4,600 tons d.w., 349 ft. l.o.a., 47·66 ft. breadth, 22·5 ft. draught, 8-cyl. Götaverken diesel by the shipbuilders, 3,000 b.h.p., 16 knots.

SCHIEKERK. *Dutch.* Cargo. Built by N.V. Mch. & Schps. van P. Smit, Jun., for N.V. Vereenigde Nederlandsche Scheepsv. Maats., The Hague. 9,830 tons gross, 12,250 tons d.w., 528·75 ft. l.o.a., 69·2 ft. breadth, 29·5 ft. draught 9-cyl. B. & W. diesel by the shipbuilders, 11,250 b.h.p., 18 knots.

SCOTTISH TRADER. *British.* Bulk carrier. Built by Austin & Pickersgill Ltd., Sunderland, for Trader Navigation Co. Ltd., London. 11,563 tons gross, 15,800 tons d.w., 507·42 ft. l.o.a., 68·58 ft. breadth, 29·5 ft. draught, 4-cyl. Doxford diesel by Hawthorn Leslie, 4,800 b.h.p., 16½ knots (trials).

SEA SAPPHIRE. *Swedish.* Tanker. Built by Ch. Nav. de La Ciotat, La Ciotat, for Salénrederierna A/B, Stockholm. 34,000 tons gross, 55,250 tons d.w., 800·5 ft. l.o.a., 104·2 ft. breadth, 38 ft. draught, 2 grd. turbs. by Turbin A/B-De Laval, 20,000 s.h.p., 17 knots.

SEGERO. *Swedish.* Cargo. Built by A/B Oskarshamns Varv, Oskarshamn, for Rederi A/B Rex, Stockholm. 6,600 tons gross, 9,280 tons d.w., 410·2 ft. l.o.a., 57 ft. breadth, 27·9 ft. draught, 6-cyl. Götaverken diesel, 5,000 b.h.p., 14¾ knots.

SAINT MATTHIEU. *This cargo ship, 7,350 tons d.w., has been completed by the Chantiers et Ateliers de Provence, Port de Bouc, for the Soc. Anon de Gerance & d'Armement. The vessel has been specially designed for the West African trade and has been fitted for carrying lumber, both in the holds and as deck cargo. There are five holds served by a number of 3-, 4-, 5-, 12- and 15-ton derricks and by a 50-ton Stulcken derrick.*

SAN JUAN PIONEER. *A large cargo vessel which can carry a capacity cargo of oil or ore, or a combination of both. The vessel, 46,300 tons gross, has been built at the Tsurumi Dock Co. Ltd., Yokohama. The same cargo tanks are used either for ore or oil—an uncommon arrangement, but one which was used successfully in another Japanese-built ship, the Mando Theodoracopulos, completed in 1960. The new vessel is owned by San Juan Carriers, an affiliate of the Marcona Mining Group. The ship is under charter to transport iron ore from Peru to the Nippon Kokan raw material depot at Ogishima in Tokyo Bay, and to carry oil from Sumatra to Los Angeles on her return journey. Two sister ships, San Juan Prospector and San Juan Pathfinder, were ordered from the Tamano shipyard of Mitsui Shipbuilding & Engineering Co. Ltd., and the former was also delivered in 1962. The San Juan Pioneer has five cargo holds, three of which have been designed as dual-purpose holds capable of carrying either ore or oil. There are six wing cargo or water ballast tanks on each side of the ship and one midship cargo or water ballast tank.*

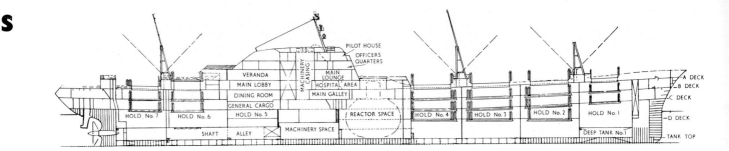

SAVANNAH. On 22nd May, 1819, an earlier S.S. Savannah, 320 tons gross, started on her voyage from Savannah, Georgia, to Liverpool. She was the first vessel to use steam on a transatlantic crossing. The new Savannah, 12,220 tons gross, delivered in 1962 is nearly as epoch-making as the former, for she ushers in the atomic era of merchant shipping. The Savannah is a nuclear-powered cargo/passenger ship developed by the U.S. Atomic Energy Commission and the Maritime Administration of the U.S. Department of Commerce. She was designed by George G. Sharp Inc. of New York and was built by the New York Shipbuilding Corporation of Camden, New Jersey. The Savannah is essentially a shelterdeck vessel of advanced design with a raked stem and a modified cruiser stern and accommodates 60 passengers and a crew of 109. About 10,000 tons of dry cargo is carried and she is constructed with six complete decks. She is propelled by a De Laval double-reduction geared turbine developing 22,000 s.h.p. and has a service speed of 20 knots. Her cargo handling gear and general equipment is of the latest type and she is fitted with stabilizers. The Savannah is really an experimental ship and she is not expected to compete economically with conventional vessels, but to pave the way for more advanced and competitive designs in the future. The first nuclear-powered non-naval vessel was the Soviet ice-breaker Lenin but she is a specialized ship whereas the Savannah is intended to demonstrate the employment of nuclear power in the normal trade and commerce of the world. She is to prove that nuclear-powered merchant ships are dependable and safe enough for acceptance in world ports.

As is common knowledge, a reactor is simply an atomic furnace which produces the heat with which to generate the steam needed to turn the ship's turbines and propeller shaft. In the type of reactor designed and built by Babcock & Wilcox, New York, for the Savannah water is circulated under pressure through the heart, or core, of the reactor as the fissioning process takes place. The water removes the intense heat created in the reactor core by the splitting of the fuel atoms and transfers this heat to a secondary system of piping located in a device called a 'heat exchanger.' Water in this secondary system is changed to steam for propulsion of the vessel. The nuclear fuel in the Savannah's reactor comprises approximately 17,000 lb. of enriched uranium oxide. A single core of the fuel is expected to supply enough energy to operate the ship for $3\frac{1}{2}$ years without replacement.

Reactor Safety

The Savannah's hull is built on a conventional transverse framing system, except for the inner bottom. This inner bottom is 'egg crated' below the reactor compartment with transverse floors running crosswise of the ship at every frame, or rib, of the vessel and with a deep vertical keel and many keelsons running in the fore and aft directions. The great strength thereby provided in the inner bottom assures very high resistance to damage to both ship and reactor in the unlikely event of grounding. The reactor compartment itself is located amidship between two upright, longitudinal collision bulkheads, or partitions, made of heavy steel. The bulkheads protect each side of the reactor. Between the bulkheads and the hull of the ship, three strengthened decks of the vessel offer additional protection from collision. Inboard of the bulkheads are collision mats made up of alternate layers of inch thick steel and three-inch redwood for a total mat thickness of 24 inches. Thus, in the event of a broadside collision opposite the reactor space, the ramming ship would have to penetrate a total of 17 feet of stiffened ship structure, the heavy collision bulkheads and two feet of collision mat before reaching the heavy reactor containment shell, or vessel. This steel containment shell rests in a cradle of steel where its bottom half is surrounded by a four-foot thickness of reinforced concrete. The steel cradle, the concrete and the containment shell itself would also have to be pierced before the actual reactor plant could be damaged. In case of sinking, provision has been made to allow for automatic flooding of the containment shell of the reactor to prevent its collapse in deep waters.

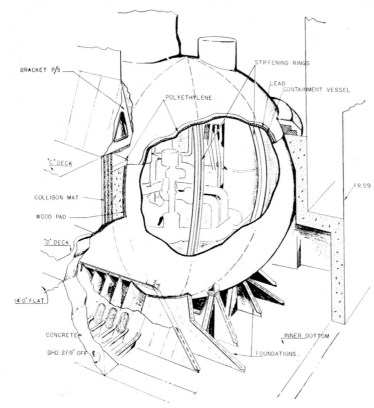

BRACKET P/S

STIFFENING RINGS

LEAD
CONTAINMENT VESSEL

POLYETHYLENE

'C' DECK

COLLISON MAT

WOOD PAD

'D' DECK

FR.99

14'0" FLAT

CONCRETE

BHD. 21'9" OFF.

INNER BOTTOM

FOUNDATIONS.

Reactor containment shell in the Savannah

SAVANNAH—*continued*

Radiation Protection

Primary radiation shielding around the Savannah reactor consists of a 17-foot high tank of high strength carbon steel located within the containment shell and covered with a layer of lead from two to four inches thick. The tank will permit a wall of water 33 inches thick to surround the reactor and, when filled, constitutes the first line of resistance to radiation from within the reactor. Surrounding this primary shielding is the heavy steel containment shell already mentioned. The top half of the shell is covered by a six-inch layer of lead plus a six-inch layer of polyethylene, each of which acts as additional radiation protection. The bottom half of the vessel, as previously mentioned, is surrounded by four feet of concrete shielding which protects against radiation as well as collision. The containment shell is designed to withstand the greatest possible pressure surge in the event of a serious accident so that there can be no hazardous release of radioactivity to the surroundings. Power plant liquid and solid radioactive wastes are collected in tanks for disposal into a specially designed barge in port. Gaseous wastes will normally be disposed of at sea through the radio mast.

SEIWA MARU. *Japanese.* Tanker. Built by Mitsubishi S.B. & E. Co. Ltd., Nagasaki, for Taiheiyo Kaiun K.K., Tokyo. 29,009 tons gross, 49,863 tons d.w., 736 ft. l.o.a., 100·33 ft. breadth, 37·5 ft. draught, 9-cyl. U.E.C. diesel by the shipbuilders, 16,500 b.h.p., 15¾ knots.

SEMATAN MARU. *Japanese.* Bauxite carrier. Built by Sanoyasu Dockyard Co. Ltd., Osaka, for Daiichi Chuo Kisen Kaisha, Tokyo. 9,500 tons gross, 15,000 tons d.w., 472·5 ft. b.p., 67·42 ft. breadth, 28 ft. draught, 6-cyl. Sulzer diesel by Uraga, 6,600 b.h.p., 16¼ knots.

SENFTENBERG. *East German.* Ore carrier. Built by Warnowwerft, Warnemünde, for Deutsche Seereederei, Rostock. 8,609 tons gross, 11,350 tons d.w., 498 ft. l.o.a., 63·2 ft. breadth, 27·25 ft. draught, 7-cyl. diesel by D.M.R., 5,850 b.h.p., 15 knots.

SENNAR. *Sudanese.* Refrigerated cargo. Built by Brodogradiliste Uljanik, Pula, Yugoslavia, for Sudan Shipping Lines Ltd., Port Sudan. 3,835 tons gross, 395·2 ft. l.o.a., 53·82 ft. breadth, 22·2 ft. draught, 6-cyl. B. & W. diesel.

SENYU MARU. *Japanese.* Coal carrier. Built by Sanoyasu Dockyard Co. Ltd., Osaka, for Izumi Kisen K.K., Tokyo. 5,050 tons gross, 7,500 tons d.w., 370 ft. b.p., 54·42 ft. breadth, 23·25 ft. draught, 6-cyl. B. & W. diesel by Mitsui, 4,200 b.h.p., 13½ knots.

SERVAASKERK. *Dutch.* Cargo. Built by C. van der Giessen, Krimpen, for N.V. Vereenigde Nederlandsche Schpsv. Maats., The Hague. 9,831 tons gross, 12,150 tons d.w., 528·25 ft. l.o.a., 69·33 ft. breadth, 29·5 ft. draught, 9-cyl. B. & W. diesel by P. Smit, Jun., 10,600 b.h.p., 18 knots (trials).

SHAVIT. *Israeli.* Cargo. Built by Uraga Dock Co., Yukosuka, for Zim Israel Nav. Co. Ltd., Haifa. 7,000 tons gross, 9,650 tons d.w., 451·2 ft. l.o.a., 60·42 ft. breadth, 27 ft. draught, 6-cyl. Sulzer diesel by the shipbuilders, 6,600 b.h.p., 15 knots.

SHINO MARU. *Japanese.* Tanker. Built by Iino S.B. & E. Co. Ltd., Maizuru, for Iino Kaiun K.K. 29,400 tons gross, 48,900 tons d.w., 727·42 ft. l.o.a., 100·2 ft. breadth, 37·82 ft. draught, 8-cyl. Sulzer diesel by the shipbuilders, 16,000 b.h.p., 16½ knots.

SHINKO MARU. *Japanese.* Ore carrier. Built by Kure S.B. Co. Ltd., Kure, for Yamashita Kisen K.K., Tokyo. 13,228 tons gross, 21,000 tons d.w., 559·82 ft. l.o.a., 74·33 ft. breadth, 30·33 ft. draught, 6-cyl. diesel by Ishikawajima, 6,600 b.h.p., 13¼ knots.

SHINSEI MARU No. 6. *Japanese.* Cargo. Built by Namura S.B. Co., Osaka, for Hara Shosen K.K., Osaka. 3,100 tons gross, 4,800 tons d.w., 48 ft. breadth, 20·66 ft. draught, 4-cyl. diesel by Ito Tekko, 2,700 b.h.p., 12 knots.

SHINSUI MARU. *Japanese.* Tanker. Built by Kasado Dock Co. Ltd., Kudamatsu, for Nisshin Kaiun K.K., Tokyo. 1,508 tons gross, 2,221 tons d.w., 245·82 ft. l.o.a., 38·33 ft. breadth, 17·25 ft. draught, 6-cyl. diesel by Hanshin, 1,550 b.h.p., 11½ knots.

SHIRLEY LYKES. *American.* Refrigerated cargo. Built by Bethlehem Steel Co., Sparrows Point, for Lykes Bros. Steamship Co. Inc., New Orleans. 10,200 tons gross, 10,960 tons d.w., 495 ft. l.o.a., 69·2 ft. breadth, 29·58 ft. draught, 2 grd. turbs. by G.E.C., 11,000 s.h.p.

SHOKAI MARU. *Japanese.* Collier. Built by Nagoya S.B. Co. Ltd., Nagasaki, for Muromachi Kaiun K.K., Tokyo. 3,650 tons gross, 5,300 tons d.w., 337·9 ft. l.o.a., 48 ft. breadth, 21·75 ft. draught, 6-cyl. Kobe Hatsudoki-U.E.C. diesel, 2,700 b.h.p., 12½ knots.

SHOKEI MARU. *Japanese.* Cargo. Built by Shioyama Dockyard Co. Ltd., Osaka, for Matsushima Tanko K.K., Oshima, Fukuoka. 1,594 tons gross, 2,266 tons d.w., 259·2 ft. l.o.a., 39·42 ft. breadth, 15·9 ft. draught, 6-cyl. B. & W. diesel by Mitsui, 1,680 b.h.p., 11 knots.

SHORYU MARU. *Japanese.* Ore carrier. Built by Namura S.B. Co., Osaka, for Taiheiyo Kisen K.K., Tokyo. 10,300 tons gross, 15,000 tons d.w., 67·42 ft. breadth, 26·9 ft. draught, 6-cyl. Sulzer diesel by Mitsubishi H.I.R., 6,600 b.h.p., 13½ knots.

S

S

SIERRA MAESTRA. *Cuban.* Cargo. Built by Warnowwerft, Warnemünde, for Empresa Consolidada de Nav., Santiago de Cuba. 6,747 tons gross, 10,220 tons d.w., 516·5 ft. l.o.a., 65·9 ft. breadth, 27·58 ft. draught, 6-cyl. diesel by D.M.R., 7,200 b.h.p., 15½ knots.

SIFNOS. *Greek.* Refrigerated cargo. Built by Schps. 'De Hoop,' Lobith, for Reefer & General Shipping Co. Inc., Piraeus. 4,015 tons gross, 4,500 tons d.w., 359 ft. l.o.a., 49 ft. breadth, 19·42 ft. draught, 6-cyl. M.A.N. diesel, 4,200 b.h.p., 15 knots.

SIGHAUG. *Norwegian.* Bulk carrier. Built by Kockums M/V A/B, Malmö, for I/S Sighaug, Oslo. 16,663 tons gross, 25,350 tons d.w., 577 ft. l.o.a., 75 ft. breadth, 33·9 ft. draught, 6-cyl. M.A.N. diesel by the shipbuilders, 16,845 b.h.p., 14½ knots.

SIGURD JARL. *Norwegian.* Cargo. Built by Fr. Lürssen, Vegesack, for Det Nordenfjeldske D/S, Trondheim. 1,388 tons gross, 1,930 tons d.w., 239·5 ft. l.o.a., 38·2 ft. breadth, 19 ft. draught, 5-cyl. Sulzer diesel, 1,670 b.h.p., 13¼ knots.

SILJA. *Norwegian.* Bulk carrier. Built by A/S Bergens M/V, Bergen, for Hagb. Waage, Oslo. 14,834 tons gross, 22,900 tons d.w., 560·2 ft. l.o.a., 72 ft. breadth, 34·25 ft. draught, 8-cyl. Götaverken diesel, 10,000 b.h.p., 15½ knots.

SIMFEROPOL. *Russian.* Cargo. Built by United Polish Shipyards, Gdansk, for U.S.S.R. 9,344 tons gross, 508 ft. l.o.a., 66·25 ft. breadth, 29·2 ft. draught, 6-cyl. Sulzer diesel, 7,800 b.h.p., 16 knots.

SINEGORSK. *Russian.* Tanker. Built by Rauma-Repola O/Y, Rauma, for U.S.S.R. 3,360 tons gross, 4,400 tons d.w., 344·82 ft. l.o.a., 48·58 ft. breadth, 20·42 ft. draught, 5-cyl. diesel by B. & W., 2,900 b.h.p., 14 knots.

SINGÖ. *Swedish.* Cargo. Built by Kieler Howaldtswerke A.G., Kiel, for Rederi A/B Rex, Stockholm. 4,822 tons gross, 7,010 tons d.w. 360·25 ft. l.o.a., 52·2 ft. breadth, 22·75 ft. draught, 8-cyl. M.A.N. diesel by the shipbuilders, 3,925 b.h.p., 13 knots.

SINOUTSKERK. *Dutch.* Refrigerated cargo. Built by C. van der Giessen, Krimpen, for N.V. Vereenigde Nederl. Scheepv. Maats., The Hague. 9,831 tons gross, 12,150 tons d.w., 528·25 ft. l.o.a., 69·42 ft. breadth, 29·5 ft. draught, 9-cyl. diesel by Gebr.-Stork, 10,600 b.h.p., 18 knots.

SIR JOHN CROSBIE. *Canadian.* Refrigerated cargo. Built by Port Weller D.D. Ltd., Port Weller, for Newfoundland Engineering & Construction Co. Ltd., St. John's. 1,859 tons gross, 2,150 tons d.w., 253 ft. l.o.a., 42·2 ft. breadth, 10-cyl. Werkspoor diesel, 2,300 b.h.p., 13 knots.

SIREFJELL. *Norwegian.* Refrigerated cargo. Built by Kieler Howaldtswerke A.G., Kiel, for Olsen & Ugelstad, Oslo. 4,108 tons gross, 5,650 tons d.w., 355 ft. l.o.a., 52 ft. breadth, 24·66 ft. draught, 6-cyl. M.A.N. diesel by the shipbuilders, 4,000 b.h.p., 14½ knots.

SIRPA DAN. *Danish.* Cargo. Built by Bijker's Aannemings, Gorinchem, for J. Lauritzen, Copenhagen. 1,859 tons gross, 2,325 tons d.w., 268·42 ft. l.o.a., 40·42 ft. breadth, 18 ft. draught, 10-cyl. diesel by Smit-Bolnes, 1,700 b.h.p., 12½ knots.

SKAUSTRAND. *Norwegian.* Bulk carrier. Built by Mitsubishi S.B. & E. Co. Ltd., Nagasaki, for A/S Skaugaas, Oslo. 15,894 tons gross, 24,724 tons d.w., 580 ft. l.o.a., 75·33 ft. breadth, 33 ft. draught, 7-cyl. Sulzer diesel by Uraga, 9,100 b.h.p., 16 knots.

SKRYPLEV. *Russian.* Fish carrier. Built by Burmeister & Wain, Copenhagen, for U.S.S.R. 4,700 tons gross, 2,600 tons d.w., 336 ft. l.o.a., 52·58 ft. breadth, 18 ft. draught, 6-cyl. diesel by the shipbuilders, 3,530 b.h.p., 14 knots.

SKYCREST. *British.* Cargo. Built by Soc. des Forges de la Méditerranée, La Seyne, for Crest Shipping Co. Ltd., Nassau. 9,400 tons gross, 13,662 tons d.w., 463 ft. l.o.a., 61 ft. breadth, 30·5 ft. draught, 6-cyl. Sulzer diesel by the shipbuilders, 5,400 b.h.p., 14¼ knots.

SKYCREST. The Crest Shipping Co. Ltd., of Nassau, Bahamas, took delivery of this cargo vessel from the Société des Forges et Chantiers de la Méditerranée, La Seyne. The vessel has been built as a shelterdecker with a deadweight of 13,662 tons and has a hull of almost entirely welded construction. Her double bottom and shelterdeck are longitudinally framed, and the rest of the ship transversely framed. There are five cargo holds with two transverse deep tanks arranged in No. 3 hold. The total grain capacity of the five holds is about 720,421 cu. ft. For cargo handling there is a 50-ton Stulcken type heavy-lift derrick serving either No. 1 or No. 2 hold, and ten 10-ton derricks. There are six 5-ton and four 5/8-ton electric winches.

SOMERSET. *This is a sister ship of the cargo liner Piako and was built by John Brown & Co. (Clydebank) Ltd. for the Federal Steam Navigation Co. Ltd., London. The Somerset, 10,250 tons d.w., also has a Velle Shipshape crane. The owners of the Piako and Somerset are companies of the P. & O. group. The Somerset has five cargo holds with tweendecks above them, and has been designed for the carriage of refrigerated and general cargo. There is insulated cargo capacity of 449,086 cu. ft. and about 70,370 cu. ft. for general cargo. General cargo is carried in No. 1 hold upper and lower tweendecks, No. 4 hatch trunk and in the forecastle, the remaining spaces being insulated. Chilled meat lockers are fitted port and starboard in Nos. 2, 3 and 4 upper tweendecks. Two cargo tanks suitable for the carriage of bulk liquid cargoes including tallow are arranged in the forward part of No. 1 hold.*

SKYROS. *Danish*. Refrigerated cargo. Built by Fredrikshavns Vaerft, Fredrikshavn, for Det Forenede D/S, Copenhagen. 2,661 tons gross, 3,200 tons d.w., 362·42 ft. l.o.a., 51·9 ft. breadth, 20 ft. draught, 6-cyl. B. & W. diesel by Elsinore, 3,900 b.h.p., 15½ knots.

SOBOLEVO. *Russian*. Cargo. Built by Schiffswerft Neptun, Rostock, for U.S.S.R. 3,455 tons gross, 5,000 tons d.w., 341·82 ft. l.o.a., 47·33 ft. breadth, 20·75 ft. draught, 6-cyl. diesel by M.A.N., 3,250 b.h.p., 15 knots.

SOMERSET. *British*. Refrigerated cargo. Built by John Brown & Co. (Clydebank) Ltd., for the Federal Steam Navigation Co. Ltd., London. 10,627 tons gross, 10,250 tons d.w., 488·2 ft. l.o.a., 66 ft. breadth, 28·2 ft. draught, 8-cyl. Sulzer diesel by shipbuilders, 9,750 b.h.p., 16½ knots.

SONATA. *Norwegian*. Bulk carrier. Built by Kockums M/V A/B, Malmö, for Skips A/S Jojolo, Gothenburg. 10,325 tons gross, 15,220 tons d.w., 492 ft. l.o.a., 65·2 ft. breadth, 29·82 ft. draught, 6-cyl. M.A.N. diesel by the shipbuilders, 6,120 b.h.p., 14½ knots.

SONIC. *Greek*. Bulk carrier. Built by Kawasaki Dockyard Co. Ltd., Kobe, for Tiger Shipping Co. S.A., Piraeus. 29,000 tons gross, 49,500 tons d.w., 746 ft. l.o.a., 100·66 ft. breadth, 37·82 ft. draught, grd. turb. by the shipbuilders, 20,250 s.h.p., 16½ knots.

SOTE JARL. *Norwegian*. Refrigerated cargo. Built by Fr Lürssen, Vegesack, for Det Nordenfjeldske D/S, Trondheim. 1,380 tons gross, 1,930 tons d.w., 240 ft. l.o.a., 38·42 ft. breadth, 19 ft. draught, 5-cyl. Sulzer diesel by Buckau-Wolf, 1,670 b.h.p., 13 knots.

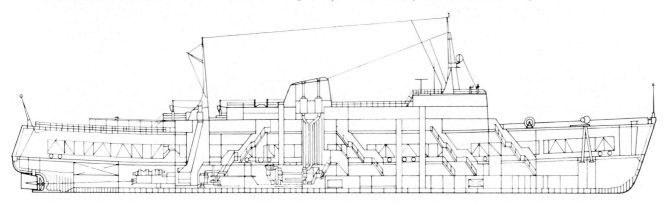

SOVETSKI AZERBAIJAN. *The first of a series of train ferries for service in the Caspian Sea between Baku and Krasnovodsk. The second of the class, Sovetski Turkmenistan, was launched in November, 1962. They were both built by the Krasnoye Sormovo Shipyard 'A. Zhdanov,' at Gorki, and have been fitted with diesel-electric propulsion and triple-screws. An athwartships bow propeller has been fitted forward to increase manoeuvrability. They can each carry thirty 50-ton railway cars, which are loaded and unloaded through the stern. Accommodation has been provided for 290 passengers in two- and four-berth cabins as well as larger cabins.*

SPEYBANK. *This vessel, which has been completed by Swan, Hunter & Wigham Richardson Ltd. for the Bank Line, is the first of a new class for these owners. The second, Marabank, is under construction. The two are vessels of 9,100 tons gross with single-screw diesel machinery giving a speed on trials of 16 knots. The Bank Line has a fleet of about 40 ships, with which it maintains a number of regular services, largely in cross trades, and also engages in tramping. The bale capacity (including deep tanks) of the Speybank is approximately 610,810 cu. ft. She has five main cargo holds and tweendeck spaces available for general cargo, and special cargo spaces in Nos. 3 and 4 upper tweendecks, port side. The propelling machinery consists of a Wallsend-Sulzer turbocharged diesel engine having five cylinders of 760 mm. bore and 1,550 mm. stroke. There are two exhaust gas turbo-blowers. The engine develops a power of 6,000 b.h.p. at about 111 r.p.m. It operates on heavy fuel oil with viscosity up to 3,500 seconds Redwood No. 1.*

SOVIETSKY AZERBAIJAN. *Russian.* Train ferry. Built by Krasnoye Sormovo Yard, Gorki, for U.S.S.R. 6,050 tons displ., 439·58 ft. l.o.a., 60 ft. breadth, 15 ft. draught, tr-sc. diesel-electric, 5,800 s.h.p., 14½ knots.

SOYA-ANDREA. *Swedish.* Tanker. Built by A/B Götaverken, Gothenburg, for Rederi A/B Soya, Stockholm. 25,911 tons gross, 40,550 tons d.w., 699·75 ft. l.o.a., 96·25 ft. breadth, 35·9 ft. draught, 2 Parsons grd. turbs., 17,500 s.h.p., 17 knots.

SPAARNEKERK. *Dutch.* Refrigerated cargo. Built by N.V. Mch. & Schps. P. Smit, Jun., Rotterdam, for N.V. Vereenigde Nederlandsche Scheepv. Maats., The Hague. 10,200 tons gross, 12,200 tons d.w., 528 ft. l.o.a., 69·2 ft. breadth, 29·5 ft. draught, 9-cyl. B. & W. diesel by the shipbuilders, 10,600 b.h.p., 18 knots.

SPENSER. *British.* Refrigerated cargo. Built by T. van Duijvendijks Schps., Lekkerkerk, for The Booth S.S. Co. Ltd., Liverpool. 1,549 tons gross, 2,470 tons d.w., 312·66 ft. l.o.a., 44·33 ft. breadth, 17·67 ft. draught, 8-cyl. Sulzer diesel, 2,400 b.h.p., 14 knots.

SPEYBANK. *British.* Cargo. Built by Swan, Hunter & Wigham Richardson Ltd., Wallsend-on-Tyne, for Bank Line Ltd., London and Glasgow. 9,100 tons gross, 12,000 tons d.w., 486·2 ft. l.o.a., 63·2 ft. breadth, 29·33 ft. draught, 5-cyl. Sulzer diesel by Wallsend, 6,000 b.h.p., 15 knots.

SPRINGBANK. *British.* Cargo. Built by Harland & Wolff Ltd., Belfast, for Bank Line Ltd., Glasgow. 6,461 tons gross, 10,162 tons d.w., 483·33 ft. l.o.a., 62·75 ft. breadth, 26 ft. draught, 6-cyl. B. & W. diesel by the shipbuilders, 5,800 b.h.p., 15 knots.

SPROGO. *Danish.* Train and car ferry. Built by Elsinore S.B. & E. Co. Ltd., Elsinore, for Danish State Railways. 3,836 tons gross, 358 ft. l.o.a., 58 ft. breadth, 15 ft. draught, tw-sc. two 7-cyl. B. & W. diesels by the shipbuilders, 7,800 b.h.p., 18 knots.

STAD VLAADINGEN. *Dutch.* Cargo. Built by Flensburger Schiffs.-Ges., Flensburg, for Nieuwe Halcyon Lijn N.V., Rotterdam. 11,048 tons gross, 15,570 tons d.w., 534·33 ft. l.o.a., 66·58 ft. breadth, 30 ft. draught, 8-cyl. M.A.N. diesel, 5,350 b.h.p., 14 knots.

SPRINGBANK. *Harland & Wolff Ltd. completed this 6,461 tons gross cargo vessel and her sister ship the Olivebank in 1962 for the Bank Line. The Springbank is the third of a group of four ordered from Belfast by these owners. The main difference between the Springbank and her predecessors is the shape of the funnel, which in previous vessels was orthodox, raked fore and aft with straight sides.*

S

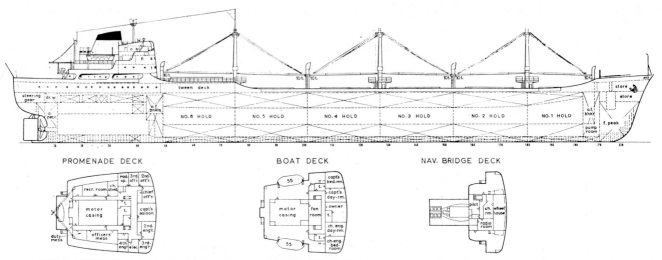

PROMENADE DECK   BOAT DECK   NAV. BRIDGE DECK

STYLEHURST. *Special attention has been given to the design of this 21,990 tons d.w. bulk carrier to ensure that the stowage will be better than in a conventional bulk carrier. This new ship has an extended poop deck over No. 6 hold forming a tweendeck for cargo, and an unusual arrangement of ducting in the keel for draining the ballast tanks and bilges. The Stylehurst has been constructed by Ateliers et Chantiers de la Seine Maritime for the Greenhurst Shipping Co. Ltd., London (managers Hadjilias & Co. Ltd.) under the supervision of F. J. Trewent & Proctor Ltd., London. In addition to providing a fast ship, the design of the Stylehurst has given her owners as large a ship as is possible for operation in the St. Lawrence Seaway, based on ordinary cubic, bearing in mind that at a later date the permissible draught for ships sailing into that area will be increased from the present figure. The Stylehurst has been built as a single-deck bulk carrier with wing tanks and hopper-sided double bottom tanks. In comparison with other bulk carriers the design of the Stylehurst enables her to offer exceptionally good stowage. Utilizing the lower holds only, with a capacity of 1,018,821 cu. ft., the vessel can lift her full deadweight of grain cargo stowing at about 47 cu. ft./ton without the use of shifting boards or feeders. When making use of the tweendecks above No. 6 hold, with a total capacity of 1,065,426 cu. ft., the vessel can lift its full deadweight of grain cargo stowing at about 50 cu. ft./ton, having shifting boards in the tweendecks only. No. 6 tweendeck and hold are suitable for common loading. The wing tanks are not intended for the carriage of grain, but if they are used the stowage rate will be about 55 cu. ft./ton. This ship is propelled by a 900 mm. bore Sulzer diesel engine, the first of this type to be built in France. A feature of the engine room is the arrangement made for making the utmost use of steam from the main engine waste heat boiler, and supplementing the turbo-alternator which is supplied with steam from this boiler with a motor-alternator obtaining its power from a D.C. generator built around the intermediate propeller shaft.*

STAD ZWOLLE. *Dutch.* Cargo. Built by Flensburger Schiffs.-Ges., Flensburg, for Nieuwe Halcyon Lijn N.V., Rotterdam. 11,048 tons gross, 15,570 tons d.w., 534·33 ft. l.o.a., 66·58 ft. breadth, 30 ft. draught, 8-cyl. M.A.N. diesel, 5,350 b.h.p., 14 knots.

STADT EMDEN. *German.* Bulk carrier. Built by Lübecker Flender-Werke A.G., Lübeck, for Schulte & Bruns, Emden. 19,945 tons gross, 30,500 tons d.w., 623·42 ft. l.o.a., 85·33 ft. breadth, 32·2 ft. draught, 6-cyl. M.A.N. diesel, 9,000 b.h.p., 14¾ knots.

STALAND. *Norwegian.* Tanker. Built by Swan, Hunter & Wigham Richardson Ltd., Wallsend, for Helmer Staubo & Co., Oslo. 31,650 tons gross, 48,000 tons d.w., 746·75 ft. l.o.a., 102·66 ft. breadth, 38 ft. draught, 2 grd. turbs. by Wallsend Slipway, 16,000 s.h.p., 16 knots.

STATE OF PUNJAB. *Indian.* Refrigerated cargo. Built by Hindustan Shipyard Ltd., Vizagapatam, for Shipping Corp. of India Ltd., Bombay. 9,191 tons gross, 12,300 tons d.w., 504·75 ft. l.o.a., 64 ft. breadth, 29·66 ft. draught, 7-cyl. M.A.N. diesel, 7,650 b.h.p., 17 knots.

STERNÖ. *Swedish.* Cargo. Built by Oresundsvarvet A/B, Lübeck, for A. K. Fernströms Rederier, Karlshamn, 6,400 tons gross, 9,300 tons d.w., 428·75 ft. l.o.a., 58·42 ft. breadth, 27·42 ft. draught, 6-cyl. diesel by Götaverken, 5,000 b.h.p., 17 knots.

STEPHAN REITH, *German.* Cargo. Built by Orenstein-Koppel & Lbcr. Masch., Lübeck, for 'Orion' Shiffahrts-Ges. Reith & Co., Hamburg. 1,860 tons gross, 5,400 tons d.w., 290·42 ft. l.o.a., 44 ft. breadth, 8-cyl. diesel by Deutz, 1,830 b.h.p., 13 knots.

STRAAT CHATHAM. *Dutch.* Cargo. Built by Schps. & Mach. 'De Merwede,' Hardinxveld, for Koninkl. Java-China Paketv. Lijnen N.V., Amsterdam. 7,544 tons gross, 9,879 tons d.w., 454·58 ft. l.o.a., 62·2 ft. breadth, 24·25 ft. draught, 6-cyl. B. & W. diesel by P. Smit Jun., 6,800 b.h.p., 15½ knots.

STRAAT COLOMBO. *Dutch.* Refrigerated cargo. Built by N.V. Mch. & Schps. P. Smit, Jun., Rotterdam, for Koninkl. Java-China Paketv. Lijnen N.V., Amsterdam. 7,553 tons gross, 9,860 tons d.w., 454·58 ft. l.o.a., 62 ft. breadth, 28·33 ft. draught, 6-cyl. B. & W. diesel by the shipbuilders, 6,800 b.h.p., 15½ knots.

STYLEHURST. *British.* Bulk carrier. Built by At. & Ch. de la Seine Maritime, Le Trait, for Grenehurst Shipping Co. Ltd., London. 15,791 tons gross, 21,990 tons d.w., 598 ft. l.o.a., 74·33 ft. breadth, 32 ft. draught, 6-cyl. Sulzer diesel, 12,000 b.h.p., 16½ knots.

STYRSO. *Finnish.* Cargo. Built by A/S Langesunds M/V, Langesund, for Mariehamns Rederi A/B, Mariehamn. 1,566 tons gross, 3,500 tons d.w., 307·75 ft. l.o.a., 45·25 ft. breadth, 16·58 ft. draught, 6-cyl. diesel by M.A.N., 2,700 b.h.p., 14 knots.

SUNPOLYCROWN. *Norwegian.* Cargo. Built by Verolme United Shipyards, Alblasserdam, for Kristiansands Tankrederi A/S, Kristiansand. 12,500 tons gross, 18,000 tons d.w., 529 ft. l.o.a., 71·75 ft. breadth, 31 ft. draught, 8-cyl. M.A.N. diesel by Verolme Machfbk., 8,480 b.h.p., 16 knots.

SVANEFJELL. *Norwegian.* Cargo. Built by Kieler Howaldtswerke A.G., Kiel, for Olsen & Ugelstad, Oslo. 4,108 tons gross, 5,650 tons d.w., 355 ft. l.o.a., 52 ft. breadth, 24·66 ft. draught, 6-cyl. diesel by M.A.N., 4,000 b.h.p., 14½ knots.

SVEA JARL. *Swedish.* Ferry. Built by A/B Finnboda Varf, Stockholm, for Stockholms Rederi A/B Svea, Stockholm. 4,250 tons gross, 330 ft. l.o.a., 56·5 ft. breadth, 16·75 ft. draught, steam recip. by Amsterdamsche D.D., 4,500 s.h.p., 16½ knots.

SYRIA. *Egyptian (U.A.R.).* Passenger. Built by Deutsche Werft A.G., Hamburg, for United Arab Republic. 4,423 tons gross, 1,327 tons d.w., 354·33 ft. l.o.a., 54·58 ft. breadth, 14·5 ft. draught, 9-cyl. M.A.N. diesel, 3,240 b.h.p., 16 knots.

SZCZAWNICA. *Polish.* Cargo. Built by United Polish Shipyards, Szczecin, for Polish Government. 3,375 tons gross, 5,350 tons d.w., 406·42 ft. l.o.a., 54·9 ft. breadth, B. & W. diesel by Gdansk, 4,500 b.h.p., 14½ knots.

S

S

SYRIA. *This small passenger ship of 4,423 tons gross is a dual-purpose ship. For three months of the year she will carry pilgrims bound for Mecca, and for the rest of the year will be engaged in general passenger service in the Mediterranean. A special feature is the arrangement of ballast tanks to ensure symmetrical flooding. The ship was built by Deutsche Werft, Hamburg, for the United Arab Maritime Co. A sister ship, the Algazayer, was also completed in 1962. It was stipulated that with a main engine output of only 3,240 b.h.p. a trial speed of 16 knots should be attained. The accommodation provides 643 berths in three classes. In accordance with the owners' wishes the three classes in the ship are kept as much apart as possible. The cubic capacity (grain) is 47,255 cu. ft.*

T

T. S. PETERSEN. *Liberian.* Tanker. Built by Odense Staalskibs. A/B, Lindo, for California Transport Corp., Monrovia and San Francisco. 32,350 tons gross, 51,000 tons d.w., 753 ft. l.o.a., 103·25 ft. breadth, 38·5 ft. draught, 2 grd. turbs. by G.E.C., 17,500 s.h.p., 16 knots.

TACOMA MARU. *Japanese.* Cargo. Built by Mitsubishi H.I. Reorg. Ltd., Kobe, for Osaka Shosen Kaisha, Osaka. 9,300 tons gross, 12,050 tons d.w., 475·58 ft. b.p., 63·82 ft. breadth, 30·2 ft. draught, 6-cyl. Sulzer diesel, 13,000 b.h.p., 18 knots.

TAIPOOSEK. *British.* Passenger and cargo. Built by Moss Vaerft & Dokk A/S, Moss, for Shun Cheong S.N. Co. Ltd., Hong Kong. 4,000 tons gross, 6,150 tons d.w., 362·5 ft. l.o.a., 52 ft. breadth, 7-cyl. diesel by B. & W., 4,900 b.h.p., 15 knots.

TAKASHIMA MARU. *Japanese.* Fish factory. Built by Nippon Kokan, Shimizu, for Hokoku Suisan K.K., Tokyo. 9,500 tons gross, 11,300 tons d.w., 491·5 ft. l.o.a., 67·2 ft. breadth, 26·5 ft. draught, 6-cyl. B. & W. diesel by Mitsui, 6,500 b.h.p., 14 knots.

TANGO MARU. *Japanese.* Tanker. Built by Nagasaki S.B. & E. Co. Ltd., Nagasaki, for Nippon Yusen Kaisha, Tokyo. 29,300 tons gross, 47,750 tons d.w., 736 ft. l.o.a., 100·33 ft. breadth, 38·25 ft. draught, 9-cyl. U.E.C. diesel by Nagasaki Zosen, 18,000 b.h.p., 15½ knots.

TARIM. *Norwegian.* Tanker. Built by Eriksbergs M/V A/B, Gothenburg, for Wilh. Wilhelmsen, Tönsberg. 25,465 tons gross, 42,200 tons d.w., 704·82 ft. l.o.a., 95·2 ft. breadth, 36·58 ft. draught, 12-cyl. B. & W. diesel by the shipbuilders, 16,600 b.h.p., 16½ knots.

TASSO. *German.* Tanker. Built by Bremer Vulkan, Vegesack, for Mobil Oil Reederei, Hamburg. 30,763 tons gross, 50,000 tons d.w., 735 ft. l.o.a., 104·25 ft. breadth, 39 ft. draught, 2 grd. turbs. by the shipbuilders 16,200 s.h.p., 16 knots.

TEAKWOOD. *British.* Cargo. Built by Sir. J. Laing & Sons Ltd., Sunderland, for John I. Jacobs & Co. Ltd., London. 9,092 tons gross, 12,550 tons d.w., 472·58 ft. l.o.a., 62·33 ft. breadth, 30·2 ft. draught, 5-cyl. B. & W. diesel by Kincaid, 7,800 b.h.p., 15½ knots.

TEKKO MARU. *Japanese.* Cargo. Built by Nagoya S.B. Co., Nagoya, for Shinwa Kaiun Kaisha Ltd., Tokyo. 1,940 tons gross, 3,089 tons d.w., 41·82 ft. breadth, 18·82 ft. draught, 6-cyl. diesel by Ito Tekko, 1,500 b.h.p., 11 knots.

TEMPLAR. *Norwegian.* Bulk carrier. Built by A/S Akers M/V, Oslo, for Wilh. Wilhelmsen, Tönsberg. 12,153 tons gross, 18,400 tons d.w., 523·75 ft. l.o.a., 69·33 ft. breadth, 32·2 ft. draught, 5-cyl. B. & W. diesel by the shipbuilders, 8,390 b.h.p., 15 knots.

TENAX. *Liberian.* Tanker. Built by At. & Ch. de Dunkerque & Bordeaux (France Gironde), Dunkirk, for Radmar Tanker Ltd., Monrovia and New York. 31,260 tons gross, 49,000 tons d.w., 755·66 ft. l.o.a., 99·58 ft. breadth, 39·2 ft. draught, 2 Parsons grd. turbs. by C.E.M., 20,000 s.h.p., 17 knots.

TEPPO MARU. *Japanese.* Ore carrier. Built by Uraga H.I., Yokosuka, for Shinwa Kaiun Kaisha, Yokohama. 17,000 tons gross, 27,400 tons d.w., 557·58 ft. b.p., 85·25 ft. breadth, 32 ft. draught, 6-cyl. Sulzer diesel by the shipbuilders, 9,600 b.h.p., 13½ knots.

TETSUKUNI MARU. *Japanese.* Ore carrier. Built by Nagoya S.B. Co., Nagoya, for Toho Kaiun Kaisha and Nittetsu Kisen K.K., Tokyo. 12,350 tons gross, 18,800 tons d.w., 524·9 ft. l.o.a., 73·58 ft. breadth, 30 ft. draught, 7-cyl. M.A.N. diesel by Mitsubishi H.I.R., 13½ knots.

TEXAS MARU. *Japanese.* Refrigerated cargo. Built by Kawasaki Dockyard Co. Ltd., Kobe, for Kawasaki Kisen K.K., Kobe. 9,200 tons gross, 11,900 tons d.w., 512·75 ft. l.o.a., 63·5 ft. breadth, 28·5 ft. draught, 9-cyl. M.A.N. diesel by the shipbuilders, 9,000 b.h.p., 16 knots.

TEXACO NORGE. *Norwegian.* Tanker. Built by Fredriksstad M/V, Fredriksstad, for Texaco Norway A/S. 13,223 tons gross, 20,200 tons d.w., 578 ft. l.o.a., 74 ft. breadth, 30·42 ft. draught, 7-cyl. Götaverken diesel by the shipbuilders, 8,750 b.h.p., 14½ knots.

TEXACO SKANDINAVIA. *Norwegian.* Tanker. Built by A/S Fredriksstad M/V, Fredriksstad, for Texaco Norway A/S, Oslo. 13,220 tons gross, 20,000 tons d.w., 578·5 ft. l.o.a., 74 ft. breadth, 30·58 ft. draught, 7-cyl. Götaverken diesel by the shipbuilders, 8,750 b.h.p., 14½ knots.

THAUNG NAING YAY. *Burmese.* Suction dredger. Built by Simons-Lobnitz Ltd., Renfrew, for Burma Government. 1,234 tons gross, 229 ft. l.o.a., 31 ft. breadth, tw-sc. two 6-cyl. diesels by Lister-Blackstone.

THERA. *Panamanian.* Bulk carrier. Built by Ishikawajima-Harima H.I., Tokyo, for Viadoro Cia. Nav. S.A., Panama. 13,785 tons gross, 22,500 tons d.w., 578·75 ft. l.o.a., 75·5 ft. breadth, 31·58 ft. draught, 2 grd. turbs. by the shipbuilders, 8,200 s.h.p., 14¾ knots.

THERESIE. *Norwegian.* Bulk carrier. Built by A/B Götaverken, Gothenburg, for Tonnevolds Rederi A/S, Grimstad. 18,124 tons gross, 25,800 tons d.w., 584 ft. l.o.a., 78·2 ft. breadth, 29·2 ft. draught, 7-cyl. Götaverken diesel, 8,750 b.h.p., 15 knots.

THOMAS MAERSK. *Danish.* Refrigerated cargo. Built by Burmeister & Wain, Copenhagen, for A. P. Möller, Copenhagen. 9,050 tons gross, 11,100 tons d.w., 560 ft. l.o.a., 74·2 ft. breadth, 9-cyl. B. & W. diesel.

THORSTRAND. *Norwegian.* Tanker. Built by A/S Stord Verft, Lervik, for A/S Thor Dahl, Sandefjord. 21,525 tons gross, 34,005 tons d.w., 665 ft. l.o.a., 86·25 ft. breadth, 34·9 ft. draught, 9-cyl. B. & W. diesel by Akers, 15,000 b.h.p., 16¾ knots.

THORSHALL. *Norwegian.* Tanker. Built by Uddevallavarvet A/B, Uddevalla, for Skibs A/S Thor Dahl, Sandefjord. 27,040 tons gross, 42,300 tons d.w., 723·75 ft. l.o.a., 97·33 ft. breadth, 36·5 ft. draught, 2 grd. turbs. by G.E.C., 19,250 s.h.p., 17½ knots.

T

T

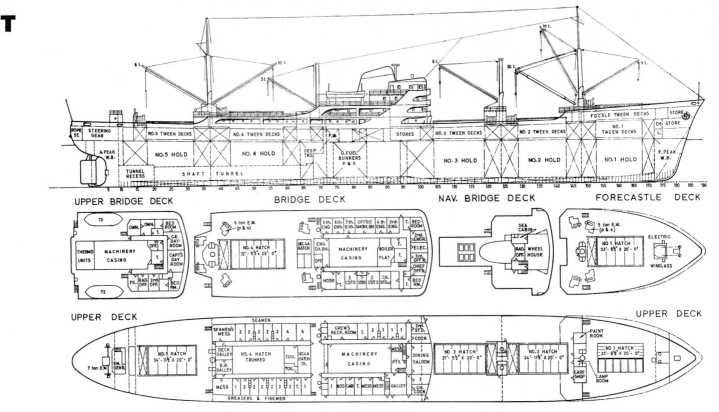

UPPER BRIDGE DECK   BRIDGE DECK   NAV. BRIDGE DECK   FORECASTLE DECK

UPPER DECK   UPPER DECK

TEAKWOOD

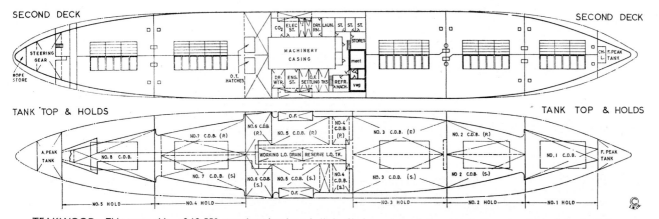

SECOND DECK — SECOND DECK

STEERING GEAR

ROPE STORE

MACHINERY CASING

CO₂ ELEC. ST. | DRY. ST. | LAUN. | ST. | ST.

STORES

meat

O.T. HATCHES

DR. WTR. ST. | ENG. ST. | O.F. SETTLING TKS | REFR. M.MACH.

veg

CH. L. | F.PEAK TANK

TANK TOP & HOLDS — TANK TOP & HOLDS

A. PEAK TANK

NO. 8 C.D.B.

NO. 7 C.D.B. (P.)

NO. 7 C.D.B. (S.)

NO.6 C.D.B. (P.)

NO.6 C.D.B. (S.)

O.F.

O.F.

NO. 5 C.D.B. (P.)

NO. 5 C.D.B. (S.)

WORKING L.O. DRAIN RESERVE L.O. TK.

NO.4 C.D.B. (P.)

NO.4 C.D.B. (S.)

NO. 3 C.D.B. (P.)

NO. 3 C.D.B. (S.)

NO. 2 C.D.B. (P.)

NO. 2 C.D.B. (S.)

NO. 1 C.D.B.

F. PEAK TANK

NO. 5 HOLD — NO. 4 HOLD — NO. 3 HOLD — NO. 2 HOLD — NO. 1 HOLD

TEAKWOOD. *This cargo ship, of 12,550 tons d.w., has been built by Sir James Laing & Sons Ltd. to the order of John I. Jacobs & Co. Ltd., the firm of shipowners best known as operators of oil tankers. The Teakwood reached an average maximum speed of 16·86 knots on sea trials. An interesting point about the main engine is that it is fitted with Stothert & Pitt lubricating oil, fresh and salt water pumps driven from the camshaft drive panel at the rear of the engine. This arrangement considerably reduces maintenance, makes the engine self-supporting and is very much cheaper than fitting two sets of electrically driven pumps, one set as standby, which would entail installing an additional generator set. The Teakwood is of conventional design with propelling machinery amidships and has two cargo holds aft and three forward. Cargo capacity is 631,950 cu. ft. bale, 696,130 cu. ft. grain. She has been constructed of large prefabricated welded sections, with transverse main frames of bulb plate section welded to the shell before erection. The upper deck and the double bottom are longitudinally framed, while the second deck has transverse framing. The bulkheads are of corrugated construction and arranged as shown on the accompanying drawing.*

THORSODD *Norwegian* Bulk carrier. Built by Uddevallavarvet A/B, Uddevalla, for A/S Thor Dahl, Sandefjord. 13,080 tons gross, 18,110 tons d.w., 555 ft. l.o.a., 70·2 ft. breadth, 30 ft. draught, 8-cyl. Götaverken diesel by the shipbuilders, 7,500 b.h.p 15½ knots.

THORUNN. *Norwegian.* Cargo. Built by Ch. de l'Atlantique, St. Nazaire, for Tönnevolds Tankrederi A/S, Grimstad 9,700 tons gross, 13,981 tons d.w., 531·5 ft. l.o.a., 69 ft. breadth, 32 ft. draught, 6-cyl. B. & W. diesel by the shipbuilders, 9,000 b.h.p., 15½ knots.

TITO CAMPANELLA. *Italian.* Bulk carrier. Built by Ansaldo S.p.A., Leghorn, for Tito Campanella Nav. S.p.A., Genoa. 13,342 tons gross, 19,200 tons d.w., 575 ft. l.o.a., 68·9 ft. breadth, 30·58 ft. draught, 7-cyl. Fiat diesel by Ansaldo Stab. Mec., 8,400 b.h.p., 15 knots.

THERA. *This bulk carrier, 22,500 tons d.w., was completed at the Tokyo shipyard of Ishikawajima-Harima Heavy Industries Co. Ltd. for the Viadoro Cia. Naviera S.A., of Panama. She is intended for the coal and grain trade. The cargo holds have a capacity of 1,043,549 cu. ft.*

THOMAS MAERSK. *Built by Burmeister & Wain for A. P. Moller, this cargo liner will operate on one of the eastern services maintained by this large Danish fleet. Part of the hold capacity is refrigerated and there are deep tanks for the carriage of vegetable oil. The heavy-lift derrick is capable of 60-ton lifts. All living quarters are air-conditioned and there are single-berth cabins for all adults.*

TOHO MARU. *Japanese.* Refrigerated cargo. Built by Usuki Tekkosho, Saeki, for Shinpo Kaiun K.K., Osaka. 1,597 tons gross, 2,550 tons d.w., 272 ft. l.o.a., 39·42 ft. breadth, 6-cyl. diesel by Nippon Hatsudoki, 1,600 b.h.p., 12 knots.

TOJO MARU. *Japanese.* Tanker. Built by Mitsubishi Nippon H.I., Yokohama, for Toho Kaiun Kaisha, Tokyo. 25,100 tons gross, 40,300 tons d.w., 694·58 ft. l.o.a., 94·82 ft. breadth, 34·75 ft. draught, 9-cyl. M.A.N. diesel by the shipbuilders, 16,500 b.h.p., 17 knots.

TOKAI MARU. *Japanese.* Tanker. Built by Ishikawajima-Harima H.I., Tokyo, for Daikyo Oil Co. 28,800 tons gross, 47,300 tons d.w., 698·5 ft. b.p., 100 ft. breadth, 9-cyl. Sulzer diesel by the shipbuilders, 18,000 b.h.p., 16 knots.

TOKALA. *Indonesian.* Cargo and passenger. Built by United Polish Shipyards, Szczecin, for Government of Indonesia. 3,437 tons gross, 2,300 tons d.w., 315·82 ft. l.o.a., 47·66 ft. breadth, 14·58 ft. draught, 6-cyl. Sulzer diesel by S.E.C.N., 1,800 b.h.p., 11½ knots.

TOMBATU. *Indonesian.* Cargo and passenger. Built by United Polish Shipyards, Szczecin, for Government of Indonesia. 3,431 tons gross, 2,300 tons d.w., 315·82 ft. l.o.a., 47·66 ft. breadth, 14·58 ft. draught, 6-cyl. Sulzer diesel by Jugoturbina, 1,800 b.h.p., 11½ knots.

TOPAZ. *British.* Coaster. Built by Ailsa S.B. Co. Ltd., Troon, for Gem Line Ltd., Glasgow. 1,956 tons gross, 2,400 tons d.w., 267·75 ft. l.o.a., 39·9 ft. breadth, 17 ft. draught, 8-cyl. Deutz diesel, 1,800 b.h.p., 12½ knots.

TORINO. *Norwegian.* Tanker. Built by Eriksbergs M/V A/B, Gothenburg, for Wilh. Wilhelmsen, Tönsberg. 25,465 tons gross, 41,500 tons d.w., 704·82 ft. l.o.a., 95·2 ft. breadth, 36·58 ft. draught, 12-cyl. B. & W. diesel by the shipbuilders, 16,700 b.h.p., 16½ knots.

TOSA MARU. *Japanese.* Cargo. Built by Onomichi S.B. Co., Onomichi, for Kobe Sambashi K.K., Kobe. 1,937 tons gross, 3,260 tons d.w., 43·5 ft. breadth, 18·33 ft. draught, 6-cyl. diesel by Ito Tekko, 1,800 b.h.p., 14 knots.

TOULOUSE. *Norwegian.* Cargo. Built by Eriksbergs M/V A/B, Gothenburg, for Wilh. Wilhelmsen, Tönsberg. 5,517 tons gross, 7,475 tons, d.w., 448·5 ft. l.o.a., 60·2 ft. breadth, 24 ft. draught, 6-cyl. B. & W. diesel by the shipbuilders, 8,400 b.h.p., 16½ knots.

TOURMALINE. *British.* Cargo. Built by Ailsa S.B. Co. Ltd., Troon, for Gem Line Ltd., Glasgow. 1,597 tons gross, 2,400 tons d.w., 267·75 ft. l.o.a., 39·66 ft. breadth, 8-cyl. diesel by Deutz, 1,800 b.h.p., 12½ knots.

TOWUTI. *Indonesian.* Cargo and passenger. Built by United Polish Shipyards, Szczecin, for Government of Indonesia. 3,432 tons gross, 2,300 tons d.w., 315·82 ft. l.o.a., 47·66 ft. breadth, 14·58 ft. draught, 6-cyl. Sulzer diesel by Jugoturbina, 1,800 b.h.p., 11½ knots.

TOYO MARU No. 2. *Japanese.* Cargo. Built by Osaka S.B. Co., Osaka, for Sawayama Kisen K.K., Kobe. 3,850 tons gross, 5,680 tons d.w., 357·33 ft. l.o.a., 52 ft. breadth, 22·42 ft. draught, 6-cyl. diesel by Hatsudoki, 2,700 b.h.p., 12 knots.

TRANSVAAL. *German.* Refrigerated cargo. Built by Deutsche Werft A.G., Hamburg, for DAL Deutsche Afrika-Linien, Hamburg. 9,835 tons gross, 13,500 tons d.w., 511 ft. l.o.a., 67·2 ft. breadth, 429·9 ft. draught, 6-cyl. M.A.N. diesel, 8,400 b.h.p., 17½ knots.

TREBARTHA. *British.* Cargo. Built by J. Readhead & Sons Ltd., South Shields, for Hain S.S. Co. Ltd., London. 10,148 tons gross, 13,500 tons d.w., 508·25 ft. l.o.a., 65·25 ft. breadth, 29·75 ft. draught, 5-cyl. Sulzer diesel by Wallsend Slipway, 6,900 b.h.p., 14½ knots.

TRATTENDORF. *East German.* Ore carrier. Built by Warnowwerft, Warnemünde, for Deutsche Seereederei, Rostock. 8,609 tons gross, 11,350 tons d.w., 498 ft. l.o.a., 63·2 ft. breadth, 27·25 ft. draught, 7-cyl. diesel by D.M.R., 5,850 b.h.p., 15 knots.

TREIN MAERSK. *Danish.* Refrigerated cargo. Built by Odense Staalskibs A/S, Odense, for A. P. Möller, Copenhagen. 9,050 tons gross, 560 ft. l.o.a., 74·25 ft. breadth, 29 ft. draught, 9-cyl. B. & W. diesel, 11,200 b.h.p., 15½ knots.

L

TOULOUSE. *This 7,475 tons d.w. open shelterdecker (10,025 tons d.w. closed) affords another example of the use of twin hatches for cargo ship holds. See also Davis Salman. In order to reduce the lateral movement of cargo when loading and discharging, and to facilitate the lowering and raising of mixed cargoes in and out of the holds, the hatches over Nos. 2 and 3 holds almost cover the entire length of these holds and extend to a little over 6 ft. from the side of the ship. The holds have centreline bulkheads and are served by 5-ton deck cranes, two of which travel fore and aft between the hatches in the centreline of the ship, and two fixed 5-ton cranes located port and starboard between Nos. 2 and 3 holds. Nos. 1 and 4 holds are served by derricks on the masts and on the front of the bridge. All hatch covers are of the MacGregor steel folding type, and those in Nos. 1 and 4 holds (where cargo will have to be moved sideways) are flush fitting to permit the movement of fork-lift trucks. There is a passageway running below deck between Nos. 1 and 4 holds, as shown in the accompanying sketch. Heavy cargo handling arrangements include a 100-ton heavy cargo derrick on the main mast and a 45-ton derrick on the fore mast.*

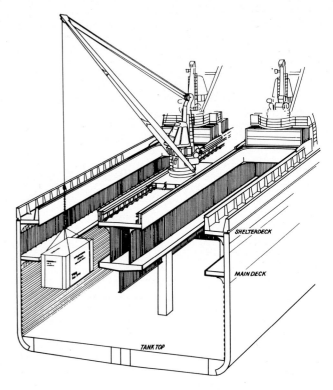

Sketch showing arrangement of the holds of the Toulouse with free access for loading and discharging cargo

TREBARTHA. *A sister ship of the Trefusis completed in 1961, this motor cargo ship was built by John Readhead & Sons Ltd. for the Hain Steamship Co. Ltd., a member of the P. & O. group. A third vessel of similar tonnage is being built by Wm. Hamilton & Co. Ltd., Port Glasgow, for delivery in 1963. Both the Trefusis and the Trebartha are on time charter, the former to Isthmian Lines Inc., the latter vessel to Lamport & Holt Line Ltd. The Trebartha has been built on conventional lines with the propelling machinery amidships, and is one of the open/closed shelterdeck type. There are five large clear holds with MacGregor single-pull patent steel hatches on the upper and forecastle decks. The cargo capacity (approximately) is bale 646,500 cu. ft., grain 733,000 cu. ft. Cargo handling gear comprises one 30-ton, two 15-ton, two 10-ton and six 5-ton derricks, all served by electric winches of the Ward-Leonard self-contained type. The winches have been supplied by Clarke, Chapman & Co. Ltd. Topping winches are also fitted to the 5-, 10- and 15-ton derricks.*

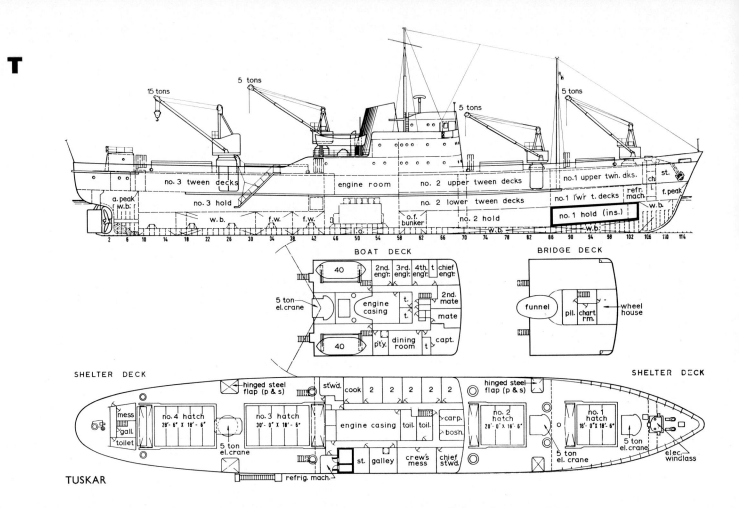

T

15 tons

5 tons

5 tons

5 tons

5 tons

no. 3 tween decks

engine room

no. 2 upper tween decks

no.1 upper twn. dks.

st.

a. peak
f.w.b.

no. 3 hold

no. 2 lower tween decks

no. 1 lwr. t. decks

refr.
mach.

ch

f. peak

w. b.

f.w.

f.w.

o.f.
bunker

no. 2 hold

no. 1 hold (ins.)

w. b.

w. b.

w. b.

2 6 10 14 18 22 26 30 34 38 42 46 50 54 58 62 66 70 74 78 82 86 90 94 98 102 106 110 114

BOAT DECK

BRIDGE DECK

40

2nd.
engr.

3rd.
engr.

4th.
engr.

t chief
engr.

funnel

pll.

chart
rm.

wheel
house

5 ton
el. crane

engine
casing

t

t

2nd.
mate

40

pty.

dining
room

t

mate

capt.

SHELTER DECK

SHELTER DECK

hinged steel
flap (p & s)

stwd.

cook 2 2 2 2

hinged steel
flap (p & s)

mess

gall.

no. 4 hatch
28'-6" X 18'-6"

no. 3 hatch
30'-0" X 18'-6"

engine casing

toil. toil.

carp.

no. 2
hatch
20'-0" X 16'-6"

no. 1
hatch
18'-0" X 18'-6"

toilet

5 ton
el. crane

bosn.

5 ton
el. crane

5 ton
el. crane

st. galley

crew's
mess

chief
stwd.

elec.
windlass

TUSKAR

refrig. mach.

164

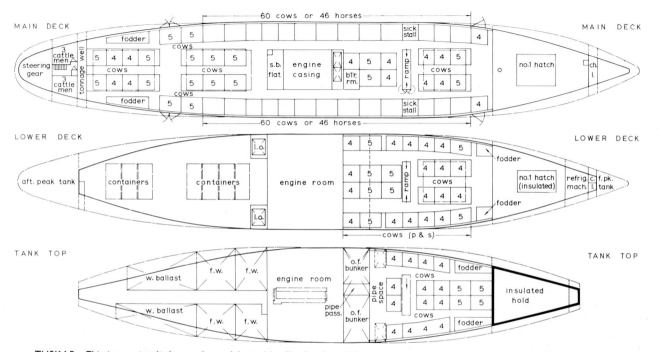

MAIN DECK

60 cows or 46 horses

fodder | 5 | 5
cows
3 cattle men
steering gear
tonnage well
3 cattle men
5 | 4 | 4 | 5 | 5 | 5 | 5
cows
5 | 4 | 4 | 5 | 5 | 5 | 5
cows
s.b. flat | engine casing | 4 | 5 | 4
b'lr. rm. | 5 | 4
ramp
sick stall | 4
4 | 4 | 5
cows
4 | 4 | 5
no.1 hatch
ch. l.
o
sick stall | 4

60 cows or 46 horses

MAIN DECK

T

LOWER DECK

aft. peak tank
containers
containers
l.o.
l.o.
engine room
4 | 5 | 4 | 4 | 4 | 5
4 | 5 | 5
ramp
4 | 5 | 5
cows
4 | 4 | 4
fodder
fodder
4 | 5 | 4 | 4 | 4 | 5
no.1 hatch (insulated)
refrig. mach.
c. i.
f.pk. tank

cows (p & s)

LOWER DECK

TANK TOP

w. ballast
f.w. | f.w.
engine room
w. ballast
f.w. | f.w.
o.f. bunker
pipe pass.
o.f. bunker
pipe space
4 | 4 | 4
cows
4 | 4 | 5 | 5
4 | 4 | 5 | 5
cows
4 | 4 | 4
fodder
fodder
insulated hold

TANK TOP

TUSKAR. *This interesting little vessel was delivered by Charles Connell & Co. Ltd., Scotstoun, to the Clyde Shipping Co. Ltd., Glasgow. The Tuskar, 2,100 tons d.w., operates mainly between Irish ports and Liverpool, and is designed for the carriage of cattle, container and refrigerated cargoes. Prominent features of the ship are the deck cranes with which she is equipped. The ship is of welded construction with a longitudinally framed bottom and deck combined with a transverse framed hull. She has four main holds with a total grain capacity of 150,000 cu. ft. The shelter tweendecks, lower tweendecks and No. 2 hold have been arranged to Ministry of Agriculture requirements for the carriage of 452 live cattle. The cattle stalls are completely portable and are supported by square tubular pillars. The gates have a tubular frame combined with a wood carcase and can be hinged either way from pillars and the ship's side. Gates and fittings*

continued overpage

T

are so constructed that projections have been eliminated. The decks in way of the cattle stalls have been laid with 2 in. thick asphalt, and foot holds have been arranged for the cattle. Steel kick-board and rump boards are fitted at the ship's side. Horses may also be carried in the main tweendecks by introducing wood divisions in the stalls and wood battens in the foot holds. Cattle and horses are shipped by means of one double and one single door on each side of the vessel. A hinged deck flap is also fitted in way of these doors to give increased head room and wooden ramps give cattle access to the lower deck and hold. Fodder bins are arranged on each deck, and draw-off cocks have been provided in each tweendeck for watering cattle. Two sludge tanks have been fitted in the double bottom and are discharged by means of two water-operated cattle sludge ejectors. Mechanical supply and exhaust ventilation has been provided for the cattle spaces. The vessel is equipped with a total of 10 hatches, one being insulated for the refrigerated cargo in No. I lower hold. The four weather deck hatches and the remaining five tweendeck hatches are fitted with MacGregor single-pull watertight covers. The covers in the tweendecks are flush with a surfacing of asphalt similar to the surrounding deck and are arranged with cattle stalls over them. A total of 5,000 cu. ft. of refrigerated cargo can be carried in No. I hold. Cargo handling facilities comprise one 15-ton and three 5-ton electrically driven level-luffing deck cranes by Clarke Chapman. The accommodation is located amidships and aft. The captain, deck and engineer officers are accommodated on the boat deck where there is a dining saloon with adjacent pantry and food hoist from the galley below. The crew accommodation is situated on the shelter deck amidships where the galley and domestic cold chambers are also located. Cattlemen are on the main deck aft, and have their own galley and mess room. The service speed is 14·5 knots.

TRENTBANK. *British.* Cargo liner. Built by Wm. Doxford & Sons (S.B.) Ltd., Sunderland, for Bank Line Ltd., London. 8,582 tons gross, 12,380 tons d.w., 487·75 ft. l.o.a., 62·25 ft. breadth, 29 ft. draught, 4-cyl. Doxford diesel, 6,640 b.h.p., 14½ knots.

TROJA. *Norwegian.* Bulk carrier. Built by Eriksbergs M/V A/B, Gothenburg, for Wilh. Wilhelmsen, Tönsberg. 12,288 tons gross, 18,175 tons d.w., 535·82 ft. l.o.a., 70 ft. breadth, 29·9 ft. draught, 6-cyl. B. & W. diesel by the shipbuilders, 8,400 b.h.p., 15½ knots.

TROJALAND. *Swedish.* Refrigerated cargo. Built by Wärtsilä Kon. Crichton-Vulcan, Abo, for Angfartygs A/B Tirfing, Gothenburg. 5,100 tons gross, 5,600 tons d.w., 441·75 ft. l.o.a., 57·66 ft. breadth, 23·33 ft. draught, 6-cyl. diesel by Götaverken, 5,450 b.h.p., 16 knots.

TROPICANA. *Liberian.* Refrigerated cargo. Built by Empresa Nacional 'Elcano,' Seville, for Tropicana Shipping S.A., Monrovia. 6,110 tons gross, 5,800 tons d.w., 450·82 ft. l.o.a., 56·9 ft. breadth, 25·42 ft. draught, 6-cyl. Sulzer diesel by the shipbuilders, 9,000 b.h.p., 18½ knots.

TRYVANN. *Norwegian.* Cargo. Built by Ast. de Cadiz, Cadiz, for D/S A/S Vard, Oslo. 2,840 tons gross, 4,100 tons d.w., 301·75 ft. l.o.a., 48 ft. breadth, 20·33 ft. draught, 5-cyl. Götaverken diesel, 2,500 b.h.p., 13 knots.

TUCURINCA. *British.* Refrigerated cargo. Built by Bremer Vulkan, Vegesack, for Surrey Shipping Co. Ltd., Bermuda. 6,738 tons gross, 451·33 ft. l.o.a., 59·5 ft. breadth, 26 ft. draught, 2 De Laval grd. turbs., 8,500 s.h.p., 17½ knots.

TUDOR. *Swedish.* Tanker. Built by A/B Lödöse Varf, Lödöse, for Elof A. Andihn, Gothenburg. 1,600 tons gross, 2,200 tons d.w., 248·25 ft. l.o.a., 37·9 ft. breadth, 6-cyl. diesel by Nydqvist, 1,575 b.h.p., 12 knots.

TUKUM. *Russian.* Tanker. Built by A/B Gävle Varv, Gävle, for U.S.S.R. 3,128 tons gross, 4,283 tons d.w., 344·82 ft. l.o.a., 48·58 ft. breadth, 20 ft. draught, 5-cyl. B. & W. diesel, 2,900 b.h.p., 14 knots.

TUSKAR. *British.* Cattle ship. Built by Chas. Connell & Co. Ltd., Glasgow, for Clyde Shipping Co. Ltd., Glasgow. 1,598 tons gross, 2,100 tons d.w., 295 ft. l.o.a., 45·25 ft. breadth, 6-cyl. Nohab Polar diesel, 2,000 b.h.p., 14½ knots.

ULYSSES. *Dutch.* Cargo. Built by C. van der Giessen, Krimpen, for Koninkl. Nederl. Stoomb. Maats. N.V., Amsterdam. 5,711 tons gross, 6,950 tons d.w., 423·5 ft. l.o.a., 57·5 ft. breadth, 24·42 ft. draught, 7-cyl. diesel by Gebr.-Stork, 4,900 b.h.p., 16¼ knots.

UNION CONCORD. *Nat. Chinese.* Cargo. Built by Mitsui S.B. & E. Co. Ltd., Tamano, for China Union Lines Ltd., Taipei. 10,134 tons gross, 12,500 tons d.w., 518·82 ft. l.o.a., 65·9 ft. breadth, 29·75 ft. draught, 8-cyl. B. & W. diesel by shipbuilders, 12,000 b.h.p., 17¼ knots.

UNZEN MARU. *Japanese.* Stern trawler. Built by Mitsui S.B. & E. Co. Ltd., Tamano, for Nippon Suisan K.K., Tokyo. 2,450 tons gross, 278·75 ft. l.o.a., 44·42 ft. breadth, 17·42 ft. draught, 6-cyl. B. & W. diesel by the shipbuilders, 2,400 b.h.p., 14 knots.

URAN. *Polish.* Stern trawling factory ship. Built by United Polish Shipyards, Gdansk, for Polish Government. 2,890 tons gross, 1,250 tons d.w., 278·82 ft. l.o.a., 45·33 ft. breadth, 17 ft. draught, 8-cyl. Sulzer diesel, 2,400 b.h.p., 12½ knots.

U

VASSA LEADER. *Finnish.* Cargo. Built by A/B Oskarshamns Varv, Oskarshamn, for Vaasan Laiva O/Y, Helsingfors. 9,040 tons gross, 13,005 tons d.w., 487·58 ft. l.o.a., 61·66 ft. breadth, 30·58 ft. draught, 6-cyl. Gebr.-Stork diesel, 7,500 b.h.p., 16 knots.

VASILIOS R. *Greek.* Cargo. Built by Austin & Pickersgill Ltd., Sunderland, for Cia. de Nav. Golfo Azul, Panama. 10,741 tons gross, 15,540 tons d.w., 526 ft. l.o.a., 67·5 ft. breadth, 31·2 ft. draught, 7-cyl. Sulzer diesel by 'De Schelde,' 10,500 b.h.p., 16½ knots.

VEGA. *French.* Tanker. Built by Ch. de l'Atlantique, St. Nazaire, for Cie. Navale des Pétroles, Paris. 33,060 tons gross, 50,500 tons d.w., 777·75 ft. l.o.a., 101·9 ft. breadth, 37·58 ft. draught, 12-cyl. B. & W. diesel by the shipbuilders, 15,000 b.h.p., 16 knots.

VEGA. *Norwegian.* Tanker. Built by A/S Bergens M/V, Bergen, for Det Bergenske Dampskibsselskab, Berge. 12,678 tons gross, 19,600 tons d.w., 556·82 ft. l.o.a., 72 ft. breadth, 30·66 ft. draught, 8-cyl. B. & W. diesel by Akers, 9,675 b.h.p., 16¼ knots.

VENABU. *Norwegian.* Bulk carrier. Built by A/S Fredriksstad M/V, Fredriksstad, for Halfdan Ditlev-Simonsen, Oslo. 12,748 tons gross, 17,950 tons d.w., 546·2 ft. l.o.a., 67·2 ft. breadth, 32 ft. draught, 6-cyl. Götaverken diesel by the shipbuilders, 7,500 b.h.p., 14¼ knots.

VESTALIS. *Norwegian.* Tanker. Built by Kockums M/V A/B, Malmö, for Smedvigs Tankrederi A/S, Stavanger. 36,000 tons gross, 58,000 tons d.w., 775 ft. l.o.a., 109·25 ft. breadth, 39·5 ft. draught, 12-cyl. M.A.N. diesel by the shipbuilders, 21,000 b.h.p., 17 knots.

VICTORIA. *Roumanian.* Cargo. Built by Galatz Shipyard, Galatz, for Roumanian Government. 3,096 tons gross, 4,500 tons d.w., 330 ft. l.o.a., 21·58 ft. draught, 5-cyl. Sulzer diesel by Reshita Eng. Wks.

VIKRAM. *Indian.* Dredger. Built by J. & K. Smit's Scheepw., Kinderdijk, for Bombay Port Trust. 1,902 tons gross, 2,280 tons d.w., 265 ft. l.o.a., 49 ft. breadth, 15·66 ft. draught, tw-sc. two 7-cyl. diesels by M.A.N., 1,200 b.h.p., 10 knots.

VILLA DE BILBAO. *Spanish.* Refrigerated cargo and passenger. Built by Union Nav. de Levante, Valencia, for Cia. Transmediterranea, Madrid. 7,760 tons gross, 7,000 tons d.w., 436·82 ft. l.o.a., 58·66 ft. breadth, 24·9 ft. draught, 6-cyl. B. & W. diesel by Maquinista, 7,500 b.h.p., 17 knots.

V

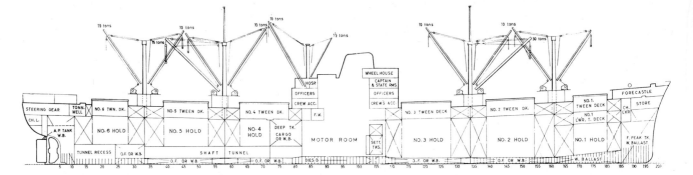

VASILIOS R. *A dry cargo ship of 15,450 tons d.w. built by Austin & Pickersgill Ltd., Sunderland, for the Compania de Navegacion, Golfo Azul S.A., Panama (London agents Rethymnis & Kulukundis Ltd.). This vessel has a service speed of 16½ knots and can make 20 knots under favourable conditions, and is one of the fastest and biggest tramp ships built in Britain up to 1963. Her propelling machinery, a Schelde-Sulzer diesel engine, was built by Koninklijke Mij. de Schelde N.V., Flushing, who carried out the entire machinery installation. The Vasilios R has been described as a super tramp and is claimed to be two years ahead of any competitor. Her owners, realizing that the trend of trampships is towards vessels of high speeds with plenty of reserve power, enabling keener fixing rates to be obtained, decided to order a vessel of this type. Her propelling machinery develops 10,500 b.h.p. and on speed trials in conditions of adverse tide and a wind of over Force 7 she attained a speed of 18·98 knots. Another feature of the ship is the speed at which she can be altered to a closed or open shelterdecker. The vessel is designed for operation in the St. Lawrence Seaway, and has a cargo capacity of 811,480 cu. ft. grain and 730,680 cu. ft. bale. There are six cargo holds, three forward and three aft of the machinery space, with a lower tweendeck in No. 1 hold. Upper deck hatches are fitted with MacGregor single-pull covers. The cargo holds and tweendecks can be ventilated by means of low-power exhaust fans fitted in the bipod masts. Accommodation has been arranged in the midship deck house and includes one double-berth cabin for the owners and three double-berth cabins for passengers, in addition to the captain's suite and rooms for the officers and crew.*

VILLE DE BREST. *French.* Refrigerated cargo. Built by At. & Ch. de la Seine Maritime, Le Trait, for Nouvelle Cie. Havraise Péninsulaire de Nav., Paris. 9,880 tons gross, 12,000 tons d.w., 509·2 ft. l.o.a., 65·42 ft. breadth, 30 ft. draught, 8-cyl. B. & W. diesel by l'Atlantique, 12,000 b.h.p., 18 knots.

VILLE DU HAVRE. *French.* Refrigerated cargo. Built by At. & Ch. de la Seine Maritime, Le Trait, for Nouvelle Cie. Havraise Péninsulaire de Nav., Paris. 9,882 tons gross, 12,000 tons d.w., 509·2 ft. l.o.a., 65·42 ft. breadth, 30 ft. draught, 8-cyl. B. & W. diesel by l'Atlantique, 12,000 b.h.p., 18 knots.

VOLUTA. This tanker of 34,750 tons d.w. with the navigating bridge and accommodation aft was built for Shell Tankers Ltd., London, by the Furness Shipbuilding Co. Ltd. This vessel is the first Shell tanker to be equipped with a simplified arrangement for generating auxiliary electrical power, comprising one steam turbo-alternator and one diesel driven alternator, in place of the two turbo-alternators and one slightly smaller diesel generator which it has hitherto been Shell practice to instal in their steam-turbine propelled ships. The tank space is divided into 10 triple tanks making 30 compartments in all. Oil cargo is carried in 24 of these compartments only, the capacity of these being 35,151 tons, 98 per cent. full at 0·82 s.g. The total of clean ballast carried in the other six tanks is 7,351 tons, 100 per cent. full at 35 cu. ft./ton. The cargo pumping system consists of three groups of tanks, each group having a 16 in. fore-and-aft main. Each centre and wing cargo tank has 14 in. and 12 in. suctions respectively. The cargo mains are each led to a 1,600 tons/hour vertical Hayward Tyler cargo pump.

VISHVA SHANTI. *Indian.* Refrigerated cargo. Built by Hindustan Shipyard Ltd., Vizagapatam, for Shipping Corp. of India, Bombay. 9,191 tons gross, 12,300 tons d.w., 504·75 ft. l.o.a., 64 ft. breadth, 29·75 ft. draught, 7-cyl. M.A.N. diesel, 7,650 b.h.p., 17 knots.

VITREA. *Dutch.* Tanker. Built by N.V. Wilton-Fijenoord, Schiedam, for Shell Tankers N.V., The Hague. 21,873 tons gross, 33,000 tons d.w., 665 ft. l.o.a., 85·25 ft. breadth, 34·5 ft. draught, 2 grd. turbs. by the shipbuilders, 11,000 s.h.p., 15½ knots.

V

VRETAHOLM. *This cargo liner, 7,800 tons d.w., was delivered by Wartsila-Koncernen A/B Crichton-Vulcan to the A/B Svenska Amerika Linien, Gothenburg. She is the third of seven vessels of the same type ordered from the yard by the Broström group. Four, including the Vretaholm, are being delivered as closed shelterdeckers while three will be open shelterdeckers. The cargo capacity is about 400,000 cu. ft. bale, of which 27,000 cu. ft. is refrigerated.*

VITUS BERING. *Russian.* Fish carrier. Built by Burmeister & Wain, Copenhagen, for U.S.S.R. 4,700 tons gross, 2,580 tons d.w., 336 ft. l.o.a., 52·58 ft. breadth, 6-cyl. diesel by the shipbuilders, 3,100 b.h.p., 14 knots.

VLADIVOSTOK. *Russian.* Whale oil and fish factory. Built by Kieler Howaldtswerke A.G., Kiel, for U.S.S.R. 17,150 tons gross, 596·75 ft. l.o.a., 78·25 ft. breadth, 27·58 ft. draught, 5-cyl. diesel by B. & W., 6,250 b.h.p., 14 knots.

VOLUTA. *British.* Tanker. Built by Furness S.B. Co. Ltd., Haverton Hill, for Shell Tankers Ltd., London. 24,400 tons gross, 34,750 tons d.w., 664·82 ft. l.o.a., 89·9 ft. breadth, 34·5 ft. draught, 2 grd. turbs. by Metropolitan Vickers, 12,500 s.h.p., 16 knots.

VRETAHOLM. *Swedish.* Cargo. Built by Wärtsilä Kon. Crichton-Vulcan, Abo, for A/B Svenska Amerika Linien, Gothenburg. 6,910 tons gross, 7,800 tons d.w., 441·75 ft. l.o.a., 57·9 ft. breadth, 26·2 ft. draught, 7-cyl. Götaverken diesel, 5,800 b.h.p., 16 knots.

VULKAN. *German.* Bulk carrier. Built by Lübecker Flender-Werke A.G., Lübeck, for Komrowski Befrachtungskontor K.G., Hamburg. 22,000 tons gross, 30,000 tons d.w., 656·2 ft. l.o.a., 85·75 ft. breadth, 32·2 ft. draught, 7-cyl. M.A.N. diesel, 10,500 b.h.p., 15½ knots.

W. HAROLD REA. *Canadian.* Tanker. Built by Collingwood Shipyards Ltd., Collingwood, Ont., for Canadian Oil Co. Ltd., Toronto. 4,009 tons gross, 5,940 tons d.w., 355·5 ft. l.o.a., 46 ft. breadth, 21·75 ft. draught, tw-sc. two 10-cyl. Fairbanks-Morse diesels, 3,200 b.h.p., 12½ knots.

W. H. ORBELL. *New Zealand.* Bucket hopper dredger. Built by Simons-Lobnitz Ltd., Renfrew, for Timaru Harbour Board, Timaru. 1,240 tons gross, 262·82 ft. l.o.a., 41·5 ft. breadth, 14·2 ft. draught, tw-sc. diesel-electric, two 8-cyl. diesels, 1,150 b.h.p., 9½ knots.

WAARDRECHT. *Dutch.* Cargo. Built by N.V. Kon. Maats. 'De Schelde,' Flushing, for N.V. Stoom. Maats. 'De Maas,' Rotterdam. 10,400 tons gross, 12,500 tons d.w., 516·42 ft. l.o.a., 65·75 ft. breadth, 6-cyl. Sulzer diesel by the shipbuilders, 6,000 b.h.p., 15 knots.

WACHTFELS. *German.* Refrigerated cargo. Built by A.G. 'Weser' Werk Seebeck, Bremerhaven, for D.D.S. 'Hansa,' Bremen. 9,718 tons gross, 12,424 tons d.w., 499·5 ft. l.o.a., 66 ft. breadth, 30·33 ft. draught, 8-cyl. M.A.N. diesel, 10,800 b.h.p., 18½ knots.

WAKASA MARU. *Japanese.* Cargo. Built by Ishikawajima-Harima H.I., Aioi, for Nippon Yusen Kaisha, Tokyo. 7,450 tons gross, 10,051 tons d.w., 438·5 ft. l.o.a., 62·33 ft. breadth, 26·25 ft. draught. 6-cyl. Sulzer diesel, 5,500 b.h.p., 14 knots.

WALLENFELS. *German.* Refrigerated cargo. Built by A.G. 'Weser,' Bremen, for D.D.G. 'Hansa,' Bremen. 9,718 tons gross, 12,424 tons d.w., 499·5 ft. l.o.a., 66 ft. breadth, 30·33 ft. draught, 8-cyl. M.A.N. diesel, 10,800 b.h.p., 18½ knots.

WAPPEN VON HAMBURG. *German.* Passenger and refrigerated cargo. Built by Blohm & Voss A.G., Hamburg, for Hafen D/S A.G., Hamburg. 3,819 tons gross, 346·58 ft. l.o.a., 50 ft. breadth, 13·33 ft. draught, tw-sc. two 16-cyl. Pielstick diesels by Ottensener Eisenwerk, 8,960 b.h.p., 21 knots.

WARKWORTH. *British.* Cargo. Built by Bartram & Sons Ltd., Sunderland, for R. S. Dalgliesh Ltd., Newcastle-upon-Tyne. 9,720 tons gross, 12,450 tons d.w., 495·42 ft. l.o.a., 62·25 ft. breadth, 27 ft. draught, 4-cyl. Doxford diesel, 4,500 b.h.p., 13 knots.

WASHINGTON. *American.* Refrigerated cargo. Built by Newport News S.B. & D.D. Co., Newport News, for States Steamship Co., San Francisco. 12,700 tons gross, 12,691 tons d.w., 565 ft. l.o.a., 76·2 ft. breadth, 31·58 ft. draught, 2 grd. turbs. by the shipbuilders, 17,500 s.h.p., 20 knots.

WASHINGTON MAIL. *American.* Cargo and passenger. Built by Todd Shipyards Corp., San Pedro, for American Mail Line Ltd., Seattle. 12,714 tons gross, 14,925 tons d.w., 563·66 ft. l.o.a., 76 ft. breadth. 31·5 ft. draught, 2 grd. turbs. by G.E.C., 17,500 s.h.p., 20 knots.

WERDENFELS. *German.* Refrigerated cargo. Built by A.G. 'Weser,' Bremen, for D.D.G. 'Hansa,' Bremen. 9,718 tons gross, 12,424 tons d.w., 499·5 ft. l.o.a., 66 ft. breadth, 30·33 ft. draught, 8-cyl. M.A.N. diesel, 10,800 b.h.p., 18½ knots.

WEST RIVER. *Liberian.* Bulk carrier. Built by Ansaldo S.p.A., Genoa, for International Nav. Corp., Monrovia and London. 10,925 tons gross, 16,600 tons d.w., 546 ft. l.o.a., 68·82 ft. breadth, 29·5 ft. draught, 8-cyl. Fiat diesel by the shipbuilders, 8,000 b.h.p., 15½ knots.

WIENIAWSKI. *Polish.* Refrigerated cargo. Built by Brodogradiliste Split, for Polish Ocean Lines. 7,100 tons gross, 501·25 ft. l.o.a., 61·82 ft. breadth, 6-cyl. diesel by Fiat, 6,000 b.h.p., 15 knots.

WILDENFELS. *German.* Refrigerated cargo. Built by A.G. 'Weser' Werk Seebeck, Bremerhaven, for D.D.G. 'Hansa,' Bremen. 9,718 tons gross, 12,424 tons d.w., 499·5 ft. l.o.a., 66 ft. breadth, 30·33 ft. draught, 8-cyl. M.A.N. diesel, 10,800 b.h.p., 18½ knots.

WAKASA MARU. *Views showing heeling tests being carried out on the 200-ton derrick. The double bottom tanks are divided longitudinally into three sections, and the wing tanks are used as ballast tanks to correct any excessive heeling.*

WAKASA MARU. *To meet the demand from shippers for a fast, heavy cargo service between South-East Asia and Central and South America, Nippon Yusen Kabushiki Kaisha, Tokyo (NYK Line) have had this ship built by Ishikawajima-Harima Heavy Industries Co. Ltd. This vessel is in many respects similar to the Hozui Maru, also delivered in 1962 by the same shipbuilders, but she is fitted with a new type of heavy derrick capable of lifting 200 tons. Although primarily intended for the heavy cargo trade, the Wakasa Maru is equally suitable for operation as a general cargo liner carrying piece goods, grain, etc., and is equipped with wooden portable bulkheads. The Wakasa Maru has three holds, Nos. 2 and 3 being for heavy cargo storage. Large cargo hatches measuring 91 ft. 10 in. long by 24 ft. 7 in. wide are provided on the upper deck, while the second deck hatches have been widened to 27 ft. 10 in. for ease of cargo handling. There are no pillars in Nos. 2 and 3 holds, and large webs have been eliminated as much as possible so as not to obstruct the cargo spaces. A gantry-type king post structure was chosen for the heavy-lift derrick as this was simple to manufacture. The height of the derrick, which is nearly a quarter of the length of the ship, is restricted by the height of a new bridge in Japan under which the Wakasa Maru must pass on her assigned route. The rise in the centre of gravity due to the height of the gantry is offset by using high tensile steel. The gantry is unstayed and the feet are supported at the upper deck and second deck, the reinforcements being well extended to the double bottom by way of the deep tank. The longest outreach possible, with the minimum length of boom, is effected by making the sheaves integral with the derrick boom. The foot of the boom is split so as to share the load equally at two points. The boom rotates on roller bearings, and can serve either hatch. The axial load is supported at upper deck level. The falls and topping lift are led from the centreline of the post to a winch platform and thence to a 30-ton steam winch.*

W

WAPPEN VON HAMBURG. *This passenger ship, when not in service between Hamburg and Heligoland, will be used for cruises in different parts of the world. This twin-screw vessel was built by Blohm & Voss A.G., Hamburg, and is owned by the Hafen-Dampfschiffart A.G., Hamburg. She is the fastest vessel yet built for the Hamburg-Heligoland service, taking passengers daily from Hamburg at 7 a.m. and returning in the evening after a three to four hours' stay on the island. Since she is also to be used as a cruise ship there are a number of well furnished cabins. In addition the ship has been designed to operate as a conference ship and also as a vessel for trade fairs. In the event of war, with her speed of 21 knots, she could serve as a hospital ship. When she is operating on the ferry service between Hamburg and Heligoland the Wappen von Hamburg can carry 1,700 passengers, and when cruising 140 persons can be accommodated. All the cabins have been luxuriously fitted out and each has a shower and separate toilet. To facilitate manoeuvring when berthing and leaving harbour there are two Pleuger 150 h.p. bow propulsion units fitted. Stabilizers have also been provided.*

WISLICA. *Polish.* Cargo. Built by United Polish Shipyards, Szczecin, for Polish Government. 3,687 tons gross, 5,340 tons d.w., 407·82 ft. l.o.a., 54·25 ft. breadth, 20·82 ft. draught, 9-cyl. B. & W. diesel, 4,900 b.h.p., 15½ knots.

WOLFSBURG. *German.* Refrigerated cargo. Built by Howaldtswerke Ham. A.G., Hamburg, for Hamburg-Amerika Linie, Hamburg. 6,850 tons gross, 8,400 tons d.w., 519·9 ft. l.o.a., 63 ft. breadth, 24·42 ft. draught, 8-cyl. M.A.N. diesel by shipbuilders, 10,800 b.h.p., 18¾ knots.

WOLLONGONG. *Australian.* Ore carrier. Built by Broken Hill Pty. Co. Ltd., Whyalla, for Bulkships Ltd., Melbourne. 12,586 tons gross, 16,400 tons d.w., 539·2 ft. l.o.a., 66·9 ft. breadth, 29·66 ft. draught, 5-cyl. Doxford diesel by Com. Govt. E. Wks., 5,500 b.h.p., 14¼ knots.

WORLD EXPLORER. *Liberian.* Bulk carrier. Built by Short Bros. Ltd., Sunderland, for Cia. de Nav. Omsil S.A., Monrovia and London, 11,971 tons gross, 20,500 tons d.w., 560·66 ft. l.o.a., 71·75 ft. breadth, 32 ft. draught, 5-cyl. Sulzer diesel by G. Clark, 7,500 b.h.p., 14¼ knots.

WYSPIANSKI. *Polish.* Cargo liner. Built by Brodogradiliste 3 Maj, Rijeka, for Polish Ocean Lines. 5,731 tons gross, 10,500 tons d.w., 486·66 ft. l.o.a., 62·66 ft. breadth, 25 ft. draught, 6-cyl. Sulzer diesel by the shipbuilders, 7,800 b.h.p., 16½ knots.

WORLD EXPLORER. *Built by Short Brothers Ltd. for the Compania de Navegacion Omsil S.A., this bulk carrier, 20,500 tons d.w., has joined the fleet of the Niarchos group. The World Explorer has been specially designed for the carriage of grain, coal and ore. The ship is divided into four holds by corrugated transverse bulkheads, and the cargo space has been designed with top wing tanks and hopper bilge tanks, thus making the holds self-trimming. The eight cargo hatchways are covered by MacGregor single-pull steel hatch covers which are opened and closed by two Clarke Chapman electric winches. There is no cargo handling gear. The propelling machinery in the World Explorer is arranged aft and consists of a 5-cylinder Clark-Sulzer turbocharged two-stroke diesel engine developing 7,500 b.h.p. at 119 r.p.m.*

YAMAMIME MARU. *Japanese.* Cargo. Built by Hitachi S.B. & E. Co. Ltd., Mukaishima, for Sansei Kogyo K.K., Tokyo. 3,535 tons gross, 5,640 tons d.w., 346·2 ft l.o.a., 49·9 ft. breadth, 21·5 ft. draught, 8-cyl. diesel by Ito Tekkosho, 2,380 b.h.p., 12 knots.

YAMATOSHI MARU. *Japanese.* Refrigerated cargo. Built by Hitachi S.B. & E. Co. Ltd., Osaka, for Yamashita Kisen K.K., Tokyo. 8,900 tons gross, 11,980 tons d.w., 30·2 ft. draught, 7-cyl. diesel by the shipbuilders, 10,500 b.h.p., 17 knots.

YAMANASHI MARU. *Japanese.* Cargo. Built by Yokohama S.B. Co. Ltd., Yokohama, for Nippon Yusen Kaisha, Tokyo. 10,100 tons gross, 12,095 tons d.w., 528·25 ft. l.o.a., 68·42 ft. breadth, 29·75 ft. draught, 9-cyl. M.A.N. diesel by the shipbuilders, 17,500 b.h.p., 19½ knots.

YAWA MARU. *Japanese.* Cargo. Built by Hitachi S.B. & E. Co. Ltd., Mukaishima, for Kyowa Sangyo Kaiun K.K., Osaka. 2,150 tons gross, 3,252 tons d.w., 18·58 ft. draught, 8-cyl. diesel by Niigata, 2,000 b.h.p., 11½ knots.

YUHO MARU. *Japanese.* Ore carrier. Built by Mitsubishi H.I.R., Kobe, for Nissho Kisen K.K. and Tanda Sangyo Kisen K.K., Tokyo. 29,354 tons gross, 46,000 tons d.w., 725·2 ft. l.o.a., 100·2 ft. breadth, 37·5 ft. draught, 8-cyl. Sulzer diesel by shipbuilders, 16,000 b.h.p., 17 knots.

YUYO MARU. *Japanese.* Tanker. Built by Hitachi S.B. & E. Co. Ltd., Innoshima, for Morita Kisen K.K., Osaka. 30,474 tons gross, 51,188 tons d.w., 682 ft. l.o.a., 100·58 ft. breadth, 36·42 ft. draught, 8-cyl. B. & W. diesel by the shipbuilders, 16,800 b.h.p., 16½ knots.

YUZAN MARU. *Japanese.* Cargo. Built by Shioyama Dockyard Co. Ltd., Osaka, for Maruei Kisen & Tokutei Sempaku Kodan, Tokyo. 1,999 tons gross, 3,105 tons d.w., 286 ft. l.o.a., 42 ft. breadth, 18·25 ft. draught, 6-cyl. diesel by Ito Tekko, 2,100 b.h.p., 12 knots.

YAMINIME MARU. *This 5,640 tons d.w. cargo ship was completed by the Mukaishima shipyard of the Hitachi Shipbuilding & Engineering Co. Ltd. for the Sansei Kogyo K.K. Between 96 and 98 per cent. of all the hull joints are welded. She has been specially designed as a coal carrier.*

YUYO MARU. *This 51,188 tons d.w. tanker was delivered to Morita Kisen by the Innoshima shipyard of Hitachi Shipbuilding & Engineering Co. Ltd. This ship incorporates a wide range of automation, and the number of crew members has been reduced from 54 to 48 men. With the completion of this ship the yard has constructed a total of about one million deadweight tons of tankers during the past 10 years.*

ZENIT. *Russian.* Training ship. Built by Neptun Werft, Rostock, for U.S.S.R. 4,374 tons gross, 344·2 ft. l.o.a., 47·33 ft. breadth, two 8-cyl. grd. diesels by Gorlitzer, 2,500 b.h.p., 14 knots.

ZLETOVO. *Yugoslav.* Bulk carrier. Built by Brodogradiliste Uljanik, Pula, for Jugoslavenska Tankerska Plovidba, Rijeka. 13,750 tons gross, 18,500 tons d.w., 569·9 ft. l.o.a., 92·66 ft. breadth, 29·5 ft. draught, 6-cyl. B. & W. diesel by the shipbuilders, 7,500 b.h.p., 15 knots.

Merchant Ships Launched during 1962

(TONNAGES ARE GIVEN IN TONS GROSS)

The following statistics are acknowledged to 'Lloyd's Register of Shipping Annual Summary of Merchant Ships Launched during 1962.'

WORLD OUTPUT

At 8,374,754 tons, the total launched during 1962 was 434,749 tons more than in 1961. This increase follows three years of falling output during which new orders have been difficult to obtain, and launchings from the various shipbuilding countries during 1962 show considerable differences in trend as compared with 1961. Notable increases are shown for Japan, Sweden and the United States of America while considerable reductions in output are seen in Great Britain and Northern Ireland and in the Netherlands.

Tonnage launched in 1962 as compared with 1961:

	Tons	Tons		Tons	Tons
Japan	2,183,147	(+383,805)	Italy	348,196	(+ 13,912)
Great Britain and			Denmark ..	230,470	(+ 19,848)
Northern Ireland	1,072,513	(−119,245)	Poland ..	189,412	(− 25,500)
Germany (West) ..	1,009,698	(+ 47,291)	Yugoslavia ..	147,685	(− 73,890)
Sweden	841,022	(+ 98,954)	Finland ..	140,135	(+ 37,331)
France	480,578	(+ 34,406)	Canada ..	129,162	(+ 45,343)
U.S.A.	449,050	(+106,284)	Spain ..	125,254	(− 26,152)
Netherlands ..	418,494	(−152,343)	Belgium ..	76,681	(− 2,276)
Norway	376,444	(+ 13,482)			

JAPAN

After falling from a peak of 2,432,506 tons in 1957 to 1,722,577 in 1959, output has now climbed back to 2,183,147 tons in 1962. This is 26 per cent. of the world total as compared with 23 per cent. for 1961.

The output for 1962 includes 861,000 tons of oil tankers, 766,000 tons of specialized bulk carriers, and 78,000 tons for the fishing industry in all its aspects.

(continued on page 181)

LAUNCHED ANNUALLY

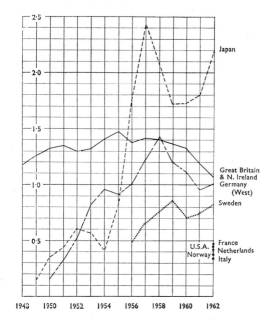

Courtesy of Lloyd's Register of Shipping

MERCHANT SHIPS LAUNCHED IN THE WORLD DURING 1962 (excluding ships of less than 100 tons gross)

Courtesy of Lloyd's Register of Shipping

COUNTRY OF BUILD		STEAMSHIPS		MOTORSHIPS		TOTAL			TOTAL, 1961	
		No.	Tons Gross	No.	Tons Gross	No.	Tons Gross	Percentage of World Tonnage	No.	Tons Gross
British Commonwealth	Great Britain and N. Ireland ...	14	376,791	173	695,722	187	1,072,513	12·81	247	1,191,758
	Australia	1	22,334	7	21,693	8	44,027		7	17,008
	Canada: Coast	5	79,892	34	24,325	45	129,162	2·40	19	83,819
	Great Lakes ...	1	17,500	5	7,445					
	India	1	420	4	21,796	5	22,216		6	28,737
	Other Commonwealth Countries	—	—	14	5,947	14	5,947		16	9,933
Argentina...		—	—	4	11,805	4	11,805	0·14	1	300
Belgium		1	29,699	8	46,982	9	76,681	0·92	12	78,957
Brazil		1	7,500	9	22,731	10	30,231	0·36	8	26,168
China (Nationalist)		—	—	—	—	—	—		2	4,744
Denmark		1	29,000	34	201,470	35	230,470	2·75	37	210,622
Egypt (U.A.R.)		—	—	5	4,352	5	4,352	0·05	—	—
Faroe Is.		—	—	1	273	1	273	0·00	1	211
Finland		—	—	43	140,135	43	140,135	1·67	39	102,804
France		4	94,881	80	385,697	84	480,578	5·74	66	446,172
Germany (West)...		11	350,233	223	659,465	234	1,009,698	12·06	262	962,407
Greece		—	—	6	1,515	6	1,515	0·02	4	602
Hungary		—	—	1	120	1	120	0·00	6	5,550
Indonesia		—	—	11	2,388	11	2,388	0·03	5	1,392
Irish Republic		—	—	2	16,501	2	16,501	0·20	2	15,302
Israel		—	—	—	—	—	—		1	200
Italy		3	90,300	48	257,896	51	348,196	4·16	37	334,284
Japan		24	776,583	534	1,406,564	558	2,183,147	26·07	643	1,799,342
Madagascar		—	—	2	508	2	508	0·01	—	—
Netherlands		5	117,784	146	300,710	151	418,494	5·00	165	570,837
Norway		—	—	95	376,444	95	376,444	4·49	84	362,962
Poland		—	—	44	189,412	44	189,412	2·26	59	214,912
Portugal		—	—	6	11,634	7	11,934	0·14	7	11,652
Angola		—	—	1	300					
South Africa		—	—	1	360	1	360	0·00	1	170
Spain		5	27,501	87	97,753	92	125,254	1·50	89	151,406

MERCHANT SHIPS LAUNCHED IN THE WORLD DURING 1962 (excluding ships of less than 100 tons gross)—*continued*

COUNTRY OF BUILD	STEAMSHIPS		MOTORSHIPS		TOTAL			TOTAL, 1961	
	No.	Tons Gross	No.	Tons Gross	No.	Tons Gross	Percentage of World Tonnage	No.	Tons Gross
Sweden	5	180,925	69	660,097	74	841,022	10·04	74	742,068
Turkey	2	2,396	5	2,240	7	4,636	0·06	5	1,345
United States of America:									
Atlantic Coast	24	289,717	9	4,652	}				
Gulf Ports	6	66,549	37	15,156	} 90	449,050	5·36	56	342,766
Pacific Coast	4	50,959	4	18,132	}				
Great Lakes	—	—	6	3,885	}				
Yugoslavia	—	—	25	147,685	25	147,685	1·76	29	221,575
WORLD TOTAL* ...	118	2,610,964	1,783	5,763,790	1,901	8,374,754	100·00	1,990	7,940,005

* Returns are not available for The Peoples' Republics of China, East Germany and Russia (U.S.S.R.)

OIL TANKERS OF 100 TONS AND UPWARDS

COUNTRY OF BUILD	STEAM		MOTOR		TOTAL		COUNTRY OF BUILD	STEAM		MOTOR		TOTAL	
	No.	Tons Gross	No.	Tons Gross	No.	Tons Gross		No.	Tons Gross	No.	Tons Gross	No.	Tons Gross
Great Britain and N. Ireland ...	13	374,067	10	28,682	23	402,749	Japan	12	413,926	70	446,627	82	860,553
Australia	1	22,334	—	—	1	22,334	Madagascar ...	—	—	1	240	1	240
Canada	1	9,500	2	8,085	3	17,585	Netherlands ...	3	116,534	5	18,040	8	134,574
Other Commonwealth Countries	—	—	1	500	1	500	Norway	—	—	16	179,898	16	179,898
Argentina	—	—	1	1,500	1	1,500	Poland	—	—	2	26,136	2	26,136
Belgium	1	29,699	—	—	1	29,699	Spain	1	21,608	1	6,618	2	28,226
Denmark	1	29,000	3	72,461	4	101,461	Sweden	5	180,925	18	298,590	23	479,515
Finland	—	—	9	34,290	9	34,290	Turkey	—	—	2	940	2	940
France	2	64,946	3	73,338	5	138,284	U.S.A.	3	63,526	—	—	3	63,526
Germany (West) ...	9	323,897	39	69,006	48	392,903	Yugoslavia ...	—	—	2	1,900	2	1,900
Italy	2	47,300	8	34,048	10	81,348	WORLD TOTAL ...	54	1,697,262	193	1,300,899	247	2,998,161

No less than 22 ships are of more than 30,000 tons each and include the *Nissho Maru* of 74,869 tons, which is the largest oil tanker ever built.

GREAT BRITAIN AND NORTHERN IRELAND

Output has continued the gradual fall from a peak of 1,473,937 tons in 1955 to 1,072,513 tons in 1962. This is 13 per cent. of the world total as compared with 15 per cent. in 1961.

Oil tankers total 403,000 tons, and bulk carriers 160,000 tons. The oil tankers include 10 of between 30,000 and 33,000 tons, which are the largest ships built in this country during the year.

GERMANY (WEST)

After falling from a peak of 1,429,261 tons in 1958 to 962,407 tons in 1961, there has now been a partial recovery in output to 1,009,698 tons in 1962. More than two-thirds (68 per cent.) is for registration in other countries.

Oil tankers total 393,000 tons and bulk carriers 322,000 tons.

SWEDEN

The output of 841,022 tons for 1962 shows an increase of 98,954 tons over the previous year and is only just short of the highest ever recorded.

Oil tankers, 480,000 tons, represent 57 per cent. of output; bulk carriers total 162,000 tons. Over 70 per cent. of all tonnage launched is for registration in other countries, largely Norway.

FRANCE

Output of 480,578 tons is 34,406 tons more than the previous year.

Oil tankers total 138,000 tons and bulk carriers 207,000 tons.

Sixty-four per cent. of all tonnage launched is for registration in other countries and includes a passenger ship of 23,000 tons for Israel.

UNITED STATES OF AMERICA

Output of 449,050 tons is 106,284 tons more than in 1961.

Only 64,000 tons are oil tankers and tonnage comprises mostly general cargo ships between 10,000 and 15,000 tons.

NETHERLANDS

Output of 418,494 tons is 152,343 tons less than the previous year and is the lowest since 1956.

Oil tankers total 135,000 tons and bulk carriers only 44,000 tons.

Fifty-eight per cent. of the tonnage launched is for export, largely for the United Kingdom.

NORWAY

The year 1962 was a record for this country with an output of 376,444 tons.

Tonnage launched includes 180,000 tons of oil tankers and 120,000 tons of bulk carriers.

Only 6 per cent. of the total is for export.

ITALY

A steady fall in output from 550,795 tons in 1958 to 334,284 tons in 1961 has been halted by a small increase to a present figure of 348,196 tons.

An outstanding feature was the launch of the *Michelangelo*, a passenger ship of 43,000 tons.

Oil tankers total only 81,000 tons but bulk carriers are 154,000 tons.

Only 8 per cent. of the total is for export.

DENMARK

Output of 230,470 tons is 19,848 tons more than in 1961 and is little short of the highest ever recorded.

Oil tankers total 101,000 tons.

Fifty-eight per cent. of the tonnage is for export.

POLAND

Output of 189,412 tons is 25,500 tons less than in 1961.

Oil tankers total 26,136 tons but further details of type and of registration have not been made available.

YUGOSLAVIA

Output of 147,685 tons shows a decrease of 73,890 tons from the previous year's record figure but this is probably due to the incidence of an increased number of larger ships on the stocks.

No less than 76 per cent. of the total launched is for export.

FINLAND

The year 1962 was a record for this country with an output of 140,135 tons, most of which is for registration in other countries.

CANADA

Output of 129,162 tons is 45,343 tons more than in 1961.

Bulk carriers include 88,000 tons for the Great Lakes.

SPAIN

Output of 125,254 tons is 26,152 tons less than the previous year and includes a large number of small fishing craft.

Forty-seven per cent. of the total is for export.

BELGIUM

Output has fallen steadily from 164,816 tons in 1959 to a present figure of 76,681 tons which includes 77 per cent. for export.

SIZE AND TYPE

The largest ships launched in the world during 1962 were:

		Tons	Launched in
s.s.	*Nissho Maru	74,869	Japan
s.s.	*Naess Champion	54,749	Japan
s.s.	*Esso Libya	53,464	Netherlands
s.s.	*Esso Spain	53,423	W. Germany
s.s.	*Esso Lancashire	48,899	Sweden
s.s.	*Esso Warwickshire	48,815	W. Germany
s.s.	†San Juan Pioneer	44,513	Japan
s.s.	†San Juan Prospector	44,513	Japan
s.s.	Michelangelo	43,000	Italy
s.s.	*Taiwa Maru	41,000	Japan
s.s.	‡Argyll	39,665	Japan
M.S.	*Taikohsan Maru	39,400	Japan
M.S.	*Ise Maru	39,364	Japan
M.S.	*Berge Charles	38,000	France
s.s.	*(Not yet named)	37,190	Sweden
s.s.	*Polarvik	36,800	Sweden
M.S.	*Vestalis	36,797	Sweden
s.s.	*Caltex Greenwich	35,720	Japan
s.s.	*Caltex Southampton	35,700	Japan
s.s.	†Universe Defender	34,696	Japan
s.s.	*Sea Sapphire	34,000	France

* Oil Tanker   † Ore/Oil Carrier   ‡ Bulk Carrier

30,000/34,000 tons—26 steam and 13 motorships: 35 oil tankers, 1 ore/oil carrier, 3 ore/bulk carriers.

25,000/30,000 tons—12 steam and 16 motorships: 18 oil tankers: 10 ore/bulk carriers.

20,000/25,000 tons—4 steam and 19 motorships: 11 oil tankers, 1 ore/oil carrier, 10 ore/bulk carriers, 1 passenger liner.

15,000/20,000 tons—8 steam and 31 motorships: 33 ore/bulk carriers, 4 oil tankers, 1 whale factory, 1 general cargo.

10,000/15,000 tons—30 steam and 111 motorships: 61 general cargo, 59 ore/bulk carriers, 18 oil tankers, 2 passenger liners, 1 bitumen carrier.

PROPULSION

			Gross tonnage of ships	
Diesel ..	..	..	5,715,526	
Diesel-electric ..	..	..	48,264	
Total Motorships			—	5,763,790
Turbine ..	..	..	2,598,205	
Reciprocating ..	..	..	7,483	
Reciprocating and Turbine ..			5,276	
Total Steamships			—	2,610,964

OIL TANKERS

As compared with 1961, the 2,998,161 tons of oil tankers launched during 1962 showed an increase of 195,272 tons.

Leading countries of build in tons gross as compared with 1961:

				Tons	Tons
Japan ..	..	..	..	860,553	(+209,792)
Sweden ..	..	..	..	479,515	(+ 58,301)
Great Britain and Northern Ireland				402,749	(+ 9,286)
Germany (West) ..	..	..		392,903	(+162,485)
Norway ..	..	..	..	179,898	(+ 3,951)
France ..	..	..	..	138,284	(− 42,408)
Netherlands ..	..	..		134,574	(− 81,738)
Denmark ..	..	..	..	101,461	(− 5,903)

REGISTRATION

Excluding tonnage launched in Poland, for which details of registration have not been made available, the tonnage intended for registration elsewhere than in country of build is 3,450,499 tons, which is 41·2 per cent. of the total output.

The countries which built the largest amounts for export, shown also as a percentage of total output in those countries, are:

Japan: 876,794 tons (40·2 per cent.) of which 256,318 tons are oil tankers.

West Germany: 683,881 tons (67·7 per cent.) of which 309,259 tons are oil tankers.

Sweden: 596,618 tons (70·9 per cent.) of which 359,726 tons are oil tankers.

France: 308,833 tons (64·3 per cent.) of which 102,946 tons are oil tankers.

Netherlands: 243,541 tons (58·2 per cent.) of which 102,164 tons are oil tankers.

The following analysis shows additions to the fleets of countries:

	Launched in country	−Export	+Import	Net increase
	('000 gross tons)			
Great Britain and Northern Ireland	1,073	165	569	1,477
Norway	376	21	970	1,325
Japan	2,183	877	—	1,306
Liberia	—	—	555	555
U.S.A.	449	—	—	449
Sweden	841	597	123	367
Germany (West)	1,010	684	1	327
Italy	348	27	1	322
Netherlands	418	244	109	283
Greece	2	—	242	244
France	481	309	2	174
Canada	129	—	19	148
Denmark	230	134	50	146
India	22	—	50	72
Spain	125	59	—	66
Israel	—	—	60	60
Belgium	77	59	33	51
Turkey	5	—	34	39
Argentina	12	—	27	39
Brazil	30	—	9	39
Yugoslavia	148	112	—	36
Finland	140	123	18	35

Abbreviations

English, French, German

bp.	Between perpendiculars. Entre les perpendiculaires. Zwischen den Senkrechten.
bhp.	Brake horse power. Chevaux effectifs. Bremspferdestärke, Bremsleistung.
Bulk	Bulk carrier. Chargement en vrac. Frachtschiff für Massengut.
C.	Compound. Machine à vapeur compound. Verbund, Compound.
Cg.	Cargo. Cargaison, chargement. Fracht, Ladung.
Col.	Collier. Bateau charbonnier. Kohlenschiff.
cu. ft.	Cubic feet. Pieds cubes. Kubikfuss.
Cy.	Cylinder. Cylindre. Zylinder.
Dsl.	Diesel. Diesel. Diesel.
Dsl/elec.	Diesel electric. Diesel électrique. Diesel-elektrisch.
d.w.	Deadweight. Capacité, port en lourd. Tragfähigkeit.
Elec.	Electric. Electrique. Elektrisch.
Exh.	Exhaust. Echappement. Abgas (-Leitung).
Exh-t.	Low pressure exhaust turbine. Turbine à échappement à basse pression. Niederdruck-Abgasturbine.
Fcty.	Factory ship. Batiment-usine. Verarbeitungsschiff (z.B. Walfang-Mutterschiff).
Fe	Ferry. Bac. Fährschiff, Fähre.
Fruit	Fruit carrier. Transport de fruits. Obsttransportschiff.
F.V.	Fishing vessel. Bateau de pêche. Fischdampfer, Fischerboot.
Grd.	Geared. à engrenage. Ueber-oder Untersetzungs-Getriebe.
Grt.	Gross tons. Tonnage brut. Bruttoregister Tonnen.
hp.	Horse power. (HP) puissance en chevaux. Pferdestärke, Pferdekraft.
ihp.	Indicated horse power. Chevaux de force indiqués. Indizierte Pferdestärke.
k.	Knots. Nœuds. Knoten.
L.	Liner. Navire régulier. Linienschiff.
Ltd.	Limited. Société à responsabilité limitée. G.m.b.H. (Limited).
M.	Motorship. Navire à moteur. Motorschiff.
Mo.	Motor. Moteur. Motor.
o.a.	Overall length. Longueur hors tout. Länge über alles, Gesamtlänge.
o.p.	Opposed piston. Pistons opposés. Gegenüberliegende Kolben.
Ore	Ore carrier. Cargo pour transport de minerai. Erzschiff.
Pass.	Passenger. Paquebot. Fahrgastschiff.
Quad.	Quadruple. Quadruple. Vierfach.
Ref.	Refrigerated. Bateau frigorifique. Kühlschiff.
r.p.m.	Revolutions per minute. Tours par minute. Umdrehungen pro Minute.
S.	Steamship. Navire à vapeur. Dampfschiff, Dampfer.
sc.	Screw. Hélice. Schraube.
shp.	Shaft horse power. Chevaux à l'arbre moteur. PS an der Schraubenwelle gemessen.
Stm.	Steam. Vapeur. Dampf.
Sugar	Sugar carrier. Transport de sucre. Zuckertransportschiff.
Ten.	Tender. Canot de bord. Beiboot.
Tk.	Tanker. Bateau citerne. Tanker.
Tr.	Trawler. Chalutier. Schleppnetz-Fischerboot.
Trl.	Triple. Triple. Dreifach.
Tr-exp.	Triple expansion. Expansion triple. Dreifach-Expansion.
Trsp.	Transport. Transport. Transportschiff.
Tw.	Twin. Double. Zweifach, doppelt.